The Canadian Fire Officer's Guide To Emergency Management

Edited By Ron Kuban, Ph. D.

PENDRAGON PUBLISHING LTD. • 1996 • CALGARY, ALBERTA, CANADA

Production supervision, design and layout by:
Prairie Dawg Designs,
a division of Pendragon Publishing Ltd.
Calgary, Alberta, Canada
Cover Design by:
Prairie Dawg Designs
Cover Photo:
Gerry Emas, Edmonton Emergency Response Department

The material contained in this book was developed with great care to ensure its accuracy and relevance. It is offered as a guide. Therefore, nothing in this book absolves its readers from using their sound judgement in the appropriate application of its content.

Printed In Canada ISBN 0-9699417-1-4

Turning Point Consulting Corp.
3116 - 36B Avenue
Edmonton, Alberta, Canada
T6T 1H4

Internet - http://www.turningpointcorp.com

This book is dedicated to all those who devotedly gave of themselves so others would survive disaster.

INTRODUCTION

We are truly in the information age. There is so much information available that we must be selective in what we read or watch. The same is true of the myriad of seminars, workshops, conferences which are available and beckon our participation, to say nothing of the trade magazines and books on the topic.

Why should you read this book? If you are a member of a municipal council, a municipal administrator/manager, or a member of the Fire Department this book has a lot of valuable information for you. This information will help put in perspective the extraordinary demands for emergency services, the wide variety of conditions for this service and real–life examples. The contributions of a variety of experts from different fields provide a series of unique insights which are not commonly available. The information will either be useful to you in a very direct way or will stimulate/provoke thought which could provide useful results in the future.

On the other hand, if your disaster plans have been thoroughly prepared, every responsible party has full knowledge of it and is fully equipped/trained to carry out its required functions under any circumstances, you may be wasting your time with this book. However, before you toss it back on the shelf give it some serious thought. Is everything really that well prepared? Have all your emergency exercises gone smoothly? Has everything worked well with the various responding agencies, including mutual aid? Do you actually have all the apparatus, equipment, materials, fully–trained personnel, or communications resources required to effectively manage those incidents which are within your Fire Department's responsibility?

Could it be that most people in your community, including its elected officials and policy makers, are not fully aware of the emergency preparedness process, the community's current shortcomings, or the implications of these shortcomings in a disaster? Could it be that very few people in your community actually know how difficult it would be to respond effectively to the many challenges of disaster. Instead, do they appear to cross their fingers hoping that these events will never happen? Does the Fire Department know what is in the municipal emergency plan and which types of emergencies are designated as Fire Department responsibility?

If you can truly say that your department and your partnering organizations are completely prepared for any eventuality, you either deserve everyone's respect and admiration, or you are being naive. If you truly have it 'in the bag,' this book is not for you. Ask for your money back or better yet, give it to someone in a neighbouring community who may be less prepared than you. Think of the pleasure you will then have knowing that the poor soul may actually read the book and end up with a football–size lump in the pit of his stomach from worrying about how he can possibly become as well prepared and confident as you. Don't forget that you can also provide assistance and help your colleague to get rid of the pent up stress when he too has it 'in the bag.'

While preparing for crises or disasters we must also remember the day–to–day work that must be done and the continually widening scope of fire operations. It is this routine operational readiness that is the foundation for success in large scale emergency responses. Many Fire Departments, despite long and exhausting efforts, are severely challenged in combatting even ordinary emergencies. How many Fire Departments, for example, currently have all of the apparatus, equipment and materials that they believe necessary to meet their anticipated challenges? How many of them are fully confident that each of their members is completely trained to effectively and quickly perform any expected task?

Many Fire Departments will be confident that they can tackle anything and succeed. However, a large number of them would quietly acknowledge that "We do the best we can. After all we can't afford to equip or train for everything that is expected of us." Hopefully this book will provide the latter group with some food for thought.

Ever wondered who has the greater expectation of Fire Departments? Is it the residents of the municipality, members of Council or Fire Department staff? The general population typically knows little about Fire Department operations; what is done, how it is done, what is needed to do the job, or what can be reliably expected from the Fire Department? Consider then these questions: Are representatives of the public included in the emergency planning process? Should they be? The same can be asked of Council. Prior to being elected for office, most Councillors were members of the general public and have brought that low level of awareness to the Council chamber.

Councillors can not suddenly become fire protection experts simply by being elected. However, they are suddenly thrust into a policy making role that can significantly affect the local Fire Department either positively or negatively. This book will also help elected officials who, like Fire Department members, often give up a great deal of time and energy for the benefit of their community.

What about the expectations of the Fire Department? Are they too high or too low? Who decides?

The policies which establish the local Fire Department, identify the services it should provide and determine its level or quality of service are typically all set by Council. The Fire Department then implements those policies. It would seem only logical, therefore, that Council would provide adequate funding to allow full implementation of their policies. However, that is not always the case. This becomes a point of severe irritation particularly to those in volunteer services who provide their time and skills at little or no cost. Is there really a balance between the expectations of the citizens, Council and the Fire Department? Often there is not.

Full–time Fire Departments have similar concerns. Fire suppression and many other emergency response actions are labour intensive endeavours. The cost of personnel often represents a major segment of Fire Department budgets. Unfortunately, the number of Fire Department personnel is increased only in a limited amount (i.e., much less than municipal growth) or, more frequently, is significantly reduced.

A common explanation is that "we do more with less because of technological developments." Is this really the case? In some instances the answer is yes and in many others no. Many activities, despite technological developments, will remain labour intensive until other technologies outside of Fire Departments are used to reduce the need for labour.

Many Fire Departments have trouble providing enough personnel for 'routine' emergency operations. It is, therefore, particularly critical to consider some of the suggestions in this book, about lining up potential partners and learning how to work effectively with them. In doing so, the performance expectations of our citizens, Council, Fire Department staff and partners may perhaps become closer to reality.

Do you feel a bit concerned? Possibly a bit provoked? Good! Now it is time for you to read this book.

Are you likely to disagree with parts of this book? Almost certainly. Do take the time, however, to make note of those things that you disagree with, or of different approaches which you have found successful and pass that information to the respective writer(s). You will then be instrumental in ensuring an even better second edition.

My best wishes go to every reader who takes the extra time to ensure a safer community for all.

Tom Makey
Fire Commissioner
Alberta

PREFACE

Sir Winston Churchill had this to say about writing a book.

> "Writing a book is an adventure. To begin with, it is a toy, then an amusement. Then it becomes a mistress, and then it becomes a monster, then it becomes a tyrant. And, the last phase is that just as you are about to become reconciled to your servitude, you kill the monster and reel him about to the public."

Our 'adventure' has led to the 'monster' now being paraded before you in the hope that it provides guidance in all facets of emergency management. We hope that you treat the beast gently.

This book started as a question almost five years ago. The question was "why do we not have something that guides Canadian practitioners through all phases of emergency management?" It was a question I asked repeatedly during my doctoral research into the management of community–wide crises. At the time I was saturated by field reports, research data and academic writing on all aspects of emergency management. I quickly observed that much of what was published on the topic was easily divided into two general categories. One was academic based for academic circles; the other was experience–based observations and recommendations by and for practitioners. Sadly, the two groups seemed to rarely exchange ideas.

Two broad ideas shaped this book. One, emergency practitioners need to understand the result of research and its meaning on practice. And two, there is a simultaneous need to address this field of study and practice from a Canadian perspective.

The need for a Canadian perspective is not intended to demean in any way the tremendous effort of research, publication, training and development which occurred, and is occurring, elsewhere in the world. Rather, it is intended to build upon this hard work and place it in terms more meaningful to Canadian emergency planners, responders and crisis managers.

This book is directed primarily to Fire Officers. Its narrative was developed by a number of people from varied perspectives and approaches. That variety is intentional.

Layout of the content

The book has four unique parts. They are:

1. The context to disasters and crises.
2. Emergency preparedness.
3. Disaster response.
4. Disaster recovery and business continuity.

This book is not intended to be all inclusive. Given the scope of its topic area it can not be. The book is designed to serve as a GUIDE. And, in that role it provides context to the discussion, highlights significant issues and makes recommendations for practice.

Chapter one provides a brief overview of research findings regarding disasters and their effects on people and organizations. It is context setting. Chapter two is an in–depth analysis of the law and emergency management. It is not intended to turn you into a law expert. However, it should help you to better understand the connection between Fire Service operations and the law.

Chapter three discusses emergency planning as a process leading to a much needed outcome. Hazard analysis, which is part of that process, is important enough to be discussed separately in Chapter four. No plan can exist without some allocation and expenditure of resources. And, since disasters are so resource intensive, many communities will have to rely on help from 'others.' Chapter five details where external support may be found. Chapter six looks at a rare but needed resource, the Dangerous Goods Response Team (DGRT). What is it, how is it formed and what equipment it needs. Then, because no plan is complete without it being tested and exercised, Chapter seven covers that aspect of planning.

The first two chapters of the response part discuss the organizational components of the response effort. Chapter eight discusses the various Fire Command systems which are currently available. Then, Chapter nine adds another organizational perspective, the management of the crisis or disaster at community level. The two sets of systems are presented as complimentary systems.

Chapter ten covers the major issues and challenges relating to the health of Fire Service personnel at the scene. Chapter eleven looks at the challenges of small and isolated communities during the emergency management process.

Chapter twelve discusses the recovery phase which includes short and long–term recovery activities. Perhaps, it raises more questions than answers. This is because Fire Officers must understand the issues of short and long–term recovery, so that they can better assist their community through this stage

The last Chapter contains a brief summary of the book's content. It also highlights key issues for future consideration.

Acknowledgements

Sir Issac Newton 1642–1727 is believed to have said that "if I have seen further, it is because I have stood on the shoulders of giants." Indeed, this book would not have been possible without the many researchers and practitioners whose dedication, hard work and keen observations paved the road ahead.

Nor would it had been possible without each of the authors of this book. My sincere thanks to each of them for their faith in this two–year project, their hard work in producing their respective content areas and their undertaking this task despite otherwise hectic lives. I am indebted to each of them for their worthy contribution.

My thanks to each of the photographers who contributed their visual talent to this book. I am particularly grateful to the Fire Departments of Edmonton, Fort Saskatchewan, Strathcona and Yellowknife for their assistance with the search for photographs. Special thanks go to an exceptionally talented and supportive photographer – Gerry Emas (Edmonton Emergency Response Department). He has been tremendously helpful.

Special thanks are also extended to Tom Makey (Alberta's Fire Commissioner) for his introductory remarks, Anne–marie Demers (Managing Editor of the Emergency Preparedness Digest), Suzanne Van Iperen (Strathcona County Fire Department), Wayne Daley, Emergency Preparedness Canada, for his comments on Chapter 12 and Don Gratiuk, Director, Alberta Fire Training School, for his comments on Chapter 13.

Two people deserve my sincere sympathy for all their hard work. One is Lyle Blumhagen who, as a friend and my publisher, has been with me from the start of the 'adventure' to the slaying of the beast. The other is Julie Alcock who contributed devotedly and extensively to the editing of this book.

Last but not least, I wish to thank my partner and most devoted supporter, my wife Wendy. Her unyielding encouragement, confidence and occasional jab in the ribs have sustained me throughout the long journey. I could have asked for no better companion and friend.

To all of them my sincere thanks and heartfelt best wishes.

We the writers hope that you, the reader, will find this book practical, educational and thought provoking. May all your crises be manageable!

Ron Kuban
Edmonton, Alberta
June, 1996

Comments and case material for future editions and other publications are welcome.
Please contact Ron Kuban: by mail, 3116 – 36B Avenue, Edmonton, Alberta, Canada T6T 1H4; by phone, (403) 463– 5252; by fax, (403) 468–4224; or Internet, http://www.turningpointcorp.com

TABLE OF CONTENTS

Disasters, Crises And Their Consequences

Ron Kuban, Ph.D.
President, Turning Point Consulting Corp.

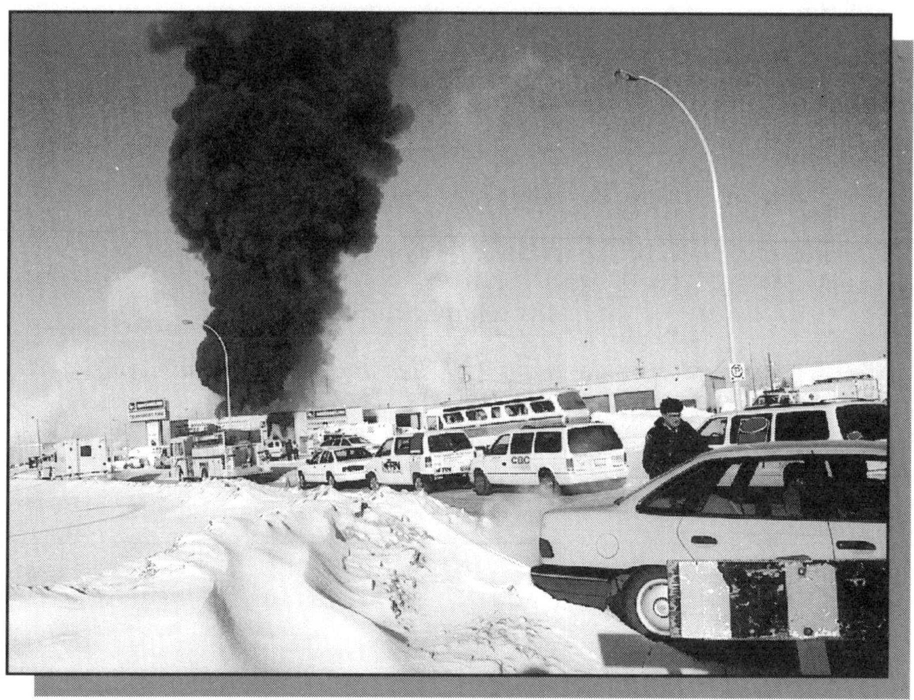

Photo Courtesy of Gerry Emas, Edmonton Emergency Response Department.

This chapter describes the nature of disasters and crises as well as their likely impact on us as individuals, our organizations and our communities. The topic is addressed through the following:

* *a review of the environment*
* *a definition of the terms emergency, disaster and crisis*
* *an outline of the myths and realities of disasters*
* *a discussion of the impact of disaster on individuals and organizations*

Any multi–disciplinary discussion relating to the management of disasters and crises must include a section to clarify the meaning of these events in personal, organizational and communal terms. This component is necessary and must lead to a clear understanding of the nature of the event for which we must train and be equipped to respond. We need, therefore, to understand what these events are, what they cause and what impact they will likely have upon us, our organizations and communities.

There are a number of significant reasons for this chapter. One is the need to clarify the terminology which emergency planners and disaster responders use to define emergencies, crises and disasters. Another reason is the need to clearly understand what makes these events disastrous and how they impact individuals, organizations and communities.

In our profession, where effective communications are so critical to success, meaningful language is ... everything! We often assume that those with whom we communicate understand what we say. After all, the terminology we use is so meaningful to us. So, why should it be less meaningful to others who are in the same emergency–response business?

In fact, the terminology used by one emergency response agency (i.e., Fire Services) may not necessarily be similar to the terminology used by its response partners (e.g., Police, Emergency Medical Services, Social Services or non–government agencies). Failure to recognize this difference can result in the failure of the planning process or, more seriously, in snags during the disaster response effort.

Consider, for example the terms emergency, disaster, crisis and response, which are central to any discussion of emergency management. They define the environment or event for which we train and in which we operate during a disaster. Therefore, these terms are often employed as if their meanings are universal and conclusive. They are not.

Equally misleading are a number of popular assumptions which exist to 'predict' the response of victims, the public, the media or the community. Because these assumptions serve as an unconscious foundation of the planning process they also serve as a basis for disaster–response action. Consequently, the accuracy (or fallacy) of these assumptions has a direct bearing on the value and effectiveness of the emergency plans which are built upon them.

There is a need, therefore, to begin this book with a chapter which defines the meaning of such terms as disaster and crisis. Equally important is the need to understand the realities and myths of the disaster (or crisis) environment. Armed with this understanding we can then develop more meaningful plans, respond more effectively and, in turn, save lives, reduce suffering and minimize damage.

OUR CHANGING ENVIRONMENT

Research into disasters and crises throughout the world has highlighted two significant patterns. One is that the frequency of these events is on the increase. The other is that the related damage figures are also increasing, and in alarming rates! These trends may be explained through the following global trends.

Increased population size and density

As our world population increases so do the risks of conflict, accidents and disasters. This is predictable, if for no other reason than the sheer size of the world's population, now at nearly five billion, and the rate of its growth. Stated more simply, there are more and more of us who live and travel across our planet. We consume more resources, generate more waste and wear– out both our infrastructure (i.e., bridges, roads, dykes, dams, sewer systems) and the environment.

Consider this as a small but poignant example. Quarantelli (1985) estimated that in the United States "44.8 percent of the Nation's 566,443 highway bridges more than 20 feet long are structurally deficient or functionally obsolete" (p. 2). No similar statistics are available about Canada, but one must wonder about our vast and aging infrastructure which is brutalized by many factors including harsh weather.

To make matters worse, the population shift to urban centres continues to escalate across the world. In many cases, the mass movement of people from dispersed rural communities to urban centres creates added stresses on the infrastructure of the recipient communities. It forces the construction of more and more high rise structures for both office and residential use. The ability of these urban centres to effectively respond to disasters is also reduced.

Moreover, as population centres continue to increase in size they become a larger, more populous and more expensive target for disasters. Unfortunately, emergency preparedness often lags behind population growth resulting in an increasing preparedness–gap.

Increased settlement in high–risk areas

Significant increases in the population of an area often create pressure on municipal officials to allow construction in and development of high–risk areas. These areas may include flood plains, earthquake faults, unstable mountain slopes and locations prone to forest or wildland fires. They may also include land near airports, industrial parks, major transportation routes, dangerous goods storage sites, hazardous–waste landfills and nuclear power plants.

Settlement in high–risk areas and in remote locations increases, in a number of ways, the risk to the local inhabitants. First, it increases the demand on the local emergency response system and further complicates its response environment. Examples include insufficient resources to meet the increased population size, improper equipment to respond to the new risks, or the commitment to wider geographical area, more dispersed population or more isolated locations.

Additionally, the development of high–risk areas into residential or even industrial zones often has a detrimental effect on these areas and increases their vulnerability to disaster. For example, increased paving and house construction in flood plains reduces the ground's ability to absorb excess water and, therefore, increases the likelihood of floods. Deforestation of mountain sides has a similar effect and could lead to flash floods.

Increased technological risks

Our insatiable thirst for technological advances has increased our exposure to disaster agents. This pattern continues at an alarming rate and is reflected in a number of issues.

First is our ever increasing specialization and inter–dependence on each other. Nearly every aspect of our lives demands the involvement of specialists or specialized equipment. No longer can we presume to have the ability to unilaterally respond to disasters. This observation is equally applicable to individuals as it is to communities.

Second, our day–to–day environment at home, at play and at work is increasingly inundated with toxic chemicals of varying hazards. according to one estimate, more than 100,000 industrial chemicals are currently in use and about 1,000 new ones are introduced annually. Their toxicity may be known when analyzed separately. However, when mixed haphazardly by floods, tornadoes or hurricanes, earthquakes, transportation accidents or major fires these chemicals present a problem of mysterious and horrendous proportion.

Third, we are continuing to produce complex and sophisticated systems (e.g., nuclear power plants), structures (e.g., dams, sky scrapers and high rise towers) and machines (e.g., nuclear generators, chemical production facilities, space shuttles). These are typically beyond the understanding of any one person. They require the response of a large team of experts, each specialized in a very small component of the whole. This complexity and the often unknown interdependence of the various parts can, and often does, significantly hamper response efforts.

Increased dependency on technology

Increases in technological risks are further exasperated by our increased dependency on technology. Many cases illustrate this dependency, but two common examples should rapidly bring the point home. One is our dependency on electricity; the other on computers.

Any significant power outage nearly anywhere in North America is bound to have significant consequences. The issue becomes particularly poignant during the winter. The abilities to heat and light one's house, cook meals, boil contaminated water, heat water for washing, travel (without traffic lights), and even communicate (using multi–line phones) are all likely to be disrupted.

The dependency on computers is evident in nearly all day–to–day activities at individual level as well as all private and public business operations. For example, a recent survey of 12,000 members of the Canadian Federation of Independent Businesses found that 84 percent are using computers, 88 percent are using FAX machines and 66 percent are using cellular phones. Additionally, all major service providers—from banking to travel, utilities, government and communications—are dependent upon computer systems. The loss or damage of their computers and computer systems during disasters, coupled with the loss of the data stored within them, can easily cripple or destroy business operations large or small.

Power failures or the incapacity of our computer systems could also significantly reduce our ability to communicate within our organization as well as external to it. Being so dependent upon these technologies we can become totally incapacitated by the disruption of power or the inability to use our computers.

Increasing world tension and terrorism

We must not ignore the reality that some disasters are caused intentionally as a result of strife and conflict. These may be due to labour strife or to an international conflict over ideology. Regardless, their outcome can be as devastating as if they were caused by nature.

To make matters worse, there are more and more groups willing to achieve their objectives through acts of terrorism and indiscriminate violence. Many cases throughout the world illustrate the point.

Canada is not immune to these types of disasters and the pattern seems to reflect an increase in both risk and vulnerability. Case in point includes sport–related riots (e.g., Edmonton, Calgary, Montreal and Vancouver), armed confrontation with activists (e.g., First Nation people and environmentalist), gang–related struggles (e.g., Montreal, Vancouver) and other political activities (e.g., FLQ, select labour unions and political movements).

GRAPPLING WITH THE KEY DEFINITIONS

Imagine extraordinary events which present major threats to human and community survival and consequently demand extreme human effort and perhaps sacrifice. What title would you provide these unusual events?

The literature on this topic is rife with the terms 'disasters,' 'emergencies,' 'catastrophes,' and 'crises.' These terms are defined in various ways and using different contexts. Occasionally different terms are used with identical meaning. Not surprisingly, the results tend to foster confusion.

The differences in terminology may be traced to the professional orientation of those who practice and those who study the various elements of emergency management. For example, the growth of the field of emergency management in the United States may be linked to three major streams: civil defense programs, the response to natural disasters, and research in the field of behavioral sciences (Drabek and Hoetmer, 1991). Petak (1985) observed that "the primary focus of research in the emergency management area has been in the general area of human response and the application of technological fixes" (p. 3).

Rosenthal, et al. (1989), on the other hand, noted that there are two major orientations in the management of out–of–the–ordinary events. One such orientation is focused on 'disasters' and is typically viewed from a sociological perspective. The other is focused on 'crises' which are typically analyzed from an organizational behaviour perspective. They noted that both perspectives are critical to a better understanding of these unique events and the style of management required to respond to them.

In fact, regardless of one's orientation, one should view out–of– the–ordinary events as points along a continuum. At the one end are uneventful situations which can be easily managed by individuals and organizations. At the other end are events which generate extreme stress and demand extensive response effort.

Day–to–day events typically include various 'incidents.' These are events which demand some low–level response, typically by those at or near the scene to return life to normal. Incidents may include vehicle accidents, small–size (and manageable) house fires and situations involving minor injuries. Invariably, this type of events can be handled by response organizations without resorting to a major call–out of their staff members or resources, and without activating mutual aid. Moreover, these events are typically handled through Standard Operating Procedures (SOPs) and other operational routines.

"Emergencies" are situations more complex than 'incidents.' They demand a more intense effort by the responding organization and, perhaps, by other response organizations in the community. They may involve mutual aid partners.

At the far end of the spectrum are events which are titled as disasters, crises and catastrophes. Because these terms often define similar outcomes, they are sometimes used interchangeably. In fact, the discussion in this book will either use the three terms interchangeably, or use the term 'crisis' to also mean disasters and catastrophes.

Let's have a closer look at the definition of the three main terms: Emergencies, disasters and crises. Please note the nature of each and the similarities among them.

Defining 'emergencies'

According to LaValle, Stoffel, and Erwin (1991) an emergency is "an unexpected event involving shortage of TIME and/or RESOURCES which places life and/or property in danger, and which requires immediate response" (p. 19). They noted that an emergency is an event slightly more complex than an accident. They defined an 'accident' as "an unpleasant and unintended happening that daily routine response can handle (daily 9–1–1 activities)" (p. 19).

Emergency Preparedness Canada (EPC) (1992) defined an emergency as "an abnormal situation in which, to limit damage to persons, property or the environment, prompt actin [sic] beyond normal procedures is required" (p. 1–1). Canada's Emergencies Act defines a national emergency as:

> An urgent and critical situation of a temporary nature that
> a) seriously endangers the lives, health and safety of Canadians and is of such proportions or nature as to exceed the capacity or authority of a province to deal with it, or
> b) seriously threatens the ability of the Government of Canada to preserve the sovereignty, security and territorial integrity of Canada and that cannot be effectively dealt with under any other law of Canada" (EPC, 1992, p.1).

Defining 'disasters'

The term 'disaster' may mean different things to different people, and consequently may be easily misunderstood. Dynes (1970) noted that the term 'disaster' may be given to a disaster agent (e.g., earthquake or hurricane), to the physical impact of that agent, to the evaluation of the physical event, to the social disruption created by the event, or to a combination of the above (p. 50). He also identified at least ten various ways to categorize disaster agents. These included a range of factors from the frequency and predictability of the disaster agent, to its scope of impact and destructive potential (pp. 52–54).

According to Fowlkes and Miller (1988) "the classic disaster, whether man–made or natural, is a social phenomenon, a cataclysm that is recognized and measured by its physical and/or economic toll on human welfare" (p. 37). Dynes (1970) viewed disasters from a sociological perspective. He noted that "a disaster is an event located in time and space, in which a community undergoes severe danger and incurs losses, so that the social structure is disrupted and the fulfilment of all or some of its essential functions is prevented" (p. 78).

The United States Federal Emergency Management Agency (FEMA) defined disaster as:

> An occurrence of a severity and magnitude that normally results in deaths, injuries, and property damage and that cannot be managed through the routine pro-

> cedures and resources of government. It usually develops suddenly and unexpectedly and requires immediate, coordinated, and effective response by multiple government and private sector organizations to meet human needs and speedy recovery (Auf der Heide, 1989, p. 51).

La Plante and Kroll–Smith defined disasters as crises which occur and unfold partly due to decisions and actions well within human control. In other words, disasters (or crises) are situations which involve and are influenced by human action and decisions, or the lack of them.

Quarantelli (1985) noted "a disaster is not simply a bigger everyday emergency" (p. 9), nor is it "simply a large–scale accident or emergency" (p. 3). He concluded that the management of disaster response is significantly different from day–to–day management operations.

Disasters are events with far–reaching consequences. Withers (1988) discussed his experiences as Canada's Chief of the Defence Staff, and later as Deputy Minister of the Department of Transport. He noted that "it is very clear . . . that a major crisis and the handling of it can drastically affect the lives of parliamentarians, civil servants and the public at large" (p. 18).

Raphael (1986) noted that "perhaps the simplest [disaster] definition is that of Cohen and Ahearn (1980): 'disasters are extraordinary events that cause great destruction of property and may result in death, physical injury, and human suffering'." (p. 5).

Defining 'crises'

According to Fink (1986) crises are analogous to major and potentially communicable illness in the human body. He argued that "it can be a fatal mistake to think that a crisis, if left unattended, will heal by itself. A crisis should be viewed as highly virulent – and should be treated accordingly" (p. 80).

Fink (1986) observed that a crisis "can occur today with little or no warning, anywhere, anytime. And it can happen to any company, large or small, public or private. It is . . . the safest of assumptions that a crisis looms on the horizon" (p. 1). He also added the following warning: "Beware and be advised: crises historically evolve in cyclical fashion and a crisis sufferer almost never has the luxury of dealing exclusively with one crisis at the time" (p. 25). However, "crises need not be the seemingly uncontrolled and uncontrollable events that their victims too often allow them to become" (p. 2).

Rosenthal, et al., (1989) noted that the typical dichotomy of disasters into either natural or man–made events is not comprehensive or meaningful enough to allow greater discussion and understanding. They recommended the use of the term "crisis" as a general all–encompassing concept.

Crises may be caused or triggered by a variety of factors which can, and often do, interact with each other. This tends to further complicate an already complex situation and further exacerbates the response effort.

For example, Shrivastawa (1989) reported on technological disasters and noted that they can be caused by the technology in use, organizational policies, human judgement, regulatory systems, infra–structural facilities, and even the public emergency preparedness organizations which respond to the disaster.

Environment Canada (1991) defined crisis from a political perspective. It noted that Privy Council's Office (PCO) has formally defined a crisis as:

> A period of danger for the government, resulting from a natural or man–made mishap, debacle, or disaster. A crisis need not pose a serious threat to human life, but it must somehow challenge the public sense of appropriateness, tradition or values, safety or security in a way that threatens the integrity of the government (p. 44).

Accordingly, crisis management is the depoliticization of the situation. In other words it is "the process of returning an event to a near normal daily activity unworthy of special attention" (p. 50).

PCO (n.d.) noted that "crises are inevitable" (p. 5) and that "a crisis is a crisis in large part because it emerges as if from nowhere and challenges our sense of what is normal and well– managed" (p. 3).

Crises are abnormal and unique events which occur with some degree of surprise to demand unusual, extensive and taxing response effort. They are, in fact, turning points with a potential for affecting individuals, family units, organizations, communities, nations and the world community in both the short and the long term. While they typically involve some degree of hazard or devastation, crises could also lead to positive outcomes and growth.

Crisis situations ultimately highlight two 'truths.' One, is that "while a crisis may strike at the heart of a corporation or a family, it is always an individual who must have the heart – and the courage – to respond" (Fink, 1986, p. 1). The other is the realization that, given the magnitude of crises, the response efforts must eventually reach a level of complexity much greater than that required in day–to–day operations, requiring the resources, experience, and capabilities provided by organizations through organized response (Drabek & Hoetmer, 1991; Dynes, 1970; Quarantelli, 1985).

DIAGNOSING 'CRISES' OR 'DISASTERS'

Definition aside, how does one diagnose a disaster? What are the categories which one can use to determine the 'type' of disaster being confronted?

Rosenthal, Hart and Charles (1989) noted that "the variety of crises is stunning. [And that] crisis analysts have been trying to impose order on this variety for years by developing typologies of crisis events" (p. 11). These efforts resulted in elaborated dichotomies such as natural versus man–made, consensual versus conflicting, or nuclear versus non–nuclear. Rosenthal, Hart and Charles (1989) concluded that "somehow these efforts have failed to cover the entire range of crisis events" (p. 11).

The above dichotomies oversimplify the nature of the disaster and often present it as being the result or reflection of a single disaster agent. In reality, few disasters are that simple. Consider for example the term technological disaster. It implies a failure of a certain technology but does not account for a variety of other possible failures, including that of community planning, human error or organizational.

Moreover, as Charles (1989) noted, when emphasis is placed on technology, as it most often is, the risk is that the problem is seen to be resolved with a technical 'fix.' This, in turn, fails to acknowledge the effects which formal and informal organizations have on the problem and its solution.

Perrow (1984) analyzed disasters from the blended perspectives of the sociological perspective and the technological factors. He noted two major dimensions of socio–technical systems which predict and explain the occurrence of crises or 'normal accidents.' The two dimensions are the 'complexity' of a system and the coupling of its parts. 'Coupling' refers to how tightly (or loosely) are the system's components dependent upon and interrelated with each other. Perrow concluded that the more complex a system is and the tighter its coupling, the more one can anticipate it to have 'normal accidents' with devastating results.

Regardless of their categories, all disasters and crises fit within a sequence of a four phase umbrella called 'emergency management'. The United States Federal Emergency Management Agency (FEMA) coined these phases: Mitigation, Preparedness, Response, and Recovery. Each of these phases address specific issues relating to disasters and crises.

Charles and Kim (1988) noted that some disasters may occur briefly while others may unfold over a period of years. However, as Dynes (1970) observed, disasters typically have seven predictable stages and associated functions. They are as follows:

> Warning (Precautionary activity), Threat (Survival action), Impact ("Holding on"), Inventory (Diagnosis of situation and decision on action), Rescue (Spontaneous, local, unorganized extrication and first aid, some preventive measures), Remedy (Organized and professional relief, medical care, preventive and security measures), Recovery (Individual rehabilitation and readjustment; community restoration of property and organizational preventive measures against recurrence) (p. 56).

Drabek (1986) described four stages of disaster: preparedness, response, reconstruction, and mitigation. "Preparedness" included both planning and warning about the disaster. "Response" involved both the pre and post impact periods. The "recovery" stage included two parts: the "restoration" period of less than six months after the impact, and the "reconstruction" period which was longer than six months. The "mitigation" stage lasted for as long as necessary until individuals and "systems" were returned to normalcy.

MYTHS ABOUT DISASTERS AND THEIR OUTCOME

Despite the extensive research to the contrary, a number of myths persist about the nature of disasters, their impact on people and the manner in which people will respond to these events. While the belief in them is wide spread, they are still ... MYTHS! It is important, therefore, to take stock in these myths, realize their true meaning and plan accordingly for more effective action during disaster–response periods.

Here, then, are some of the more common myths. Some relate to what individuals may attribute to themselves in the disaster situation, others to what is attributed to the situation, the response effort and the public's reaction to the disaster.

It will not happen here

Many individuals, organizations and communities have a sense of invincibility which fly in the face of the findings of hazard–analysis studies and reported disasters elsewhere. These people often fail to realize the unpalatable truth: The issue is when, not if, disaster strikes.

It will not happen to me (or my organization)

Much as in the point above, the sense of invincibility continues to exist despite acceptance that a disaster IS likely to occur in the local area.

If it did happen to me, I will be able to manage it and recover from it

Once again, that sense of invincibility fails to acknowledge the reality that disasters, by their definition, will overwhelm (even if only initially) those who are affected by them.

We have insurance

Canadians have a wide variety of insurance programs to choose from and thus protect themselves, their lives, vehicles, homes, possessions, employment, social security, health and business operations. Some of these programs (e.g., vehicle insurance) are mandatory. And yet, many Canadians fail to carry sufficient insurance, even when it is mandated. Moreover, those who do carry insurance, often assume that their coverage will meet all their needs during a disaster.

Catastrophic disasters in the United States have highlighted the folly of trusting the complete cost of the recovery process to insurance coverage. Not all disaster events are covered by insurance. And, even in cases when a disaster is within a policy's coverage, compensation is often significantly less than the total loss incurred during (and following) the disaster.

Members of the Public could not handle the truth about the disaster or crisis

The myth is that members of the public could neither understand, nor be able to cope with, details relating to the disaster which is unfolding, or is about to unfold in their area. This myth can lead to a particularly dangerous response. It may result in members of the public receiving less information about the disaster and, therefore, being less prepared to deal with it at the time when they most need both!

People panic during crises

This myth is born by the sensational headlines in the various media which depict the public emotionally aroused, fear stricken and at a loss for the appropriate response. While all these may be true, and justifiably so, they do not represent 'panic.' Scores of research findings contradict the myth and yet it persists (Quarantelli, 1982, 1985).

The truth of the matter is, that relatively few members of the public 'panic.' Most handle their situation as best as they can by trying to find ways to overcome the disaster agent and its outcome.

Most people act in a rational way. Their behaviour may, in some cases, be inappropriate (e.g., screaming, crying, fidgeting), but it is still 'rational.' It is NOT panic which is typically a behaviour reflecting the total loss of one's senses.

Quarantelli (1979, p. 13) identified three conditions which must be present for panic to occur. Drabek et al. (1981) reported them as:

1. A perception of possible entrapment and the inability to escape
2. A sense of powerlessness to 'fight' the threat
3. A feeling of social isolation and the need to depend on one's own ability and resources.

Some people do panic during disaster situations. However, research into this area indicates that those who panic during crisis situations are often pre–disposed to panic behaviour and that the disaster agent rarely causes members of the general public to behave in a panic–like manner.

People's behaviour during crises is socially maladaptive

This myth states that people will behave in ways that will harm their neighbours and fellow community members. This maladaptive behaviour is typically stated in terms of increased looting and in the refusal to offer assistance to those in need due to the disaster agent.

The truth is that every community has some 'looting.' When conducted during non–disaster periods, this activity is often reflected in break–and–enter incidents. Quarantelli (1982, 1985) discovered that the incidents of looting often decrease during the early part of the disaster–response period and are typically conducted by outsiders. Disasters which are based on intentional violence (e.g., riots) are the exception to the rule.

The assumption that people will not be willing to assist those in need is also inaccurate. Here too, researchers have discovered that people are particularly concerned for the wellbeing of their relatives, friends, neighbours and even strangers (Dynes, 1971; Drabek et al., 1981).

The dichotomy of 'rescuer' and 'victim.'

Many disaster responders perceive themselves as 'rescuers' of the disaster's 'victims.' Both images, of 'rescuer' and 'victim,' are a myth and cloud the reality of disaster response activities (Auf der Heide, 1989; Drabek, 1986; Dynes, 1970; Quarantelli, 1985).

In fact, maintaining this myth creates very dangerous stereotypes for both responders as well as survivors. When responders are termed 'rescuers' they build themselves for failure. They create the illusion of being invulnerable, all–powerful, without– limitation and success–prone. None of these characteristics are necessarily true of themselves. Moreover, the stereotype of the responder as rescuer also creates an illusion of the victim as weak, vulnerable, helpless and unwilling to act towards self preservation (Raphael, 1986; Kuban, 1994).

As noted above, the truth of the matter is that responders may themselves become survivors of a disaster. And, the survivors of a disaster may well become the immediate responders to those in need around them. Both responders and survivors are human beings; both are in heightened state of stress and personal risk; and, both are focused on the preservation of life and limb, though not necessarily their own. The key difference between the two groups is that the responders are typically better trained and equipped to perform their response duties.

IMPACT OF CRISES AND DISASTERS ON INDIVIDUALS

By their definition, crises and disasters are exceptionally disruptive events regardless of the level in which they occur (i.e., individual, family, organization or community). The literature on the subject contains a great deal to explain what happens to people and organizations before, during and after crises. This information is particularly useful because it helps to predict many of the issues which will be encountered during disaster. This, in turn, will assist in the development of more appropriate emergency plans and more effective response procedures.

One of the common 'truths' to emerge from disasters is that individuals, not organizations, are first to respond to disasters (Anderson & Woodrow, 1989; Auf der Heide, 1989; Beare, 1980; Drabek, 1986; Dynes, 1970; Mileti, Drabek, & Haas, 1975; Quarantelli, 1978, 1982, 1985). These people are often in or near the area affected by the disaster, are immediately mobile, less cumbersome than organizations or groups and are driven by a direct and relatively unambiguous sense of the disaster and its consequences.

Another major 'truth' is that, regardless of the level of their occurrence, disasters ALWAYS affect people and always at a personal level. Raphael (1986) observed that "all who experience disaster are likely to be in some ways touched by it; they can never be exactly the same again" (p. 27). Individuals may be 'touched' by a disaster even before it strikes (e.g., during its 'warning' phase) and will definitely be affected by its impact phase or stage.

Perhaps the most striking effect of disasters and crises on individuals is the exceptionally high stress level which these events generate. Anticipation of the event, the occurrence of the event and its consequences all contribute to a level of stress which is far and beyond what is 'typical' or 'normal' (Kuban, 1995a).

The impact of the disaster and its consequences often leaves people bewildered and disoriented. The larger the disaster, the more they are likely to be uprooted from their family and work units, homes and routines. And yet, in all that chaos, people typically go out of their way to help others.

The perception that disasters bring out the worst in people is a myth! Williams (1970) reported that "well–documented humanitarian feelings surface with news of a nearby disaster" (cited in Drabek et al., 1981, p. 18). Furthermore, victims of disaster often respond with actions of altruism (Auf der Heide, 1989; Bryn, 1974; Drabek et al., 1981; Dynes, 1970; Fritz, 1961).

One of the reasons for the general attitude of goodwill is that disasters have a levelling affect on people. They don't strike any one group and, therefore, temporarily reduce status differences. Hence, class, ethnic, and other status distinctions temporarily disappear during the early disaster response period. (It is important to note, however, that disasters typically affect those who are already vulnerable more severely than those who are not).

In spite of the disruptive effects of disasters "the overwhelming picture [in disasters] is one of human resilience; of suffering that is overcome through courage and fortitude; of altruism, and human endurance" (Raphael, 1986; p. 24). Panic is also rare during disasters (Auf der Heide, 1989; Dynes, 1970; Mileti, Drabek, & Haas, 1975; Quarantelli, 1982, 1985), because "both victims and nonvictims in disaster–stricken communities seek to 'normalize' the situation by using the same interpretative frameworks they use in their daily lives" (Drabek, et al., 1981, p. 8).

Disaster responders are not immune to the above–noted effects. Health and Welfare Canada (1990) reported that even disaster workers or 'responders' who typically function well in their jobs may be overcome by the disaster situation. It noted that "at times, the stresses experienced can overcome a person's natural defences . . . and the person is suddenly confronted with a tidal wave of painful events that cannot be handled through ordinary processes of adjustment" (p. 51). It reported that, although responses vary, after a disaster "people gradually come to realize what has happened. Some cry and some get mad. Others feel confused and disorganized" (p. 92). Also, "several days after the event, some people feel nervous, have difficulty concentrating, suffer from insomnia, feel guilty or deny reality" (p, 92). These difficulties may be experienced by emergency response personnel as well as members of the public who experienced the disaster either first or second hand (Raphael, 1986).

Responders in disaster situations confront many conflicts which add stress to their already stressful environment. Raphael (1986), for example, observed that conflicts regarding roles and priorities during that time create much stress for the individual concerned. Dynes (1970) noted "that the conflict most frequently faced by [individuals in a disaster] . . . was between the family and a variety of other units, most notably occupational and community loyalties" (p. 151). Other key conflicts include the choice the individual must make between alternative disaster roles (e.g., fight the fire or save lives), between loyalty to one's organization or to fellow employees, and between loyalty to community or to extra community groups (p. 152).

However, the concern that emergency responders will not perform their duties during a massive disaster which affects their homes and family is not validated by research. Bryn (1974) reported on a study conducted by Dynes and Quarantelli of over 3,000 staff members from various organizations, and of reports on the conduct of thousands of other workers during disasters. Their study "never found a [single] case where a person abandoned an important emergency–related responsibility because of anxiety" (p. 10). However, it is important to realize that their findings relate to those who were already on duty. In fact, those off duty were more likely to verify the safety of their family members and then report to duty (Mileti, Drabek, & Haas, 1975, p. 53).

Quarantelli (1985) concluded that the role conflict for disaster responders between disaster response duties and family related responsibilities did "not result in the abandonment of, or failure to carry out occupational responsibilities" (p. 15).

Quarantelli (1982) summarized individual responses to disasters as follows: "Those who experience disasters are not immobilized by even the most catastrophic of events. They are neither devoid of initiative nor passively expectant that others will take care of them and their needs" (p. 8). It is these individuals who on the one hand staff the disaster–response organizations, and on the other are served by them.

THE IMPACT OF CRISES AND DISASTERS ON ORGANIZATIONS

While individuals are first to respond to a disaster, effective and sustained disaster response is more within the realm of organizations (Dynes, 1971; Quarantelli, 1982,

1985; Auf der Heide, 1989). In other words, individual response is critical for the more immediate needs of disaster response, while organizational resources and capabilities are required to sustain the demanding response effort to its completion. Moreover, the greater the destruction of a disaster or a crisis, the greater the need for organizational response.

Like individuals, organizations are greatly affected by disasters. For example, a tornado which kills community members may also kill needed staff members. A flood which destroys private homes may also wash away required public and organizational resources. An earthquake which paralyses phones and power lines may also neutralize critical fax machines, computer links, and broadcasting equipment. Furthermore, as Drabek et al. (1981) suggested, "too often, the emergency grows in complexity so swiftly that the ability to deal with all the responsibilities and functions is lost" (p. 279).

Rosenthal, Hart, and Charles (1989) observed that crises cause a dramatic change in bureaucratic organizations. They noted that among the key changes are: decision making becomes centralized, informal rules and improvisation become the modus operandi, bureaucratic politics flourish, the speed and volume of communication increases dramatically, decision makers prefer to rely on trusted sources, and problems emerge regarding the control of the flow of information (pp. 18–20).

Dynes (1970) noted that certain activities such as collecting information, control, and coordination are less obvious in a disaster and are often neglected. This neglect further aggravates the situation. Quarantelli (1982) suggested that the many problems faced by organizations in a disaster may be grouped into four categories: communication, coordination, authority, and personnel. Charles and Kim (1988), as well as Rosenthal, Charles, and Hart (1989), reported that the function of decision making is also critical. Each of these is discussed separately below.

Communication

Fink (1986) reported that in 1984 Americans transmitted approximately 976.4 billion messages via a variety of means. These included: "600 billion telephone calls, 250 billion interoffice memos, 125 billion first–class letters, 1 billion telegrams, Telexes, or facsimiles, 250 million electronic mail messages, 125 million priority–mail, overnight–courier letters and packages" (p. 99).

Rosenthal, Charles, and Hart (1989) wrote that "public agencies can be viewed as information processing systems" (p. 19). They added that:

> These systems determine what information is to be processed, and they entail standardized ways in which information is transmitted. They usually adapt themselves best to inputs that resemble previously processed information. They tend to be disposed to consume information that is easy to categorize, leaning towards so–called programmed decisions (p. 19).

Rosenthal, Charles, and Hart (1989) also stated that crisis information does not fit the above pattern of normal communication. Instead, they described crisis information as threatening, frightening, unfamiliar, new, surprising, unprecedented, critical, and ambiguous.

It is generally accepted that timely and accurate information is critical for effective decision making (Kepner, & Tregoe, 1975; Plunkett, & Hale, 1982). Charles, and Kim (1988), Fink (1986), and Rosenthal, Charles, and Hart (1989) reported on a wide array of disasters. They all agreed on the need of decision makers to have accurate information both before and especially during crises. As an example, when reporting on the crash of the Challenger, Charles (1989) noted that "it is quite clear . . . that crucial information did not reach important decision makers. Had the decision makers known [that information] . . . it is unlikely that the launch would have taken place" with such disastrous consequences (p. 156).

Organizations which undergo crisis must be vigilant to communicate to all groups which need the information. These groups may include employees, other response agencies, government officials, customers, investors, elected public officials, insurance companies, lawyers, families of victims, and many more. Fink (1986) noted that each group may require its own special language and perhaps be approached differently. He added that "during a crisis you have an important message to communicate. But how that message is communicated is sometimes as important as the message itself" (p. 107).

The key challenge of crisis managers is to manage the flow of crisis–related information, and find ways to effectively link that information with both the decision making and implementation process. It is a difficult process fraught with many obstacles (Rosenthal, Hart, and Charles, 1989).

One of the obstacles to the smooth flow of information within organizations and between them may be summed up in the terms power and turf. Mintzberg (1973) noted that the power of many managers is derived from the unique information which they possess. The same applies to organizations. It is not surprising, therefore, that many organizations are reluctant to share their knowledge with others.

The Privy Council's Office (PCO) (n.d.) noted that "particularly in the early stages [of crises] there tends to be a natural resistance within an organization embroiled in a crisis to be forthcoming with information. This may exacerbate the perception that events are outpacing the response" (p. 7).

Rosenthal, Hart, and Charles (1989) observed that data processing in a crisis does break down. They reported that in a crisis "the processing of incoming information as well as the monitoring of outgoing information pose serious problems of controlling the information flow. Decision makers need to cope with a peculiar variety of overload and 'underload,'" both in incoming and outgoing communications (p. 20). This situation is further complicated by the reality that the strategic data bank of most organizations is not in the memory of its computers but in the minds of its managers (Mintzberg, 1975).

One of the often stated reasons for information overload in disasters is "convergence" (Auf der Heide, 1989; Dynes, 1970; Scanlon, 1990). Fritz and Mathewson (1957) identified three major types of convergence activity—personnel, information, and material resources. They reported that by far the most difficult to disentangle is the convergence of information which leads to information "overload."

Upon the onset of a crisis, organizations are usually unclear of the extent of the disaster, its impact on their human and other resources, the location of these resources, and the role which these organizations can play in communal disaster response (Auf der Heide, 1989; Dynes, 1970; Quarantelli, 1982, 1985).
Communication in the emotionally charged crisis environment is also a major challenge. On the one hand the situation is so overwhelming that concrete and complete information is lacking, and on the other there is a significant convergence of bits of information gathered to define a situation which is beyond immediate definition or comprehension (Auf der Heide, 1989; Drabek, 1986, 1991; Dynes, 1970; Quarantelli, 1985; Rosenthal et al., 1989).

The situation is further complicated by the lack of access into the disaster's impact area. This limits the ability of members of response organizations or the media to conduct personal reconnaissance of the situation. It then increases the tendency to accept exaggerated accounts of the situation as factual descriptions of the situation (Dynes, 1970).

Reporting on the response to the mid–air collision over San Diego, California in September 1978, Scanlon (1990) wrote that:

> Communications also proved to be a headache. Telephone circuits were saturated. Radio channels were flooded. The police site commander actually turned his radio off because the constant chatter of radio squawk was too distracting. Somehow media people got hold of the number of the radio phone located in the police command van. They tied up that line with calls (p. 114).

Quarantelli (1985) stated that communication problems which organizations experience in disasters are more the outcome of human error than equipment failure. He explained that "under normal conditions, the communication system is designed to process and exchange predetermined types and quantities of information. However, during a disaster, the number of staff using the communication system increases greatly" (p. 12) thus overburdening the system.

Drabek et al. (1981) found that "communication flow [in disasters] was surprisingly dense and to a large extent unregulated" (p. xix). Rosenthal, Hart, and Charles (1989) reported that "in crisis situations there is a considerable increase in the volume and speed of upward and downward communications. Time spending [consuming] procedures are set aside. High–level officials directly communicate with low–ranking bureaucrats" (p.19). Auf der Heide (1989) observed that the difficulty with the information overload is that it forces those occupying communication and decision–making positions to perform a "communication triage. That is, they must filter out all but the most essential information to transmit. A problem can occur when the person filtering the information does not understand its significance to the overall disaster effort" (pp. 55–56).

Organizations experience at least five categories of communication problems in disasters. These communication categories are intra– organizational, inter–organizational, from the organization to the public, from the public to the organization and between systems (Quarantelli, 1982, 1985). These are discussed separately below.

Intra–organizational communication. The entry point of information into an organization, its flow across the organization's hierarchies, and its utilization may all be altered by a disaster. Because of their physical proximity to a disaster site, or their special contact with response agencies, individuals may suddenly become their organization's information source and provide information in a non–routine manner. Due to the manner of its collection, and the pressure of the situation, such information may not be communicated to the appropriate people (Auf der Heide, 1989; Drabek et al., 1981; Dynes, 1970; Quarantelli, 1982, 1985).

Organizations also face the problems of a surge of regular but extra–shift staff and of volunteers who place added demands on the whole communication system—both on its hardware and its process (Quarantelli, 1982).

Inter–organizational communication. One of the major obstacles in inter–organizational communication is that disaster response requires organizations to communicate in unusual ways and with unfamiliar organizations (Dynes, 1970; Quarantelli, 1982), some of which emerged after the disaster's impact (Drabek, et al., 1981). Quarantelli (1982) noted that the more bureaucratic an organization is in its normal communication, the more difficulty it will have shifting its communication patterns and adapting to the new environment of a disaster.

Pre–disaster inter–agency communications are typically between officials who are familiar with each other and during a period when time is available to develop this familiarity. However, disaster environments provide limited opportunity and time to get to know other individuals and organizations. This limitation hampers effective communication (Quarantelli, 1985). Such communications are based on trust and need to be developed prior to disasters through the process of joint emergency planning, training and exercising.

Communications from organizations to the public. Disasters may force some organizations to communicate with the public in spite of their staff members' inability, lack of experience or disinterest in doing so (Auf der Heide, 1989; Beare,

1980; Dynes, 1970; Quarantelli, 1982, 1985; Withers, 1988). An additional problem is that many organizations are unaware of the unique needs of risk communications. That is, providing the public with information that is meaningful in a manner that makes that information easily understood, credible and more likely to be followed.

Whatever is or may be meaningful information to response personnel is not necessarily meaningful to members of the public. For example, messages to the public are often stated in organizational expectations and requirements instead of addressing the public's individual needs and the action required by them.

Communications from the public to organizations. During disaster situations people will often approach the more visible organizations (e.g., the police) and saturate them with requests for assistance or information. Members of the public will often turn to familiar and trusted organizations. Because of that, queries by members of the public may be made to organizations which either lack the desired information, or are unauthorized to release it (Quarantelli, 1982). In either case, the added stress to the internal communication system of the organization being queried may cause it to overload and break down (Auf der Heide, 1989).

Communication among systems. Disaster response often involves not only individual organizations, but the 'systems' to which they belong. A disaster involving casualties, for example, ultimately involves the health services and the social services systems. Communications between such systems is often more complicated and structured than the communication between organizations (Auf der Heide, 1989; Quarantelli, 1985).

The existence of 'boundary personnel' in organizations facilitates the transfer of information between organizations and systems. 'Boundary personnel' are those who are members of, or, have contacts with a number of organizations (Dynes, 1970; Quarantelli, 1985; Warheit & Dynes, 1969). These inter–organizational linkages help overcome the disruptive effect of a disaster on the formal communication system of the organizations involved.

There are also 'boundary organizations' which are typified by Emergency Measures Organizations at municipal, provincial and federal levels. These organizations own and control few resources. And yet, their contribution is invaluable if conducted well. Their greatest asset is the extensive network of contacts, developed and maintained prior to the disaster. Through this network of contacts, boundary organizations could perform three critical roles. These relate to the coordination of:

1. Jurisdictions, interests and capabilities.
2. The collective planning effort (e.g., drafting of the plan, training, exercising and securing needed resources).
3. Resources and activities during the disaster response period.

Coordination

Environment Canada (1991) identified coordination as the "essential process which binds together all the arrangements that must function together to provide effective disaster response and management" (p. 4). It also noted that:

> the aim of 'co–ordination' as it applies to emergency preparedness and response is to bring together a number of disparate organizations in such a way that their skills and resources can be used in an effective manner to prepare for, respond to, or mitigate the effects of an emergency (p. 3).

Coordination is critical during all four phases of emergency management: mitigation, preparedness, response and recovery. Hoffman (1988), Emergency Preparedness Canada (1990), and Environment Canada (1991) emphasized that disaster coordination efforts must be focused on pre–set priorities, based on prior agreements, and serve as guides for action. Coordination efforts, they noted, regulate the response process and provide a degree of control.

However, the term "coordination" often means different things to different people. To some it means only the exchange of information relating to emergency response, while to others it signals centralized decision making or centralized resource allocation (Quarantelli, 1985). Regardless, Drabek and Hoetmer (1991) observed that effective emergency management requires the coordination of five key resources: "information, people, money, physical space, and equipment" (p. 63). Furthermore, according to Emergency Preparedness Canada (1990).

> Co–ordination includes the provision of policy guidance, leadership and the responsibility to bring together various players, and to lead them in a fashion that combines their expertise and resources to result in the achievement of national goals (p. 3).

Inter–agency coordination. "Routine emergencies create little demand for ongoing moment–to–moment coordination among the involved organizations" (Auf der Heide, 1989, p. 53). A disaster environment, however, is quite different. It requires "intense activities on the part of diverse organizations and brings together many people who had little contact with each other before the crisis" (Quarantelli, 1978, pp. 4–5).

Inter–agency coordination is almost always a problem in disasters because these events impose on organizations demands which cannot be met independently. Drabek and Hoetmer (1991) stated that "the larger the organization—staff, budget, and resources—and the greater the number and variety of its services, the greater its needs to interact with other organizations" (p. 6). "A disaster event reduces the autonomy of each organization since it no longer has the same control over its environment that it had previously" (Warheit, & Dynes, 1969, p. 12). Additionally, the disaster response of one organization typically has significant effect on the response efforts of another (Drabek et al., 1981; Dynes, 1970; Warheit & Dynes, 1969).

Drabek and Hoetmer (1991) observed that "organizations seek relationships with other organizations as a mean of coping with rapid change and uncertainty in the environment" (p. 61). They stated that this effort to establish new relationships is manifested through integration and coordination. They observed that although the two are often used interchangeably, they are different. "To integrate means to draw separate parts together into a unified whole. In contrast, to coordinate means to bring into common action or to harmonize" (pp. 57–58).

Quarantelli (1985) observed that during periods of disaster "organizations are forced into more and different kinds of interactions with other groups. The greater the number of contacts among organizations the more new relationships with other groups and organizations will be established" (p. 5).

Warheit and Dynes (1969) reported that there are two major types of inter–organizational relationships in disaster situations. One is the exchange of resources; the other, the exchange of information. Drabek and Hoetmer (1991) observed that "the more complex the community . . . the more important it is to establish coordination" (p. 55).

Drabek and Hoetmer (1991) stated that coordination may be voluntary or mandated. It may relate to administration, personnel practices, planning and programming, and administrative support services. (Administrative services are generally more difficult to establish than direct service linkages.) They identified a number of advantages for inter–organizational coordination. These included: "Financial stability, increased staff creativity, public support or perception of legitimacy, broader geographical representation, prestige, reduced fragmentation of services, continuity of services, [and] reduced duplication of services" (pp. 61–62).

In one sense disasters create a temporary unifying effect on groups and organizations. Individual differences and disagreements are often set aside during a disaster but resurface soon afterwards (Beare, 1980; Bryn, 1974; Dynes, 1970). Dynes (1970) wrote that "in every community there is a potential of conflict. However, during an emergency, community conflicts tend to be minimized" (p. 98). He accredited that phenomenon to the following:

1. The existence of an external threat or agent.
2. The presence of consensus on the need to act.
3. A sense of urgency.
4. The creation of a strong (community) identification.
5. The focusing on the present.
6. The breakdown of social distinctions.

Cooperation among organizations during disaster period is often short lived. Organizations which band together to respond to a disaster, often revert to their more traditional roles and functions as soon as the initial threat of the disaster ceases to exist (Dynes, 1970). Quarantelli (1982) noted that "surface cordiality notwithstanding, organizations ... often have difficulty coordinating [their] diaster responses because they have different interests, tasks and goals" (p. 9). Other obstacles to effective coordination include failure to negotiate, cooperate and communicate.

Many coordination problems stem from failure to share information among agencies. "In disasters, communication difficulties are often hard to separate from coordination difficulties, and the greatest coordination difficulties are inter–organizational" (Auf der Heide, 1989, p. 79).

Another major obstacle to effective coordination is the vast number of agencies which are required and often involved in disaster response. The 1982 United States Census of Governments identified over 82,000 separate "governments" (Auf der Heide, 1989, p. 57). In a disaster, each affected government agency interacts with a multitude of private, public and volunteer organizations which bring their own procedures, values, and resources into the already chaotic environment of the disaster area. Some of these organizations may be "established" while others may be "emergent." Some may have direct emergency response focus while others may have no relevant experience in disaster response. Some may have credibility while others may not. Each of these factors influences significantly the cooperation among agencies (Auf der Heide, 1989; Dynes, 1970; Warheit, & Dynes, 1969).

Drabek et al. (1981) reported that "those who must manage a disaster response . . . are surprised at the number and diversity of groups who will arrive to help with their special expertise" (p. xviii). Rosenthal, et al. (1989) reported that in crisis situations

> different actors hold different perceptions stemming from differences in tasks, jurisdictions, education, geographic location, level of preparedness, and other political and administrative considerations. Consequently, decision makers and agencies are drawn into a crisis at different moments, from different points of view, and with different purposes. This diversity more often than not prevails upon attempts to coordinate or integrate crisis management efforts (p. 436).

Unfortunately, many organizations continue to operate independently and fail to coordinate their efforts within the overall response plan. Quarantelli (1985) wrote that even local agencies, such as fire and police, which normally work together may encounter difficulties in integrating their efforts in a disaster. He noted that this lack of coordination is based on three major problems: Lack of consensus on the meaning of coordination, strained relations caused by new tasks, and the difficulty of communicating at community level during a disaster. He concluded that "the greater the scope of a disaster and the greater the numbers of responders, the less is the likelihood of success of any overall organizational coordination" (p. 18). Efforts to bring about this coordination often lead to the establishment of martial law or the appointment of one or more agencies as central decision makers (Quarantelli, 1985). That move is not necessarily the correct one.

Drabek and Hoetmer (1991, p. 58) identified seven key obstacles to the coordination of community emergency response efforts. These are:

1. The tendency of organizations to seek autonomy.
2. Staff commitment to professional ideologies and work autonomy.
3. Differences in organizational technologies and resource needs.
4. Fear that the identity of the group or organization will be lost.
5. Concern about the redirection of scarce resources.
6. The proliferation of organizations and interest groups across multiple political jurisdictions.
7. Differences in costs and benefits from participating in coordination.

Warheit and Dynes (1969) observed that "inter–organizational relationships tend to occur most frequently between organizations that consider each other as being legitimate" (p. 12). Auf der Heide (1989) wrote that "when organizations have interacted and coordinated with each other beforehand, they have had fewer problems doing so in a disaster" (p. 82). At the basis of these relationships is the issue of trust. Comfort (1989) documented a number of disasters and concluded that "the factor of trust was crucial to action at each level of disaster operations, both by its presence and its absence" (p. 335). She also wrote

> Developing trust in disaster operations is an elusive task. It cannot be bought or forced. It can only be earned on the basis of demonstrated performance toward a shared goal. Under the urgent constraints of time and uncertainty characteristic of disaster operations, trust bridges inevitable gaps in information and facilitates action in this complex set of conditions (p. 336).

Drabek and Hoetmer (1991) emphasized the need to coordinate community resources in disaster situations. They pointed to the increasing complexity of disaster response as the most significant reason for this coordination. They observed (p. 61) that there are at least five factors which facilitate coordination:

1. Shared goals and expectations about what the organizations will and will not do.
2. Shared leaders or overlapping board members.
3. Diversity of roles and interests.
4. Similarity in technologies and resource needs.
5. High rates of environmental change.

Resource coordination. Coordination difficulties are not restricted to communication and inter–agency contacts, but also extend to material and human resources. Disasters often destroy some but not all locally available resources. Additionally, a typical lack of information and "the atypical mode in which resources respond makes it difficult to tell what resources are present, where they are, what they are doing" (Auf der Heide, 1989, p. 63).

Another predictable complication for disaster response efforts is the convergence of material and human resources onto the disaster area. Kallsen (1983) noted that external organizations usually increase the pressure on the local, already weak, logistical system (cited in Auf der Heide, 1989). Jim Hoffman, Regional Director of

Emergency Preparedness Canada, Alberta/NWT Region experienced this during the response to the July 31, 1987 Edmonton Tornado. He wrote:

> When an event draws national and international attention, a mass of resources often pours upon the scene, and often these are loaded upon volunteers or agencies not designed to cope with a mass assault. As a result, some volunteer agencies had to be reinforced by government support rather than vice–versa (APSS, 1991b, p. 36).

Scanlon and Sylves (1990) reported on the mid–air collision over San Diego in 1978. They wrote extensively about necessary resources which were wasted or unavailable, and about the outpouring of unnecessary resources which hindered the response operation. Referring to but one of many services, they wrote: "Emergency medical services proved to be extremely confused. A communications foul–up flooded the 727 crash site with ambulances, almost none of which were actually needed" (p. 111). Similar examples were reported by Charles, and Kim (1988), ECRU (1985, 1987), as well as Rosenthal, Charles, and Hart (1989).

Similarly to resource co–ordination, the practice of resource allocation in a disaster environment is drastically different from "normal times." In essence, the "boundaries between public and private goods and services [often] become blurred during disasters" (Quarantelli, 1985, p. 7) and budgetary controls are usually left till the post–disaster recovery period (Auf der Heide, 1989; Dynes, 1970; Quarantelli, 1978, 1985).

Authority and the Diversity of Decision Makers

During crises, both the pattern of decision making and the lines of authority are severely tested and altered (Dynes 1970; Drabek, et al., 1981). Rosenthal (1989) observed that the normal pattern of authority and decision making is often altered during the evolution of a crisis period. He concluded that the major reason for the alteration is expediency!

Hart and Pijnenburg (1989) related the tragedy at the Heizel Stadium in Brussels. The pattern of decision making which they reported is representative of a wide range of community–wide disasters. They noted that:

> Many important operational and tactical decisions were, as a matter of necessity, made by lower level officials confronted with acute problems and threats that left no time for consultation, or for decisions or orders from responsible command personnel. . . . (p. 215).

One crisis scenario after another reflects the same dilemma. Front line individuals are often left to respond to a rapidly expanding and chaotic situation, with little more than their experience and whatever [little] preparation which they may have for the crisis confronting them (Dynes, 1970; Quarantelli, 1985; Auf der Heide, 1989; Rosenthal, 1989; Rosenthal, et al, 1989; Turner & Toft, 1989).

One of the major factors which quickly becomes an issue in crises is that of centralization versus decentralization of decision making. According to Rosenthal, Hart, and Charles (1989) researchers "discovered evidence that suggests that some of the conventional wisdom about centralization of decision making in crisis events may need to be revised" (p. 26). Turner and Toft (1989) stated the matter more directly and concluded that "centralization is not always helpful" (p. 195).

The issue of centralization versus decentralization is as relevant to intra–organizational procedures as it is to inter–organizational cooperative efforts. Furthermore, the often–time decentralization of decision making should not stifle or prevent joint decision making. Auf der Heide (1989) noted that "although it may not be obvious initially, the need for joint decision making eventually becomes apparent in most large disasters" (p. 77).

Organizations responding to disasters typically represent a variety of jurisdictions—federal, provincial, county, municipal and numerous private companies. Their vague jurisdictional boundaries and overlapping roles and authorities are typically ignored in non– crisis periods. However, during disasters these jurisdictional issues surface with a vengeance and demand immediate resolution.

It is not uncommon for organizations to lose some of their autonomy during crisis situations (Quarantelli, 1985). However, Dynes (1967) noted that as a result of the sharing of authority and decision making the overall response organization becomes a "much more efficient problem solving entity during the emergency period than it [is] during normal times" (p. 16). In effect, it becomes more rational in its problem solving process.

Warheit and Dynes (1969) noted that "the emergency period is more likely to be characterized by pragmatic decision making based on what has to be accomplished even if legal limits have to be placed aside" (p. 13). Rosenthal, et al. (1989) presented a contradictory view. They reported the ever presence of bureaucratic politics throughout crisis management examples involving various scenarios. These disputes are often related to issues of authority or blame (Rosenthal, et al., 1989).

Quarantelli (1982) reported that authority problems during disasters are not the result of organizational breakdowns, or a grab for power by one group over another. Quarantelli (1985) also identified four predictable areas which affect organizational authority during a disaster: "(1) loss of higher echelon personnel because of overwork; (2) conflict over authority regarding new disaster tasks; (3) clashes over organizational domains between established and emergent groups; (4) surfacing of organizational jurisdictional differences" (p. 15). There are seldom disputes regarding responsibility for traditional tasks such a fire fighting, health care, and crowd control. Rather, disputes occur over responsibility for new tasks such as mass burial or mass search and rescue operations (Quarantelli, 1985).

Personnel

The imminent or actual impact of a disaster usually brings about the convergence of people onto the stricken area or into the facilities (e.g., hospitals, dispatch stations, command centres) of responding agencies (Drabek, 1986; Dynes, 1970; Fritz, & Mathewson, 1957; Quarantelli, 1985). Kartez and Lindell (1990) observed that convergence is typically "motivated by anxiety over missing kin and friends, sympathy for the stricken population and the desire to help it, and interest in an unusual or unfamiliar event" (p. 6). Fritz and Mathewson (1957) identified five types of groups based on their motivation to converge onto a disaster site. These include the returners, the anxious (for family and friends), the helpers, the curious, and the exploiters. Each group has an impact on the operation and each needs to be dealt with accordingly.

Quarantelli (1985) noted that "disasters free people from work, household, and school demands and/or the performance of daily tasks and responsibilities" (p. 10). Organizations, may also curtail activities which they consider non–essential, and may re–assign their staff to disaster response activities (Auf der Heide, 1989).

Organizations—their structure, reporting lines, roles, and responsibilities—are all greatly affected by a disaster. Off– shift personnel and volunteers are likely to converge on organizational sites adding pressure on an already confusing situation, and reducing the availability (in long–term operations) of rested and available staff reserve (Auf der Heide, 1989; Dynes, 1970). As an example, Scanlon and Sylves (1990) reported that in the 1978 San Diego air crash "over–convergence of police at the site was excessive, unnecessary, uncoordinated, and probably counter productive to recovery operations . . ." (p. 111). They also stated that "before long almost every on–duty San Diego police officer, and many who were off duty, were at the scene. . . police dispatchers had almost no idea who was on–site [consequently] . . . there were just nine uniformed officers left to cover the rest of the city during the incident" (p. 111).

Organizational performance in a disaster is also greatly affected by vacancies in critical positions. These vacancies may be the result of lack of staffing, the death of staff members, their inability to arrive at the work site, or the transfer of the incumbent to another critical disaster response position within or outside the organization (Auf der Heide, 1989; Drabek, 1986; Dynes, 1970; Quarantelli, 1982, 1985).

Organizations attempting to mobilize their human resources are first confronted by the chaos of the rapidly–evolving nature of the disaster. They must also contend with their need to expand and adjust their resources to meet this situation (Dynes, 1970; Quarantelli, 1985). McLuckie (1970) suggested that the more centralized an agency is prior to the disaster, the slower will its response be following the disaster (cited in Mileti, Drabek, & Haas, 1975). However, organizations which undergo rapid expansion and a change of leadership, lose some of their "legitimacy" within their community (Warheit & Dynes, 1969).

Decision Making

The pattern of decision making in disasters is significantly different from that practised during non–disaster periods. Communication lines are often overloaded by an increasing number of information bits which travel faster, and often through novel routes. Information filtering occurs at all levels with widespread effects on decision making (Drabek, 1986; Dynes, 1970; Rosenthal, et al., 1989).

During crisis situations, people typically allow their leaders more control over their lives (Hamblin, 1958). This control is often translated into the authority to make decisions and take the necessary action to respond to the crisis at hand. Because of the life–and–death nature of disasters, decisions must be made rapidly, often in a whirlwind of activity and emotions (Withers, 1988).

Dynes (1970) reported that organizations do not react automatically to the increased demands which disasters impose on them. The predictable delays may be attributed to a number of factors including: limited knowledge of the extent, magnitude, and evolution of the disaster; uncertainty regarding the status of organizational resources and response capabilities; and, uncertainty regarding the capability, intention, and resource deployment of other organizations. In other words, immediate response is ruled by uncertainty (Fink, 1986; Quarantelli, 1982, 1985; Rosenthal, et al., 1989). Yet, as Rosenthal, Hart, and Charles (1989) noted "crises may be viewed as 'occasions for decision'" and may also provide an opportunity to resolve an underlying organizational or environmental problem (p. 9).

Decision making in a crisis situation is not easy, particularly due to the added stressors inherent to the event and its consequences. Fink (1986) noted that "effective decision making is a technique. High–quality decision making in the midst of crisis–induced stress is a process with mechanics to it" (p. 150). He added that managers must become familiar and practised at it.

Ritti and Funhouser (1977) wrote that decisions are "a process starting with an initial awareness of the need for some action and carrying through to the point of final evaluation and, if need be, reconstruction of the situation" (p. 238). In some instances this reconstruction of reality is due to what Janis (1982) had termed "groupthink." Rosenthal, Hart, and Charles (1989) observed that crisis decision makers can succumb to groupthink "whereby the preservation of group harmony and amiability between group members overrides the group's ability to critically assess decision problems, process strategic information, and intelligently choose a course of action" (p. 21).

As noted above, communication in a disaster is influenced to a great degree by trust. Crisis decision makers and other disaster responders often rely on trusted and liked sources.

Rosenthal, Hart, and Charles (1989) also noted that crisis decision makers tend to reduce the uncertainty of their current situation by referring to previous crises. This practice often ignores the strong likelihood of significant differences which might exist between the two situations. To use a military analogy, it is like fighting the next war based on the experiences of the last one. Comfort (1989) stated that action in crises "is most effective if it is based not upon previously defined rules, but on the best information available at the time" (p. 334).

Fink (1986) stated that crisis decision makers are affected by a number of cognitive distortions or maladaptive coping methodologies. These include viewing the outcome of the crisis and crisis response efforts as being 'overdetermined,' fear, being convinced that there are no good alternatives, fearing the loss of self–esteem, as well as polarized thinking or viewing everything as black–or–white, life–or–death (pp. 144–145). He also noted that some psychologists claim that decision makers who are placed under the above conditions actually "regress and move into more primitive styles of thinking and of coping. They become defensive, they become arbitrary. They may begin to make decisions based purely on . . . 'gut reaction', rather than on a cerebral thought process" (p. 145). Additionally, as Rosenthal (1989) noted, when crisis "decision makers have difficulties redefining the situation, they tend to become obsessed with one dominant goal–means perspective" at the exclusion of much of the whole picture (p. 248).

Auf der Heide (1989) noted that "although it may not be obvious initially, the need for joint decision–making eventually becomes apparent in most large disasters" (p. 77). This further complicates the problem of decision making because it introduces added variety of needs, resources, values, interests, trust levels, communication patterns, and many more aspects which have the potential to create conflicts (Dynes, 1970; Quarantelli, 1978, 1985). This environment is further complicated when political and technical advisers become decision makers. Rosenthal, Hart, and Charles (1989) noted that "in some crises there may be such a shortage of expertise that a few available experts – from a psychiatrist in a hijacking case to radiation specialists in a nuclear plant accident – may gain a vital monopoly in exerting influence" (p. 18). Such influence, they noted, tends to be destructive.

Decision making during the 'impact' phase and the early part of the 'response' phase is often de–centralized and conducted at the lowest levels of responding organizations (Auf der Heide, 1989; Drabek, 1985, 1986; Drabek et al., 1981; Dynes, 1970, 1978; Rosenthal, Charles, and Hart, 1989). Once response efforts become more structured and involve more resources, the style of decision making changes and becomes more centralized. Crises generally necessitate the abandonment of routine forms and procedures of decision making (Hart & Pijnenburg, 1989)

Yet, for all their "threat" and subsequent damage, crises also have a constructive side to them. Rosenthal, Hart, and Charles (1989) noted that "crises have been aptly phrased 'occasions for decision.' They require critical decisions under conditions of uncertainty and time pressure" (p. 17). These decisions may lead to opportunities to make things better. Barton (1993) observed that "some managers use crisis to their advantage—their swift and effective decision making may save millions of dollars in lost revenue and preserve their company's reputation" (p. 3).

Fink (1986) noted that crises bring with them many often forgotten opportunities. He stated:

> Be aware that the crisis, the turning point, holds out to you the potential for achievement; for obtaining your personal or business goals; for achieving admiration from your peers and for receiving admiration from your peers and subordinates, and praise or promotion from your superiors; for facilitating self–enhancement and for moving up (p. 133).

SUMMARY

This chapter describe those events which, by their definition, overwhelm individuals and organizations. These are not your day– to–day events and their consequences are severe. They are often situations which present threat or injury to people, significant damage to property and the likelihood of long–term consequences.

Crises and disasters may be encountered at individual, familial, organizational and communal levels. At each level their impact can be felt through the individual. Survivors and responders alike are likely to be affected and traumatized.

The research on the impact of crises and disasters on individuals and organizations is extensive. It highlights the need for effective preparedness based on the reality of the disaster/crisis environment.

These events CAN be managed, but require inter–organizational and consequently inter–jurisdictional effort. The skills most required of effective crisis managers are communication, decision making and coordination.

Crises and disasters are turning points in the lives of individuals, organizations and communities. Managed well they can lead to growth, development and greater security against future disasters. Mismanaged, they become an invitation to catastrophe and devastation. And, that is their challenge.

Picture 1.1

Disaster scenes attract attention and cause convergence.
(Photo Courtesy of Gerry Emas, Edmonton Emergency Response Department.)

Picture 1.2

Disasters can occur anywhere, even in the heart of large urban centres.
(Photo Courtesy of Gordon Sweetnam, Calgary Fire Department.)

Legal Foundations of Fire and Emergency Services

Larry A. Reynolds B.A., B.Ed., LL.B., LL.M.

Larry A. Reynolds is a fellow with the University of Alberta *Eco-Research* Chair in Environmental Risk Management and with the Social Sciences and Humanities Research Council of Canada, a sessional instructor with the Alberta Fire Training School, and a practising lawyer in Alberta and the Northwest Territories.

The study of fire and emergency services law in Canada must begin with an examination of its legal foundations. This chapter will examine many of the components of the legal framework which underlies fire and emergency services law in Canada at the federal, provincial, territorial and municipal levels.

1.0 INTRODUCTION

Fire and emergency services across Canada are being asked to provide an increasing array of services with diminishing resources. The relative effectiveness and efficiency of fire and emergency services are no longer measured on an empirical basis in relation to a clearly defined set of criteria. Rather, evaluation is increasingly seen in terms of the ability of fire and emergency services to meet the various objectives of the diverse group which employ and operate such services - including public institutions such at the federal, provincial, territorial and municipal levels of government, and private interests including business and industry. At the same time, fire and emergency services must also meet the requirements of society as a whole, with the task of ensuring that such requirements are met falling to the legal system.

Consequently, the challenge facing fire and emergency services in Canada is in providing effective and efficient services which satisfy both the objectives of the employers and operators of such services and the requirements of society as reflected in the legal system. To meet this challenge it is necessary for fire and emergency services professionals to develop an understanding of those facets of the legal system which impact upon fire and emergency services. Unfortunately, for many fire and emergency services personnel the operation of the legal system is surrounded in a certain mystique, with the study of law generally limited to those who are members of the legal profession. While assistance from qualified legal counsel should play an important role in the operation of every fire and emergency services organization, it is equally important that fire and emergency services personnel have a sound understanding of the basic concepts of the law as it affects the performance of their duties. After all, fire and emergency services personnel may be asked to make a decision in a matter of seconds which the legal system may review for several years, and fire and emergency services departments rarely have their lawyer present at the scene of a rescue operation!

This chapter is intended to introduce fire and emergency services personnel to the Canadian legal system through an examination of the primary components of the legal system which affect fire and emergency services in Canada.* The chapter will commence with an examination of the constitutional foundation upon which Canadian law (including fire and emergency services law) is based. This is followed by a survey of the fire and emergency services legislation which has been enacted across the Country. Consideration will then be given to alternative approaches to the provision of fire and emergency services. Finally, the current status of administrative and civil law as it impacts upon fire and emergency services across Canada will be explored.

AUTHOR'S NOTE:

* The material contained in this Chapter is intended solely for educational purposes and should not be considered to be legal advice. It is recommended that the reader consult legal counsel to obtain legal advice should such advice be required.

2.0 CONSTITUTIONAL JURISDICTION

2.1 Federal System

In order to understand the law as it applies to fire and emergency services in Canada it is first necessary to understand the constitutional framework within which the legal system operates. Canada is a federal state wherein the power to govern is divided between a central authority commonly referred to as the "Federal Government" and a group of regional authorities which may be collectively referred to as "provincial governments". The legal framework created by a federal system of government is described by Professor P. W. Hogg in *Constitutional Law in Canada*:

> In a federal state governmental power is distributed between a central (or national or federal) authority and several regional (or provincial or state) authorities, in such a way that every individual in the state is subject to the laws of two authorities, the central authority and a regional authority. For example, anyone in Ontario is subject to the laws of the Parliament of Canada (the central authority) and the Legislature of Ontario (the regional authority). The central authority and the regional authorities are "coordinate", that is to say, neither is subordinate to the other. The powers of the Legislature of Ontario are not granted by the Parliament of Canada, and they cannot be taken away, altered or controlled by the Parliament of Canada. And the Legislature of Ontario, even acting in concert with all the other provincial Legislatures, is likewise incompetent to take away, alter or control the powers of the Parliament of Canada.[1]

Professor Hogg goes on to offer the following comments with respect to the development of a system for the distribution of powers in the Canadian federal system:

> At confederation in 1867, the framers of the British North America Act not only contemplated a continuing colonial relationship between the new Dominion of Canada and the United Kingdom, they sought to model the new Dominion's institutions upon those of the United Kingdom. However, the federal character of Canada forced some fundamental departures from British concepts. Legislative power had to be distributed between the federal Parliament and the provincial Legislatures. This meant that each legislative body was given the power to make laws in relation to certain classes of subjects, and denied the power to make laws in relation to other classes of subjects. Moreover, as we have seen, the courts assumed the power to determine whether or not the Parliament or a Legislature had acted within its powers in enacting a statute, and to declare the statute invalid if it were outside the powers of the enacting body. It followed that there was no legislative body in Canada which was sovereign in the sense of being able to make or unmake any law whatsoever.

1 P. W. Hogg, *Constitutional Law in Canada*, 3rd ed., Toronto: Carswell, 1992 at p. 98.

> While federalism was inconsistent with one omnicompetent Legislature like the United Kingdom Parliament, the idea of parliamentary sovereignty remained an important influence in Canadian constitutional theory. The Constitution Act, 1867 for the most part limited legislative power only to the extent necessary to give effect to the federal principle. Any power withheld from the federal Parliament was possessed by the provincial Legislatures, and vice versa. If there was room for doubt on this point, the Privy Council scotched it by repeatedly enunciating the principle of exhaustive distribution of legislative powers: "whatever belongs to self-government in Canada belongs either to the Dominion or to the provinces, within the limits of the British North America Act". The federal Parliament and provincial Legislatures, provided they stayed within the limits imposed by the scheme of federalism, received powers as "plenary and ample" as those of the United Kingdom Parliament.[2]

The authority to enact legislation was originally given to the federal Parliament and to the provincial Legislatures by the *British North America Act, 1867.*[3] Specifically, Part VI of the Act expressly allocates to the federal Parliament and to the provincial Legislatures those classes of subjects for which they have jurisdiction to enact legislation.

The distribution of powers between the federal and provincial governments is considered to be exhaustive (subject to certain limited exceptions such as matters protected by the *Canadian Charter of Rights and Freedoms*).[4] That is, all subjects will fall within one or more of the heads of power found in the *Constitution Act, 1867.*

2.2 Fire and Emergency Services

Constitutional authority to legislate with respect to matters concerning fire and emergency services in Canada is shared between the federal and provincial governments.

2.2.1 Federal Jurisdiction

Section 91 of the *Constitution Act, 1867* specifically provides the federal Parliament with the exclusive jurisdiction to legislate with respect to those matters concerning fire and emergency services which fall within the following classes of subjects:

> It shall be lawful for the Queen, by and with the Advice and Consent of the Senate and House of Commons, to make Laws for the Peace, Order, and good Government of Canada, in relation to all Matters not coming within the Classes of Subjects by this Act assigned exclusively to the Legislatures of the Provinces; and for greater Certainty, but not so as to restrict the Generality of the foregoing Terms of this Section, it is hereby declared that (notwithstanding anything in the Act) the

2 *Supra,* note 1 at pp. 302-304.
3 Renamed the *Constitution Act, 1867* in 1982.
4 Part I of the *Canada Act, 1982* (U.K.), c. 11.

exclusive Legislative Authority of the parliament of Canada extends to all Matters coming within the Classes of Subjects next hereinafter enumerated; that is to say—

1A The Public Debt and Property.
7. Militia, Military and Naval Service, and defence.
10. Navigation and Shipping.
24. Indians, and Lands reserved for the Indians.
27. The Criminal Law, except the Constitution of Courts of Criminal Jurisdiction, but including the Procedure in Criminal Matters.
28. The Establishment, Maintenance, and Management of Penitentiaries.[5]

2.2.2 Provincial Jurisdiction

Section 92 of the *Constitution Act, 1867* specifically provides provincial Legislatures with the exclusive jurisdiction to legislate with respect to those matters concerning fire and emergency services which fall within the following classes of subjects:

92. In each Province the Legislature may exclusively make Laws in relation to Matters coming within the Classes of Subject next hereinafter enumerated; that is to say—

5. The Management and Sale of the Public Lands belonging to the Province and of the Timber and Wood thereon.

10. Local Works and Undertakings other than such as are of the following Classes:—

(a) Lines of Steam or other Ships, Railways, Canals, Telegraphs and other Works and Undertakings connecting the Province with any other or others of the Provinces, or extending beyond the limits of the Province;

(b) Lines of Steam Ships between the province and any British or Foreign Country;

(c) Such Works as, although wholly situate within the Province, are before or after their Execution declared by the parliament of Canada to be fore the general; Advantage of Canada or for the Advantage of Two or more of the Provinces.

13. Property and civil Rights in the Province.

15. The Imposition of Punishment by Fine, Penalty, or Imprisonment for enforcing any law of the Province made in relation to any matter coming within any of the Classes of Subjects enumerated in this Section.

5 *Supra,* note 3 at s. 91 (1A), (7), (10), (24), (27), (28).

16. Generally all Matters of a merely local or private Nature in the Province.[6]

2.2.3 Residual Powers

While several of the Classes of subjects enumerated in sections 91 and 92 of the *Constitution Act, 1867* apply to a variety of matters concerning fire and emergency services, some of these matters which have arisen since 1867 are *prima facie* (at first glance) not addressed by the enumerated classes of subjects. Further, the constitutional distribution of powers is considered to be exhaustive, thereby precluding the later inclusion of additional classes of subjects to address new matters.

In order to address this issue the Fathers of Confederation included within the enumerated classes of subjects certain broadly defined classes of subjects which operate to allow the Federal and provincial governments to assume constitutional jurisdiction to legislate with respect to new matters for which constitutional authority is not otherwise directly provided.

The nature and purpose of these residual powers are summarized in *Constitutional Law of Canada* as follows:

> It goes without saying that the framers of the Constitution could not foresee every kind of law which has subsequently been enacted; not could they foresee social, economic and technological developments which have required novel forms of regulation. But they did make provision for new or unforeseen kinds of laws. The last of the enumerated provincial classes of subject in s. 92 is "generally all matters of merely local or private nature in the province" 9s. 92(16). And for matters which do not come within this or any other enumerated class of subjects, the opining words of s. 91 give to the federal Parliament the residuary power "to make laws for the peace, order, and good government of Canada in relation to all matters not coming within the classes of subject assigned exclusively to the Legislatures of the Provinces". Thus, any matter which does not come within any of the specific classes of subjects will be provincial if it is merely local or private (s. 92(16)() and will be federal if it has a national dimension (s. 91, opening words).[7]

2.2.3.1 Federal Residual Power

The federal residual power is found in the preamble to section 91, which provides, *inter alia*:

91. It shall be lawful for the Queen, by and with the Advice and Consent of the Senate and House of Commons, to make Laws for the Peace, Order, and good Government of Canada...

---

6 *Supra*, note 3 at s. 92 (5), (8), (10), (13), (15), (16).
7 *Supra*, note 1 at p. 339.

In order for a matter to come within federal jurisdiction pursuant to the "Peace, Order and good Government" (P.O.G.G.) power, the matter must meet one of three tests which have been established by the courts:

a) Gap Test

The P.O.G.G. power will be used to fill gaps in the constitutional distribution of powers. This test requires that the matter under consideration fall partially within an existing class of subject, but that the class of subject fails to completely deal with the matter.

For example, section 92(11) of the *Constitution Act, 1867* gave to the provinces the constitutional jurisdiction to legislate with respect to "The incorporation of Companies with Provincial Objects". However, the Act made no provision for the Federal Government to incorporate companies with federal objects. In order to remedy this apparent deficiency the courts have held that the power to incorporate companies with federal objects rests with the federal government pursuant to the P.O.G.G. power.[8]

b) National Concern Test

The P.O.G.G. power will be used to give the federal government constitutional jurisdiction to legislate with respect to matters of national concern. The test is that set out in *A.G. Ontario v. Canada Temperance Federation*:

> In their Lordships' opinion, the true test must be found in the real subject matter of the legislation: if it is such that it goes beyond local or provincial concern or interests and must form its inherent nature be the concern of the Dominion as a whole then it will fall within the competence of the Dominion Parliament as a matter affecting the peace, order and good government of Canada, although it may in another aspect touch on matters specially reserved to the provincial legislatures.[9]

The national concern test has been applied by the courts to bring a number of matters pertaining to fire and emergency services within federal jurisdiction pursuant to the P.O.G.G. power. Examples include:

i) In *Johannesson v. West St. Paul*[10] the Supreme Court of Canada held that while aeronautics did not fall directly within any of the enumerated heads of power in the *Constitution Act, 1867* it did satisfy the national concern test, and was therefore a matter falling within federal jurisdiction. As a result, the provision of fire and emergency services at aeronautic facilities such as airports is a federal responsibility.[11]

8 *Citizens Insurance Co. v. Parsons* (1881), 7 App. Cas. 96.
9 [1946] A.C. 193 at pp. 205-206 per Viscount Simon.
10 [1952] 1 S.C.R. 292 (S.C.C.).
11 This responsibility may be carried out directly by federal fire and emergency services or indirectly by retaining private fire and emergency services. See discussion section 4.3, *infra*.

ii) In *Pronto Uranium Mines v. Ontario Labour Relations Board*[12] the Ontario High Court upheld the constitutional validity of the *Atomic Energy Control Act*, which federal legislation purported to regulate atomic energy in Canada on the basis that it met the national concern test. Consequently, the federal government has the constitutional jurisdiction to provide fire and emergency services with respect to atomic energy facilities.[13]

c) Emergency Test

The P.O.G.G. power will be used to give the federal government constitutional jurisdiction to legislate on a temporary basis with respect to matters which constitute an emergency. This test has been applied by the courts to give the federal government constitutional authority to enact legislation which includes the *War Measures Act*[14] and the *Anti-Inflation Act*.[15]

2.2.3.2 Provincial Residual Power

The provincial residual power is found in section 92(13) and section 92(16) of the *Constitution Act, 1867* which provide:[16]

92. In each Province the Legislature may exclusively make Laws in relation to Matters coming within the Classes of Subject next hereinafter enumerated; that is to say—

13. Property and Civil Rights in the Province.

16. Generally all Matters of a local or private Nature in the Province.

2.2.4 Territorial Jurisdiction

Section 146 of the *British North America Act* provided for the admission into Canada of additional provinces and territories.[17] In 1870 Rupert's Land and the North-Western Territory were admitted into Canada by order-in-council made pursuant to section 146.[18] Upon admission, the federal Parliament carved the province

---

12 [1956] O.R. 862 (Ont. H.C.). See also *Denison Mines v. A.G. Canada*, [1973] 1 O.R. 797 (Ont. H.C.), which found federal jurisdiction through both the P.O.G.G. power and works pursuant to section 92(10)(c).
13 See O'Donnell, "An inquiry into Provincial Jurisdiction over Uranium Development in Saskatchewan" (1948), 48 *Sask. L. Rev.* 293.
14 This legislation was enacted during World War I, World War II and during the 1970 "October Crisis". The Act empowers the Federal Government to legislate with respect to a broad range of matters.
15 *Re Anti-Inflation Act*, [1976] 2 S.C.R. 373 (S.C.C.).
16 Some writers are of the view that section 92(16) was originally intended as the only provincial residuary power, but that section 92(13) has to a large degree taken over this role. See P. W. Hogg, *Constitutional Law of Canada, supra*, note 1 at 370 and A. S. Abel "What Peace, Order and Good Government? (1968), 7 *West. Ont. L. Rev.* 1.
17 *Supra*, note 3.
18 *Rupert's Land and North-Western Territory Order*, 1870 (U.K.), R.S.C. 1985, Appendix II, No. 9.

of Manitoba out of Rupert's Land[19] and amalgamated the remainder of Rupert's Land and the North-Western Territory, renaming the new territory the Northwest Territories.

In 1880 all remaining British territories in the north, including the arctic islands, were admitted into Canada by the *Adjacent Territories Order, 1880* (U.K.),[20] and were subsequently incorporated into the Northwest Territories. In 1898 the Yukon Territory was created from the western portion of the Northwest Territories[21] and in 1905 the provinces of Alberta[22] and Saskatchewan[23] were also carved out of the Northwest Territories.

The constitutional jurisdiction of the Northwest Territories and the Yukon Territory to legislate with respect to matters concerning fire and emergency services differs from that enjoyed by the federal and provincial governments in that constitutional legislation does not provide Canadian territories with the power to legislate. Rather, the *Constitutional Act, 1871* empowers the federal Parliament to enact laws for the territories:[24]

> 4. The Parliament of Canada may from time to time make provision for the administration, peace, order, and good government of any territory not for the time being included in any Province.

The federal Parliament has in turn delegated to the Northwest Territories and to the Yukon Territory extensive powers of self-government including the establishment of a legislative "Council" for each territory.[25] These Councils may in turn enact legislation in the form of "ordinances" with respect to a list of subjects similar to those allocated to the provincial legislatures pursuant to section 92 of the *Constitution Act, 1867*.[26]

In the *Northwest Territories Act* the federal Parliament has delegated to the Council of the Northwest Territories the power to legislate with respect to those matters concerning fire and emergency services which fall within the following classes of subjects:

> 16. The Commissioner in Council may, subject to this Act and any other Act of Parliament, make ordinances for the government of the Territories in relation to the following classes of subjects:
>
> (h) property and civil rights in the Territories;

19 *Manitoba Act*, 1870, s. 35.
20 R.S.C. 1985, Appendix II, No. 14.
21 *Yukon Territory Act*, 1989, R.S.C. 1985, Appendix II, No. 19.
22 *Alberta Act*, 1905, R.S.C. 1985, Appendix II, No. 20.
23 *Saskatchewan Act*, 1905, R.S.C. 1985, Appendix II, No. 21.
24 *Constitution Act*, 1871 (U.K.), R.S.C. 1985, Appendix II, No. 11, s.4.
25 See *Northwest Territories Act*, R.S.C. 1985, c. N-27, s.9 and *Yukon Act*, R.S.C. 1985, c. Y-2, s.9.
26 See *Northwest Territories Act*, R.S.C. 1985, c. N-27, s.16 and *Yukon Act*, R.S.C. 1985, s.17.

(s) the expenditure of money for territorial purposes;

(t) generally, all matters of a merely local or private nature in the Territories;

(u) the imposition of fines, penalties, imprisonment or other punishments in respect of the contravention of the provisions of any ordinance.[27]

Similar powers have been delegated to the Yukon Territory pursuant to section 17 of the *Yukon Act*.[28]

2.2.5 Municipal Jurisdiction

Section 92(8) of the *Constitution Act, 1867* empowers the provinces to create municipal institutions:

92. In each Province the Legislature may exclusively make Laws in relation to Matters coming within the Classes of Subject next hereinafter enumerated; that it to say—

8. Municipal Institutions in the Province.[29]

The term "municipal institutions" has been broadly interpreted by the courts. In *Smith v. City of London* the court commented that the term:

... appears to give compendious expression to the state of affairs which exists in a defined populated area inhabitants of which are incorporated and intrusted with privileges of local self-government or administration, responsive to the needs, the health, the safety, the comfort and the orderly government of an organized community.[30]

As a result, section 92(8) allows for the creation of a wide array of municipal institutions, generally referred to today as "local public authorities", which include:

a) municipalities such as cities, towns, villages, counties, municipal districts and regional municipalities;

b) school boards and districts;

c) public health boards and districts; and

d) various miscellaneous districts, boards and commissions.

---

27 *Ibid.*, at s. 16.
28 *Supra*, note 26 at s. 17.
29 *Supra*, note 3 at s. 92(8). Similar powers are granted to the Northwest Territories and Yukon Territory by the federal Parliament. See *Northwest Territories Act*, R.S.C. 1985, c. N-27, s. 16(c) and the *Yukon Act*, R.S.C. 1985, c. Y-2, s. 17(c).
30 (1909), 20 O.L.R. 133 (Ont. Div. Ct.).

While section 92(8) grants to the provinces the power to create municipal institutions, it does not of itself provide these institutions with any power.[31] Rather, the general rule with respect to the powers of municipal institutions is that they possess only those powers which have been expressly granted by provincial legislation or are necessarily incidental to those expressed powers. The rule was well summarized by Chief Justice Falconbridge in *Journal Printing Co. v. McVeity*:

> We are of the opinion that no rights exist except such as are expressly or by implication given by the statute.[32]

Of course, the provinces can only delegate to municipal institutions those powers which they themselves possess pursuant to section 92 of the *Constitution Act, 1867*.[33]

The application of the above rule to expressly granted powers seldom causes difficulty. However, identification of those powers which are implied as being necessarily incidental to the expressly granted powers is often more difficult. The test which the courts have adopted to make this decision is whether the expressly granted power can be properly and effectively exercised without resort to the implied power. This test is set out by Hogg J.A. in *Township of Nelson v. Stoneham*:

> It is stated in 8 Hals., 2nd ed., 0. 72, that where a corporation is created by statute, its powers are limited by the statute creating it and extend no further than is expressly stated therein or is necessarily and properly required for carrying into effect the purposes of its incorporation or may be fairly regarded as incidental to or consequential upon those things which the Legislature has authorized. In Craies work on Statute Law, 5th ed., p. 105, the following passage is to be found: "If a statute is passed for the purpose of enabling something to be done, but omits to mention in terms some detail which is of great importance (if not actually essential) to the proper and effectual performance of the work which the statute has in contemplation, the Courts are at liberty to infer that the statute by implication empowers that detail to be carried out."[34]

Thus for example, there is a strong argument that the power granted to Nova Scotia municipalities to "organize fire companies"[35] necessarily implies the power to "purchase fire and emergency service equipment", even though such power is not expressly provided in the legislation.

---

31 *A.G.Ontario v. A. G. Canada*, [1896] A.C. 348.
32 (1915), 33 O.L.R. 166 at p. 174 (Ont. C.A.). See also *Murray and Brighton Townships Public School Trustees v. United Counties of Northumberland and Durham*, [1939] D.L.R. 738 (Ont. S.C.); *Re Hassard and City of Toronto* (1908), 16 O.L.R. 500 (Ont. Div. Ct.).
33 See *Smith v. City of London, supra*, note 30; Clarke v. Wawken, [1930] 1 W.W.R. 319 (Sask. C.A.); *Brandon v. Manitoba Municipal Commissioner*, [1931] 3 W.W.R. 65; affirmed [1931] W.W.R. 225.
34 (1957), 7 D.L.R. (2d) 39 at p. 42 (Ont. C.A.).
35 Nova Scotia *Municipal Act*, R.S.N.S. 1989, c. 295, s. 133.

While provincial and territorial legislation may *prima facie* provide local public authorities with powers for the provision of fire and emergency services, such powers may be illusory if in the exercise of these powers a local public authority comes into conflict with other provincial/territorial legislation. This issue is of particular concern with respect to municipalities, whose by-laws may conflict with provincial/territorial legislation. The law in this area is summarized in *The Law of Canadian Municipal Corporations* as follows:

> Although it is said that by-laws are similar to statutes, they are still "inferior" laws and cannot usurp the authority of or be contrary to the higher law. Since a by-law is a form of local legislation, it for this reason that it must not be at variance with provincial legislation. It is a cardinal rule of municipal law that all by-laws are subject to the general law of the realm and are subordinate to it and any by-laws which are repugnant to or inconsistent with general provincial legislation are void and of no effect (a), or else are superseded to the extent that the legislature has acted (b).[36]

The test which has been developed by Canadian courts for determining the existence of a conflict between provincial/territorial and municipal legislation is the one set out by Morden J.A. in *Re Attorney General for Ontario et al. and City of Mississauga*:

> In my view if the competing pieces of legislation are intended to advance the same policy and the provision in the statute covers the same ground as the by-law in a way to give rise to the interpretation that the statutory provision is intended "... completely, exhaustively, or exclusively [to express] what [shall be] the law governing the particular conduct...to which its attention is directed...", then there is a case of conflict. I quote from *Ex parte McLean* (1930), 43 C.L.R.472 at p. 483, which was adopted in *O'Sullivan v. Noarlunga Meat Ltd.*, [1957] A.C. 1 at p. 24, and quoted in *R. v. Morin* (1965), 52 D.L.R. (2d) 644 at pp. 646-7, [1966] 1 C.C.C. 265, 53 W.W.R. 234. If, in covering the same ground the subordinate legislation works at cross purposes to the provincial statute, then the case for conflict is reinforced. This is not intended to be an exhaustive definition of a conflict which will result in the rendering inoperative of the subordinate legislation but merely as one instance thereof and one which, in my view, is applicable to the case.
>
> I should also say that I see no objection to borrowing, in this field, relevant principles of accommodation which have been developed in cases involving alleged federal-provincial areas of conflict. In both fields great care is, and should be, taken before it is held that an otherwise properly-enacted law is inoperative. These principles of accommodation are, it seems to me, a useful and logical way of determining whether there has been an implied withdrawal of the power delegated to the municipal council, if the issue of conflict is approached with such a question in mind.[37]

36 Ian Mac F. Rogers, *The Law of Canadian Municipal Corporations*, 2nd ed., Toronto: Carswell, 1971. See also *St. Leonard v. Fournier* (1956), e D.L.R. (2d) 315 (N.B.C.A.); *Saumur v. Quebec*, [1953] 2 S.C.R. 299 (S.C.C.).

37 (1981), 124 D.L.R. (3d) 385 (Ont. C.A.).

3.0 FIRE AND EMERGENCY SERVICES LEGISLATION

Federal, provincial and municipal governments have exercised their constitutional jurisdiction to enact a wide range of legislation with respect to matters pertaining to fire and emergency services.

3.1 Federal

The Federal Government has exercised its constitutional jurisdiction to enact legislation with respect to matters pertaining to fire and emergency services in a variety of areas, including the following:

3.1.1 Aeronautics

Federal legislation does not expressly address those matters pertaining to fire and emergency services involving aeronautics. However, authority for such services may be found in the general powers for the establishment and operation of aeronautics facilities found in the *Aeronautics Act*, which provides that:

> 4.2 The Minister is responsible for the development and regulation of aeronautics and the supervision of all matters connected with aeronautics and, in the discharge of those responsibilities, the Minister may
>
> b) construct, maintain and operate aerodromes and establish and provide other facilities and services relating to aeronautics;
>
> e) control and manage all aircraft and equipment necessary for the conduct of an services of Her Majesty in right of Canada;[38]

3.1.2 Criminal Matters

The Federal Government has enacted legislation in the *Criminal Code*[39] which provides for a variety of criminal offences relating to fire. For example, the *Criminal Code* makes it an offence to commit arson with a disregard for human life:

> 433. Every person who intentionally or recklessly causes damage by fire or explosion to property, whether or not that person owns the property, is guilty of an indictable offence and liable to imprisonment for life where
>
> a) the person knows that or is reckless with respect to whether the property is inhabited or occupied; or
>
> b) the fire or explosion causes bodily harm to another person.[40]

38 R.S.C. 1985, c. A-2, s. 4.2 (b), (e). See also s. 4.9 (e), (t), (u).
39 R.S.C. 1985, c. C-34.
40 *Ibid.,* at s. 433. See also ss. 434-436.1 for related arson offences.

Federal legislation has also made it a criminal offence to make a false alarm of fire. Section 437 of the *Criminal Code* provides:[41]

437. Every one who wilfully, without reasonable cause, by outcry, ringing bells, using a fire alarm, telephone or telegraph, or in any other manner, makes or circulates or causes to be made or circulated an alarm of fire is guilty of

a) an indictable offence and liable to imprisonment for a term not exceeding two years; or

b) an offence punishable on summary conviction.

3.1.3 Explosives

The Federal Government has enacted legislation for the regulation and control of explosives. The *Explosive Act*[42] provides the Federal Government with a wide array of powers which include:

a) Licensing requirements for the manufacture,[43] storage,[44] sale[45] and possession[46] of explosives.

b) Permit requirements for the importation of explosives.[47]

c) Establishment of an explosives inspection system which includes the appointment of inspectors and chemists.[48]

d) Direction by the Minister that an inquiry take place, subject to the *Canadian Transportation Accident Investigation and Safety Board Act*,[49] in the event of an accidental explosion or when an accident has been caused by an explosive.[50]

e) Establishment of a number of quasi-criminal offenses relating to explosives, including:

i) Failing to allow an inspection.[51]

ii) Obstructing an inspection.[52]

41 *Ibid.*, at s. 437.
42 R.S.C. 1985, c. E-17.
43 *Ibid.*, at s. 6(a)(e).
44 *Ibid.*, at s. 6(c).
45 *Ibid.*, at s. 6(b).
46 *Ibid.*, at s. 6(d).
47 *Ibid.*, at s.9.
48 *Ibid.*, at ss. 13-14.
49 R.S.C. 1985, c. 23.4.
50 *Supra*, note 42 at s. 15.
51 *Ibid.*, at s. 16(a).
52 *Ibid.*, at s. 16(b), (c).

iii) Failing to comply with the order, directions or requirements of inspectors.[53]

iv) Trespassing in an explosives factory or magazine.[54]

v) Providing false or misleading information in an application for an explosives license or permit.[55]

vi) Committing any act which is likely to cause an explosion or fire in or about any explosives factory or magazine or any vehicle in which explosives are being transported.[56]

vii) Manufacturing, selling, possessing, importing or delivering an explosive if not authorized by the Act.[57]

viii) Seizure and disposal of explosives which have been abandoned or have deteriorated or constitute a danger to persons or property.[58]

3.1.4 Railways

In its railways legislation the federal government has enacted special provisions relating to fire prevention. Specifically, both public and private railways are required to ensure that their right-of-ways are free from combustible material such as dry grass and weeds. For example, the *Railway Act* provides:

> 223. The company shall at all times maintain and keep its right-of-way free from dead or dry grass, weeds and other unnecessary combustible matter.[59]

3.1.5 Hazardous Materials

The Federal Government has enacted legislation for the regulation and control of hazardous materials. The *Hazardous Products Act*[60] provides the federal government with a wide array of powers which include:

a) Prohibiting the advertising, sale and importation of products designated by the Federal Government as "Prohibited".[61] Prohibited products pertaining to fire and emergency services include:

---

53 *Ibid.*, at s. 16 (d).
54 *Ibid.*, at s. 18.
55 *Ibid.*, at s. 19.
56 *Ibid.*, at s. 20.
57 *Ibid.*, at s. 21.
58 *Ibid.*, at s. 27.
59 R.S.C. 1985, c.R-3. See also *Government Railways Act*, R.S.C. 1985, c. G-u, s. 63.
60 R.S.C. 1985, C. H-3.
61 *Ibid.*, at s. 4(1). A listing of prohibited products is found in Schedule I, Part II of the Act.

- Clothing products which do not meet applicable flammability standards.[62]

- Candles which re-ignite spontaneously.[63]

- Smoke detectors and heat detectors which do not meet applicable standards.[64]

b) Restricting the advertising, sale and importation of products designated by the federal government as "restricted".[65] Restricted products pertaining to fire and emergency services include:

- Fire extinguishing fluids containing halogenated aliphatic hydrocarbons where such products are packaged as consumer products.[66]

- Carpeting products which do not meet applicable flammability standards.[67]

c) Regulating the importation and sale of products designated by the federal government as "controlled".[68] Classes of controlled products identified by the Act which pertain to fire and emergency services include:[69]

- Class A - Compressed Gas.

- Class B - Flammable and Combustible Material.

- Class C - Oxidizing Material.

- Class D - Poisonous and Infectious Material.

- Class E - Corrosive Material.

- Class F - Dangerously Reactive Material.

d) The power to require that manufacturers of products disclose to the Minister information relating to the formula, composition, chemical ingredients or hazardous properties of products, and such other information as the Minister deems necessary for the purpose of determining whether the product is likely to be a danger to the health or safety of the public.[70]

---

62 *Ibid.*, at Schedule I, Part I, nos. 4, 5, 13.
63 *Ibid.*, at Schedule I, Part I, no. 29.
64 *Ibid.*, at Schedule I, Part I, no. 33.
65 *Ibid.*, at s. 4(2). A listing of restricted products is found in Schedule I, Part II of the Act.
66 *Ibid.*, at Schedule I, Part II, no. 6.
67 *Ibid.*, at Schedule I, Part II, no. 30.
68 *Ibid.*, at ss. 13-14.
69 *Ibid.*, at Schedule II, Section 2. Regulations enacted pursuant to section 15(1)(a) of the Act specify for each Class listed in Schedule II the products included in that class.
70 *Ibid.*, at s. 10.

e) Establishment of a hazardous products inspection system which includes the appointment of inspectors and analysts.[71]

f) Establishment of a number of quasi-criminal offences relating to hazardous products, including:

i) Failing to assist an inspector.[72]

ii) Obstructing an inspection.[73]

3.1.6 National Defence

Federal legislation does not expressly address those matters pertaining to fire and emergency services involving national defence. However, authority for such services may be found in the general powers for the establishment and operation of national defence facilities found in the *National Defence Act*:

4. The Minister holds office during pleasure, and has the management and direction of the Canadian Forces and of all matters relating to national defence and is responsible for

a) the construction and maintenance of all defence establishments and works for the defence of Canada;[74]

3.1.7 National Parks

The Federal Government has enacted legislation pertaining to fire and emergency services in national parks. Specifically, the *National Parks Act* provides as follows:

7.(1) The Governor in Council may, as he deems expedient, make regulations for

e) the prevention and extinguishing of fire on or threatening park lands, and requiring persons residing or being in the vicinity to report any such fire or to assist in its extinguishment.[75]

3.2 Provincial/Territorial

The provincial governments have exercised their constitutional jurisdiction, and the territorial governments have exercised their delegated powers, to enact legislation with respect to matters pertaining to fire and emergency services in a variety of areas, including the following:

---

71 *Ibid.*, at ss. 21, 22.
72 *Ibid.*, at s. 22(2).
73 *Ibid.*, at s. 23.
74 R.S.C. 1985, c. N-5, s. 4(a).
75 R.S.C. 1985, c. N-14, s. 7(1)(e).

3.2.1 Administration Of Fire And Emergency Services

Every province/territory in Canada has established an administrative framework for the purpose of regulating and controlling fire and emergency services within their respective jurisdictions.[76]

3.2.2 Crown Lands

The provinces and territories have also enacted legislation for the provision of fire and emergency services on lands owned by the provincial and territorial Crown.[77]

3.2.3 Emergencies

The provinces and territories have enacted a wide variety of legislation with respect to emergencies.[78]

76 See for example the Alberta *Municipal Government Act*, R.S.A. 1980, c. M-26.1, ss. 3-9; *Forest and Prairie Protection Act*, R.S.A., 1980, c. F-14, ss. 4-28; and *Safety Codes Act*, R.S.A 1980, c. S-0.5; British Columbia *Fire Service Act*, R.S.B.C. 1979, c.133, ss.2-8; Manitoba *Fires Prevention Act*, R.S.M. 1987, c. F80, s2. 2-31, 35-50, 57; New Brunswick *Fire Protection Act* R.S.N.B. 1973 c. F-13 s.s. 2-24 and *Forest Fires Act*, R.S.N.B. 1973, c. F-20, s.s. 2-30; Newfoundland *Fire Prevention Act*, R.S.N. 1990, c. F-11, s.s. 3-11 and *Forestry Act*, R.S.N. 1990, c. F-23, ss. 4, 88, 97-108; Northwest Territories *Fire Prevention Act*, R.S.N.W.T. 1988, c.F-6, ss. 2-5 and *Forest Protection Act*, R.S.N.W.T. 1988, c.F-10, ss. 16-21; Nova Scotia *Fire Prevention Act*, R.S.N.S. 1989, c. 171, ss. 3-20 and *Forest Act*, R.S.N.S. 1989, c. 179, ss. 4, 5(d), 21 (1)(2), 22-31; Ontario *Fire Marshals Act*, R.S.O. 1990, c.F.17, ss.2-8 and *Forest Fires Prevention Act* R.S.O. 1990, c.F.24, ss.2,4,8,9; Prince Edward Island *Fire Prevention Act* R.S.P.E.I. 1988 c. F-11, ss. 2-15, 26-49 and *Forest Management Act*, R.S.P.E.I. 1933, c. F-14, s. ((1)(a); Saskatchewan *Fire Prevention Act*, R.S.S. 1978, c. F-15.01, ss. 3-17; and *Forest Act*, R.S.S. 1978, c. F-19, s. 4(e); and Yukon *Fire Prevention Act*, R.S.Y. 1986, c. 67, s. 2-6 and *Forest Protection Act*, R.S.Y. 1986, c.71, s. 3.

77 See for example the Alberta *Forest and Prairie Protection Act*, R.S.A. 1980, c. F-14; British Columbia *Forest Act*, R.S.B.C. 1979, c.140. ss.110-116, 120-124; Manitoba *Fire Prevention Act*, R.S.M. 1987, c. F-80, and *Forests Act*, R.S.M.1987, c. F-150; New Brunswick *Forest Fires Act* R.S.N.B. 1973, c. F-20; Newfoundland *Forestry Act*, R.S.N. 1990, c. F-23; Northwest Territories *Forest Protection Act*, R.S.N.W.T. 1988, c.F-10; Nova Scotia *Fire Prevention Act*, R.S.N.S. 1989, c. 171; and *Forest Act*, R.S.N.S. 1989, c. 179; Ontario *Forest Fires Prevention Act*, R.S.O. 1990 c.F.24; Prince Edward Island *Fire Prevention Act*, R.S.P.E.I. 1988, c. F-14, s. 9(1); Saskatchewan *Forest Act* R.S.S. 1978, c. F-19; and Yukon *Forest Protection Act* R.S.Y. 1986, c. 71.

78 See for example the Alberta *Municipal Governemt Act*, R.S.A. 1980, c. M-26.1, s. 551, and *Safety Codes Act,* R.S.A. 1980, c. S-0.5, s 43; British Columbia *Emergency Program Act,* R.S.B.C. 1979, c.106; Manitoba *Emergency Measures Act* R.S.M. 1987, c. E80; Newfoundland *Emergency Measures Act*, R.S.N. 1990, c.E-8; Northwest Territories *Civil Emergency Measures Act*, R.S.N.W.T. 1988, c. C-9; Nova Scotia *Emergency Measures Act* R.S.N.S., 1989, c.8; Ontario *Emergency Plans Act*, R.S.P. 1990, c. E.9; Prince Edward Island *Emergency Measures Act*, R.S.P.E.I. 1988, c.E-6; and Yukon *Civil Emergency Measures Act*, R.S.Y. 1986, c. 25.

3.2.4 Fire Safety Standards

Each jurisdiction has enacted fire safety standards which must be observed. These standards which are usually enacted in the form of regulations, cover a broad spectrum including building standards, burning permits, electrical standards, heating standards and occupancy limits.[79]

3.2.5 Inspection

Most jurisdictions have enacted legislation which contemplates the carrying out of inspections and the issuance of orders to ensure that fire safety standards are met.[80]

3.2.6 Investigation

The provinces and territories have also enacted a broad range of legislation which provide powers for the investigation of fires.[81]

---

79 See for example the Alberta *Safety Codes Act*, R.S.A. 1980, c. S-0.5, *Forest and Prairie Protection Act* R.S.A. 1980 c. F-14, ss. 39-40 and *Provincial Parks Act* R.S.A. 1980, c. 0-22 s. 11(i); British Columbia *Fire Services Act*, R.S.B.C. 1979, c.133, s.59; Manitoba *Fires Prevention Act*, R.S.M. 1987 c. F80, ss. 34, 68;New Brunswick *Fire Prevention Act* R.S.N.B., 1973 s. 30 and *Forest Fire Act*, R.S.N.B. 1973, c. F-20, ss. 2-30; Newfoundland *Fire Prevention Act* R.S.N. 1990, c. F-11 s. 25 and *Forestry Act*, R.S.N. 1990, c. F-23, s. 109; Northwest Territories *Fire Prevention Act*, R.S.N.W.T. 1988, c. F-6, s. 23 and *Forest Protection Act*, R.S.N.W.T. 1988, c. F-10, s. 28(d); Nova Scotia *Fire Prevention Act*, R.S.N.S. 1989, c. 171 s. 3(2) and *Forest Act*, R.S.N.S. 1989, c. 179, s. 40(b), (c), (f), (h), (i), (j); Ontario *Fire Marshals Act* R.S.O. 1990, c.F.17, ss. 19,28; Prince Edward Island *Fire Prevention Act*, R.S.P.E.I. 1988, c. F-11, s. 24; Saskatchewan *Fire Prevention Act*, R.S.S. 1978, c. F-15.0) s. 39 and *Forest Act*, R.S.S. 1978, c. F-19, c. 5f; and Yukon *Fire Prevention Act*, R.S.Y. 1986, c. 67 s. 23 and *Forest Protection Act*, R.S.Y. 1986, c. 71, s. 27.

80 See for example the Alberta *Municipal Government Act*, R.S.A. 1980, c. M-26.1, ss. 542-543, *Safety Codes Act*, R.S.A. 1980, c. S-0.5, s. 30, and *Transportation Of Dangerous Goods Control Act*, R.S.A. 1980, c. T-6.5, ss. 6-7; British Columbia *Fire Service Act* R.S.B.C. 1979, c.133, ss.21-29; Manitoba *Fires Prevention Act*, R.S.A. 1987, c. F-80, ss. 55, 57; New Brunswick *Fire Prevention Act*, R.S.N.B., 1973 c. F-13, s. 11 and *Forest Fires Act* R.S.N.B. 1973, c. F-20, s. 31; Newfoundland, *Fire Prevention Act*, R.S.N. 1990, c. F-11, ss. 12-13, 17-18; Northwest Territories *Fire Prevention Act*, R.S.N.W.T. 1988, c. F-6, ss. 11-12 and *Forest Protection Act* R.S.N.W.T. 1988 c. F-10 s. 19; Nova Scotia *Fire Prevention Act*, R.S.N.S. 1989 c. 171, s. 19 and *Forest Act*, R.S.N.S. 1989 c. 179, ss. 39(2), 32; Ontario *Fire Marshals Act*, R.S.O. 1990, c.F.17, s.18; Prince Edward Island *Fire Prevention Act*, R.S.P.E.I. 1988 c. F-11, ss. 12-14; Saskatchewan *Fire Prevention Act*, R.S.S. 1978, c. F-15.01, ss. 15-17; and Yukon *Fire Prevention Act*, R.S.Y. 1986, c.67, ss. 12, 13, 18 and *Forest Protection Act*, R.S.Y. 1986, c. 71, ss. 7 and 21.

81 See for example the Alberta *Municipal Government Act*, R.S.A. 1980, c. M-26.1, ss. 542-543, *Forest and Prairie Protection Act*, R.S.A. 1980, c. F-14, s. 30.1, *Safety Codes Act*, R.S.A. 1980, c. 0-5, s.30, and *Transportation Of Dangerous Goods Control Act*, R.S.A. 1980, c. T-6.5, ss. 6-7; British Columbia *Fire Services Act*, R.S.B.C. 1979, c.133, ss.9-20; Manitoba *Fires Prevention Act*, R.S.M. 1987, c. F80, ss. 54, 56; New Brunswick *Fire Prevention Act*, R.S.N.B. 1973, c. F-13, s. 7 and *Forest Fires Act*, R.S.N.B. 1973, c. F-20, s.9; Northwest Territories *Fire Prevention Act*, R.S.N.W.T. 1988, c. F-6, ss. 6-10 and *Forest Protection Act*, R.S.N.W.T. 1988, c. F-10, s. 20; Nova Scotia *Fire Prevention Act*, R.S.N.S. 1989, c. 171, s.9; Ontario *Fire Marshals Act*, R.S.O. 1990, c.F.17, ss.5-9; Prince Edward Island *Fire Prevention Act*, R.S.P.E.I. 1988, c. F-11, ss. 10-15; Saskatchewan *Fire Prevention Act*, R.S.S. 1978, c. F-10.01, ss. 9-15; and Yukon *Fire Prevention Act*, R.S.Y. 1986, c. 67, s. 7.

3.2.7 Offences And Penalties

Each jurisdiction has enacted legislation establishing offences with respect to its fire and emergency services. This legislation includes penalties for the commission of these offences.[82]

3.2.8 Provincial And Territorial Parks

Finally, provincial and territorial legislation usually provides in either specific or general terms for fire and emergency services in provincial and territorial parks.[83]

3.3 Municipal

As discussed earlier, a province or territory may delegate to municipalities any or all of its powers with respect to fire and emergency services. While the fire and emergency services powers delegated to municipalities vary from jurisdiction to jurisdiction, most provincial/territorial legislation delegates to their municipalities the power to:

- establish and operate fire and emergency services.
- regulate and control fire.
- enforce laws enacted to regulate and control fire.

These powers are most often exercised by municipalities through the enactment of by-laws. An example of a municipal fire and emergency services by-law is set out in Appendix B1.

The following is a synopsis of many of the fire and emergency services and powers which have been delegated to Canadian municipalities, identified according to province or territory.

---

82 See for example the Alberta *Forest and Prairie Protection Act,* R.S.A. 1980, c. F-14, s. 35 and *Municipal Government Act,* R.S.A. 1980, c. M-26.1, ss. 545-546; Manitoba *Fires Prevention Act,* R.S.M. 1987, c. F80, ss. 6(e), 7(2), 8(2), 21 (6)(13), 25(3), 32(1), 39, 44; New Brunswick *Fire Prevention Act,* R.S.N.B. 1973, c. F-13, ss. 23-26 and *Forest Fires Act,* R.S.N.B. 1973, c. F-20, s. 29; Newfoundland *Fire Prevention Act,* R.S.N. 1990, c. F-11, s. 23 and *Forestry Act* R.S.N. 1990, c. F-23, s. 110; Northwest Territories *Fire Prevention Act,* R.S.N.W.T. 1988, c. F-6, ss. 19-22 and *Forest Protection Act,* R.S.N.W.T. 1988, c. F-10, ss. 22, 23; Nova Scotia *Fire Prevention Act,* R.S.N.S. 1989, c. 171, s. 23 and *Forests Act,* R.S.N.S. 1989, c. 179, s. 29(3); Ontario *Fire Marshals Act,* R.S.O. 1990, c.F.17, s.19(5)(6)(7) and *Forest Fires Prevention Act,* R.S.O. 1990, c. F.24, s.35.; Prince Edward Island *Fire Prevention Act,* R.S.S. 1978, c. F-15.01 and *Forests Act,* R.S.S. 1978, c. F-19, s. 55; and Yukon *Fire Prevention Act,* R.S.Y. 1986, c. 71, s. 28.

83 See for example the Alberta *Provincial Parks Act,* R.S.A. 1980, c. P-22, s.11(i); British Columbia *Park Act,* R.S.B.C. 1979, c. 309, s. 3; New Brunswick *Parks Act,* R.S.N.B. 1973, c. P-2, s. 15(1)(h); Newfoundland *Provincial Parks Act,* R.S.N. 1990, c. P-32, s. 8(g); Northwest Territories *Territorial Parks Act* R.S.N.W.T. 1988, c.T-4, s. 15(g); Nova Scotia *Provincial Parks Act,* R.S.N.S. 1989, c. 367, s. 37(g); Ontario *Provincial Parks Act,* R.S.O. 1990, c.P.34, s. 21(i); Prince Edward Island *Forest Management Act,* R.S.P.E.I., 1988, c. F-14, s. 3; and Yukon *Parks Act* R.S.Y.T. 1986, c. 126, s. 21(1)(f).

3.3.1 Alberta

3.3.1.1 Establishment & Operation Of Fire & Emergency Services

There is no legislative requirement that urban municipalities in Alberta provide fire and emergency services. However, rural Alberta municipalities must provide such services pursuant to the *Forest and Prairie Protection Act* which provides:

> 7(1) The council of a municipal district is responsible for fighting and controlling all fires within the boundaries of the municipal district and the costs and expenses shall be paid by the municipal district.[84]

Provincial legislation delegates to Alberta municipalities broad powers for the establishment and operation of fire and emergency services. While not specifically defined, Alberta's new *Municipal Government Act* states that:

> 7 A council may pass bylaws for municipal purposes respecting the following matters:
>
> (a) the safety, health and welfare of people and the protection of people and property;
>
> (b) services provided by or on behalf of the municipality;[85]

By way of explanation of the broadly defined powers given to Alberta municipalities under the new *Municipal Government Act*, the Act states:

> 9 The power to pass bylaws under this Division is stated in general terms to
>
> (a) give broad authority to councils and to respect their right to govern municipalities in whatever way the councils consider appropriate, within the jurisdiction given to them under this or any other enactment, and
>
> (b) enhance the ability of councils to respond to present and future issues in their municipalities.[86]

3.3.1.2 Regulation And Control Of Fire

Powers for the regulation and control of fire under the Alberta Municipal Government *Act* fall under the same broad heads of power as those outlined above for the establishment and operation of fire and emergency services.

84 R.S.A. 1980, c. F-14.
85 *Municipal Government Act*, R.S.A. 1980, c. M-26.1, s. 7(a)(f).
86 *Ibid.*, at s. 9.

3.3.1.3 Enforcement Of Laws For The Regulation And Control Of Fire

Powers for the enforcement of laws enacted for the regulation and control of fire include the general powers outlined above, and the power to enact by-laws for:

1) Recovery of fees and costs associated with the provision of fire and emergency services.[87]

2) The imposition of penalties for the violation of by-laws to a maximum of a $10,000.00 fine and 1 year imprisonment.[88]

3) Taking such measures as are deemed necessary to remedy a contravention or prevent a re-occurrence of a contravention of either Provincial legislation which a municipality is authorized to enforce or a municipal by-law.[89]

3.3.2 British Columbia

3.3.2.1 Establishment And Operation Of Fire And Emergency Services

There is no general legislative requirement that British Columbia municipalities provide fire and emergency services. However, British Columbia municipalities are required to provide for a regular system of fire inspection of premises within their boundaries.[90] Provincial legislation delegates to British Columbia municipalities a variety of powers for the establishment and operation of fire and emergency services, which include the power to enact by-laws for:

a) The establishment of a fire department or fire brigades for the purpose of fire suppression, prevention and providing assistance in response to other classes of circumstances specified by by-law that may cause harm to persons or property.[91]

b) Acquire, accept and hold property.[92]

c) Appoint, regulate and control a fire chief and members of a fire department.[93]

d) Making agreements with other municipalities for the use of fire fighting and assistance response equipment and personnel.[94]

---

87 *Ibid.*, at ss. 8 and 549.
88 *Ibid.*, at s. 7.
89 *Ibid.*, at s. 549.
90 *Fire Services Act*, R.S.B.C. 1979, c.133, s. 26.
91 *Municipal Act*, R.S.B.C. 1979, c. 290, s. 699(1)(a).
92 *Ibid.*, at s.699(1)(a.1).
93 *Ibid.*, at s.699(1)(b)(c).
94 *Ibid.*, at s. 699(1)(d).

e) Making agreements with other persons, firms, corporations or municipalities for fire protection and assistance response.[95]

f) Construct, operate, maintain and use buildings and other improvements and provide necessary accommodation facilities or equipment for the fire department.[96]

3.3.2.2 Regulation And Control Of Fire

Powers for the regulation and control of fire include the power to enact by-laws for:

a) Regulating the conduct of persons at or near fires.[97]

b) Requiring persons to assist in the fighting of fires and in preserving property threatened by fires.[98]

c) Regulating the manufacturing, processing, storing, selling, transporting or using of combustibles, chemicals, explosives, inflammable or other dangerous things.[99]

d) Requiring the taking of precautions and the disposal of debris caused by lumbering, land clearing or industrial operation to prevent the escape of fire or damage to property.[100]

e) Regulating the construction, installation and operation of tanks, pumps and measuring devices used, or intended to be used for the sale, storage or other disposition of gasoline, oil or other flammable liquid.[101]

f) Regulating the use of fires and lights in the open air or elsewhere.[102]

g) Prohibiting persons from standing, loitering or sitting in the aisles, passages and stairways of churches, theatres, halls, skating rinks and other places of amusement or public resort.[103]

h) Requiring the owners or occupiers of real property to remove anything for a building or yard which in the opinion of the fire chief is a fire hazard or increases the danger of fire.[104]

95 *Ibid.*, at s. 699(1)(e).
96 *Ibid.*, at s. 699(2).
97 *Ibid.*, at s. 700(a).
98 *Ibid.*
99 *Ibid.*, at s. 700(b).
100 *Ibid.*, at s. 700(c).
101 *Ibid.*, at s. 700(d).
102 *Ibid.*, at s. 700(e).
103 *Ibid.*, at s. 700(f).
104 *Ibid.*, at s. 700(g).

i) Requiring the owners or occupiers of real property to clean chimneys and flues or other apparatus or things which in the opinion of the fire chief, if not cleaned, may cause a fire or increase the danger of fire.[105]

j) Authorizing the inspection of premises for conditions which may cause a fire or increase the danger to persons.[106]

k) Taking measures to prevent and suppress fires, including the demolition of buildings and structures to prevent the spreading of fire.[107]

l) Issuing permits for outdoor fires when considered safe to do so.[108]

3.3.2.3 Enforcement Of Laws For The Regulation And Control Of Fire

Powers for the enforcement of laws enacted for the regulation and control of fire include the power to enact by-laws for:

a) Directing that a matter or thing be done by a person, and upon default by that person the matter or thing be done at the expense of the person in default, with such expense recoverable in the same manner as municipal taxes.[109]

b) The imposition of penalties for the violation of by-laws as authorized by the by-laws, the *Municipal Act*[110] or the *Offence Act*[111] and the costs of prosecution.[112]

3.3.3 Manitoba

3.3.3.1 Establishment And Operation Of Fire And Emergency Services

There is no legislative requirement that Manitoba municipalities provide fire and emergency services. However, Manitoba legislation delegates to municipalities a variety of powers for the establishment and operation of fire and emergency services, which include the power to enact by-laws for:

a) Acquiring, by expropriation or otherwise, land necessary for the establishment of fire halls.[113]

---

105 *Ibid.*
106 *Ibid.*, at s. 700(h)(i).
107 *Ibid.*, at s. 700(h)(ii).
108 *Ibid.*, at s. 700(h)(iii).
109 *Ibid.*, at s. 311.
110 *Ibid.*
111 R.S.B.C. 1979, c. 305.
112 *Supra*, note 91 at s. 308.
113 *Municipal Act*, R.S.M. 1988, c. M255, s. 289(1)(a).

b) Erecting, operating and maintaining fire halls.[114]

c) Purchasing, leasing, or otherwise acquiring fire fighting equipment, apparatus and appliances.[115]

d) Appointing a fire chief and as many firemen and other assistants as may be considered necessary from time to time and for fixing their salary or remuneration.[116]

e) Establishing and regulating the government of a fire protection force, and for preventing neglect or abuse and for rendering the force efficient in the discharge of its duties.[117]

f) Delegating to the fire chief the right to maintain discipline in the fire protection force.[118]

g) Entering into an agreement with any other municipality or person for providing or obtaining throughout the whole or a part of the municipality, fire protection or assistance in the prevention and suppression of fires, on such terms as are provided in the agreement.[119]

h) Levying taxes within the municipality to meet financial obligations incurred pursuant to an agreement for the protection or assistance in the prevention and suppression of fires.[120]

i) Providing services through its fire protection force in the prevention and suppression of fires or in relation to other emergencies outside the municipality.[121]

j) Charging the owner of any real or personal property in respect to which fire protection services are provided outside of the municipality or any other municipality in which no agreement for compensation for fire protection services has been entered into.[122]

k) Providing that a fire protection force established by the municipality may provide services in emergencies of any kind, whether or not the emergency relates to fire or the danger of fire, including:

114 *Ibid.*, at s. 289(1)(b).
115 *Ibid.*, at s. 289(1)(c).
116 *Ibid.*, at s. 289(1)(d).
117 *Ibid.*, at s. 289(1)(e).
118 *Ibid.*, at s. 289(1)(f).
119 *Ibid.*, at s. 289(2).
120 *Ibid.*, at s. 289(3).
121 *Ibid.*, at s. 289(6).
122 *Ibid.*, at s. 289(7).

- emergency services for the relief of illness and injury and for the preservation of life; and

- emergency services for dealing with dangerous materials and the protection of persons and property from injury or damages arising out of dangerous materials.[123]

3.3.3.2 Regulation And Control Of Fire

Powers for the regulation and control of fire include the power to enact by-laws for:

a) Making regulations for the prevention and suppression of fires.[124]

b) Regulating the locating and construction of fire walls.[125]

c) Permitting the entering, pulling down or demolishing of houses and other buildings or structures where reasonably necessary to put out a fire or to prevent the fire from spreading.[126]

d) Requiring adult persons for the time being in the municipality to assist in the extinguishing of fires and in the prevention of spread thereof.[127]

e) Preventing interference with the efforts of persons engaged in the extinguishing of fires or preventing the spreading of fire by regulating the conduct of the public at or in the vicinity of any fire.[128]

f) Preventing or regulating the keeping or storage, within certain defined areas in the municipality, of explosives or other highly inflammable or dangerous material, or of anything the keeping or storage of which is likely to cause or contribute to the starting of a fire, or contribute to, or increase the danger of, the spreading of fires.[129]

g) Preventing or regulating the use of fire or lights in places where explosives or other highly inflammable or dangerous combustible material is kept or stored.[130]

123 *Ibid.*, at s. 289(5).
124 *Ibid.*, at s. 290(a).
125 *Ibid.*, at s. 290(b).
126 *Ibid.*, at s. 290(c).
127 *Ibid.*, at s. 290(d).
128 *Ibid.*, at s. 290(e).
129 *Ibid.*, at s. 290(f).
130 *Ibid.*, at s. 290(g).

h) Preventing or regulating the carrying on, in certain defined areas of the municipality, of trades or occupations that are dangerous because of the possibility of their causing or promoting fire.[131]

i) Requiring buildings and yards to be put in a safe condition to guard against fire or the risk of fire.[132]

j) Regulating and prohibiting, within certain defined areas, the keeping of lumber yards or wood yards, or of any inflammable debris, including derelict vehicles.[133]

k) Regulating the transportation of explosives or highly inflammable or dangerous materials in the municipality.[134]

l) Regulating the manner of disposal of ashes or combustible refuse and requiring the placing or keeping of ashes and combustible refuse in fireproof containers.[135]

m) Regulating and enforcing the proper cleaning of chimneys at stated intervals, either by licensed chimney sweeps or otherwise.[136]

n) Preventing or regulating the construction of any chimney, flue, fireplace, oven, stove, boiler or other apparatus or thing that is liable to be dangerous because of the possibility of it causing or promoting fire.[137]

o) Regulating or prohibiting persons from smoking in public places described in the by-law.[138]

p) Regulating or preventing the erection or placing of any building, erection or other structure within areas prescribed in the by-law unless the main walls and roof thereof are constructed of incombustible materials.[139]

q) Preventing structural alterations to any existing building if the existing building does not conform in structure to the building and fire regulations governing construction in any defined area.[140]

---

131 *Ibid.*, at s. 290(h).
132 *Ibid.*, at s. 290(i).
133 *Ibid.*, at s. 290(i).
134 *Ibid.*, at s. 290(j).
135 *Ibid.*, at s. 290(k).
136 *Ibid.*, at s. 290(l).
137 *Ibid.*, at s. 290(m).
138 *Ibid.*, at s. 290(n).
139 *Ibid.*, at s. 290(o).
140 *Ibid.*, at s. 290(p).

r) Regulating or prohibiting the use of a building as a public garage or machine shop unless it is provided with a concrete floor.[141]

s) Regulating the precautions to be observed and the time during which stumps, trees, logs, brush, grass, straw, shavings or refuse may be set on fire or burned in the open air.[142]

t) Requiring the construction and maintenance upon all buildings of more than three storeys in height of proper fire escapes, platforms, stairways or other means of egress.[143]

u) Requiring all buildings of four or more storeys in height to have outer doors that open freely outwards, and to be equipped with fire protection services.[144]

v) Prescribing the character, material and thickness of enclosing walls for hoists or elevators in buildings; requiring fireproof doors at openings to a hoist or elevator shaft; regulating the operation of hoists and elevators; and prescribing doors that open and close automatically as the hoist or elevator ascends or descends.[145]

w) Requiring in all buildings wherein labour is employed, sufficient means of egress in case of fire.[146]

x) Regulating the installation, insulation and position of wires and appliances used for conducting electricity, and the removal of unsafe or dangerous wires and appliances.[147]

y) Providing generally for the protection of life and property damage by fire.[148]

z) Acquiring by expropriation or otherwise land necessary for the establishment of a magazine for explosives.[149]

aa) Constructing and maintaining a magazine for explosives.[150]

bb) Compelling persons having or using explosive materials to store them in the magazine for explosives.[151]

---

141 *Ibid.*, at s. 290(s).
142 *Ibid.*, at s. 290(s).
143 *Ibid.*, at s. 290(s).
144 *Ibid.*, at s. 290(t).
145 *Ibid.*, at s. 290(u).
146 *Ibid.*, at s. 290(v).
147 *Ibid.*, at s. 290(w).
148 *Ibid.*, at s. 290(x).
149 *Ibid.*, at s. 296(a).
150 *Ibid.*, at s. 296(b).
151 *Ibid.*, at s. 296(c).

cc) Providing fees and charges for the storing of explosives, highly flammable or dangerous material in the magazine for explosives.[152]

3.3.3.3 Enforcement Of Laws For The Regulation And Control Of Fire

Power for the enforcement of laws enacted for the regulation and control of fire include the power to enact by-laws for:

a) Inflicting fines and penalties not exceeding $1,000.00, in addition to costs, for breach of any of the by-laws of the municipality, and in case of non-payment of fine and costs inflicted for any such breach, imprisonment for a period not exceeding 30 days.[153]

3.3.4 New Brunswick

3.3.4.1 Establishment And Operation Of Fire And Emergency Services

There is no legislative requirement that New Brunswick municipalities provide fire and emergency services. However, Provincial legislation delegates to municipalities a variety of powers for the establishment and operation of fire and emergency services, which include the power to enact by-laws for:

a) The purpose of preventing and extinguishing fires and protecting property from fire.[154]

b) Establishing a fire department.[155]

c) Appointing fire department officers and members.[156]

d) Providing for the purchase of vehicles and equipment.[157]

e) Appointing fire prevention officers and prescribing their duties.[158]

f) Providing for compensation to officers and members of fire departments and fire prevention officers for injuries received while performing their duties.[159]

g) Conferring upon fire prevention officers the same powers under the same conditions as are conferred upon the fire marshal by sections 11, 12, 16 and 21 of the *Fire Prevention Act.*[160]

152 *Ibid.,* at s. 296(d).
153 *Ibid.,* at s. 746.
154 *Municipalities Act,* R.S.N.B. 1973, c.M-22, s. 109(1).
155 *Ibid.,* at s. 109(1)(a).
156 *Ibid.*
157 *Ibid.,* at s. 109(b).
158 *Ibid.,* at s. 109(c).
159 *Ibid.,* at s. 109(d).
160 *Ibid.,* at s. 109(q).

3.3.4.2 Regulation And Control Of Fire

Powers for the regulation and control of fire include the power to enact by-laws for:

a) Establishing fire zones and regulating the construction, repair and occupancy of buildings and premises within such zones.[161]

b) Regulating the storage, handling, transportation and disposal of flammable liquids, solids and gases.[162]

c) Prohibiting or regulating the storage of combustible, explosive or dangerous materials.[163]

d) Regulating the installation of equipment for burning fuel.[164]

e) Regulating the cleaning of chimneys, flues, stove and furnace pipes.[165]

f) Requiring buildings and yards to be kept in a safe condition to guard against fire or other danger.[166]

g) Regulating the removal and safe keeping of ashes.[167]

h) Prohibiting or regulating the lighting of outdoor fires for the disposal of refuse and prescribing the location and construction of public and private incinerators.[168]

i) Authorizing a fire prevention officer or the chief of a fire department to enter any building at reasonable times to inspect for the purpose of fire prevention or to investigate the cause or origin of a fire.[169]

j) Authorizing the demolition of buildings or other erections to prevent the spread of fire.[170]

---

161 *Ibid.*, at s. 109(1)(3).
162 *Ibid.*, at s. 109(1)(f).
163 *Ibid.*, at s. 109 (1)(g).
164 *Ibid.*, at s. 109(1)(h).
165 *Ibid.*, at s. 109(1)(i).
166 *Ibid.*, at s. 109(1)(j).
167 *Ibid.*, at s. 109 (1)(k).
168 *Ibid.*, at s. 109(1)(l).
169 *Ibid.*, at s. 109(1)(m).
170 *Ibid.*, at s. 109(1)(o). It should be noted that where a building or other erection is demolished pursuant to this section, the municipality may be required to compensate any person having an interest in the building or other erection pursuant to section 109(4) of the Act.

3.3.4.3 Enforcement Of Laws For The Regulation And Control Of Fire

Powers for the enforcement of laws enacted for the regulation and control of fire include the power to enact by-laws for:

a) Authorizing fire prevention officers to enforce the *Fire Prevention Act* and the regulations enacted thereunder.[171]

b) Providing penalties to a maximum fine of $50.00 for a breach of a by-law enacted pursuant to section 109 of the *Municipalities Act* or for failure to observe an order of a fire prevention officer authorized by a by-law.[172]

3.3.5 Newfoundland

3.3.5.1 Establishment And Operation Of Fire And Emergency Services

While Newfoundland legislation specifically provides for the establishment and operation of the City of St. John's fire department,[173] there is no legislative requirement that other Newfoundland municipalities provide fire and emergency services.[174]

Provincial legislation delegates to Newfoundland municipalities a variety of powers for the establishment and operation of fire and emergency services, including:

a) The establishment, operation and maintenance of town and community fire departments composed of volunteer members, paid employees or both.[175]

b) The construction, acquisition, establishment, ownership and operation of fire halls, fire engines and other apparatus necessary for fire fighting and fire protection by a local service district committee.[176]

c) Acquisition of a fire hall, fire alarm system, fire engines, hydrants and other apparatus and appliances for the purpose of fire fighting and the prevention of fire.[177]

d) Making regulations with respect to the control and management of town fire departments.[178]

e) Entering into agreements with other municipalities, local service districts, or persons, for joint fire fighting.[179]

---

171 *Ibid.*, at s. 109(1)(p).
172 *Ibid.*, at s. 109(1)(r).
173 *St. John's Fire Department Act*, R.S.N. 1990, c. S-2.
174 Newfoundland municipalities are designated as cities, towns, communities and regions.
175 *Municipalities Act*, R.S.N. 1990, c. M-23, at ss. 192, 268.
176 *Ibid.*, at s. 642.
177 *Ibid.*, at s. 192.
178 *Ibid.*, at s. 193(1). It should be noted that such regulations require Ministerial approval.
179 *Ibid.*, at s. 195.

3.3.5.2 Regulation And Control Of Fire

Powers for the regulation and control of fire include:

a) Making regulations for the fighting of fires, the prevention of fire in towns and the inspection of buildings in towns for fire prevention purposes.[180]

b) Adopting all or part of the National Fire Code of Canada or other code, and supplements thereto, with or without modification.[181]

c) The officer in charge of a town fire department attaching and fixing to a private or public building or structure, fire alarms, wires and fastenings necessary for carrying on the work of the department or staying the progress of or preventing fire.[182]

d) The officer in charge of a town fire department pulling down or removing all or part of a private or public building or structure where such action is considered necessary to extinguish or stay the progress of a fire.[183]

e) The officers and members of a town fire department, their fire engines, apparatus and appliances to have the right-of-way over all traffic while proceeding to answer an alarm of fire.[184]

f) Prohibiting any person from obstructing an officer or member of a municipal fire department in the performance of their duties and from wilfully retarding the passage of an engine apparatus or appliance used by an officer or member.[185]

g) Prohibiting any person from wilfully giving a false alarm of fire to a town fire department or to another person.[186]

3.3.5.3 Enforcement Of Laws For The Regulation And Control Of Fire

Newfoundland legislation does not specifically provide for the recovery of fees and costs associated with the provision of fire and emergency service, nor does it impose specific penalties for violation of the fire and emergency services provisions of the *Municipalities Act*.[187]

---

180 *Ibid.*, at s. 193(1). It should be noted that such regulations require Ministerial approval and are subject to the provisions of the *Fire Prevention Act*, R.S.N. 1990, c. F-11.
181 *Ibid.*, at s. 193(2).
182 *Ibid.*, at s. 196.
183 *Ibid.*, at s. 197.
184 *Ibid.*, at s. 198(1).
185 *Ibid.*, at s. 201(1).
186 *Ibid.*, at s. 201(2).
187 *Ibid.*

3.3.6 Northwest Territories

3.3.6.1 Establishment And Operation Of Fire And Emergency Services

There is no legislative requirement that Northwest Territories municipalities provide fire and emergency services. However, Territorial legislation delegates to municipalities a variety of powers for the establishment and operation of fire and emergency services, which include the power to enact by-laws for:

a) Establishing and operating a fire protection service.[188]

b) Entering into agreements respecting the use of fire-fighting staff and equipment.[189]

3.3.6.2 Regulation And Control Of Fire

Powers for the regulation and control of fire include the power to enact by-laws for:

a) Dividing the municipality into fire districts of different classes.[190]

b) Determining the standards for buildings and structures in each class of fire district.[191]

c) Prohibiting or regulating the construction of buildings and structures in a fire district according to the standards of that class of fire district.[192]

d) The demolition, removal or alteration of buildings, structures, vegetation, waste or any thing that the municipal council considers to be or likely to be a fire hazard.[193]

e) Prohibiting or regulating the manufacture, processing, storage, sale, transport or use of combustibles, chemicals, explosives or other dangerous products.[194]

3.3.6.3 Enforcement Of Laws For The Regulation And Control Of Fire

Powers for the enforcement of laws enacted for the regulation and control of fire include:

---

188 *Cities, Towns and Villages Act*, R.S.N.W.T. 1988, c. C-8, s. 97.
189 *Ibid.,* at s. 99.
190 *Ibid.,* at s. 98 (1)(a).
191 *Ibid.,* at s. 98(1)(b).
192 *Ibid.,* at s. 98(1)(c).
193 *Ibid.,* at s. 98(2). It should be noted that pursuant to section 178, prior to exercising this power the municipal council must hold a hearing at which any person affected may make representations. Further, section 180 provides a statutory right of appeal from the municipal council's decision to the Supreme Court. However, no hearing is required if the municipal council is of the opinion that there is imminent danger to public health and safety, pursuant to section 179.
194 *Ibid.,* at s. 100.

a) Enactment of by-laws for the purpose of ensuring compliance with its by-laws by providing for the issuance of orders by the municipal council, a by-law officer or other employee directing a person to do any act or refrain from doing any act, and further providing that failure to obey such an order constitutes an offence.[195]

b) Enactment of by-laws providing for the inspection of buildings, structures and excavations to ensure compliance with its by-laws.[196]

c) Use of the *Summary Conviction Procedures Act*[197] to enforce municipal by-laws.[198]

d) In addition to any other remedy available to it, a municipality may enforce a by-law by applying to the Supreme Court for an injunction.[199]

e) Enactment of by-laws providing for the imposition of penalties for the violation of by-laws to a maximum fine of $1,000.00 for individuals and $5,000.00 for corporations, and in default of payment of a fine to imprisonment for up to 6 months.[200]

f) In addition to any fine that may be levied, a court, subject to its jurisdiction, may order a person convicted of an offence under a by-law to pay any fee or charge that may otherwise be payable by the person to the municipal corporation in respect of any license or permit that should have been obtained by the person.[201]

g) In addition to any fine that may be levied, a court, subject to its jurisdiction, may order a person convicted of an offence under a by-law to do or refrain from doing any activity that the court may specify.[202]

3.3.7 Nova Scotia

3.3.7.1 Establishment And Operation Of Fire And Emergency Services

Nova Scotia legislation requires that its municipalities provide fire and emergency services. *The Municipal Act*[203] requires that municipal councils appoint firewards,[204]

195 *Ibid.*, at s. 173.
196 *Ibid.*, at s. 174.
197 R.S.N.W.T. 1988, c. S-15.
198 *Supra*, note 187 at s. 176(1).
199 *Ibid.*, at s. 177.
200 *Ibid.*, at s. 182. The same maximum penalties are available even if a municipality does not specify penalties within its by-law. See section 186.
201 *Ibid.*, at s. 183(a).
202 *Ibid.*, at s. 183(b).
203 R.S.N.S. 1989, c. 295, s. 126.
204 *Ibid.*, at s. 127.

and further states that "When a fire occurs the firewards or any persons acting under their direction or authority shall endeavour to extinguish and prevent the spreading of the same."[205]

Provincial legislation delegates to municipalities a variety of powers for the establishment and operation of emergency service, including:

a) The creation of one or more zones within the municipality for the purpose of fire protection.[206]

b) The annual appointment of firewards for each zone.[207]

c) The establishment of a command structure which includes firewards and officers of fire companies.[208]

d) The organization of companies to assist in the extinguishing of fires and the preservation and protection or property at or during fires.[209]

e) The remuneration of members of fire companies.[210]

f) Entering into agreements with one or more cities, towns, municipalities, villages, commissions or person, for such length of time and or such terms as the council of the municipality may determine, for giving assistance at fires outside the boundaries of the municipality or for receiving assistance at fires within its boundaries.[211]

g) Assisting with its apparatus, machinery, implements or equipment at fires occurring outside its boundaries.[212]

3.3.7.2 Regulation And Control Of Fire

Powers for the regulation and control of fire include:

a) Commanding the assistance of person present at a fire and all inhabitants of the municipality.[213]

---

205 *Ibid.*, at s. 129(1).
206 *Ibid.*, at s. 126.
207 *Ibid.*, at s. 127.
208 *Ibid.*, at ss. 128, 134, 136, 137, 138.
209 *Ibid.*, at s. 133.
210 *Ibid.*, at s. 135.
211 *Ibid.*, at s. 132(2).
212 *Ibid.*, at s. 132(1).
213 *Ibid.*, at s. 129(1)(a).

b) Removing property from buildings on fire or in danger thereof,[214] and the power to take charge of such property.[215]

c) Entering or breaking into any building to extinguish and prevent the spread of fire.[216]

d) Pulling down or otherwise destroying any building to prevent the spread of fire.[217]

e) Excluding persons and vehicles from the vicinity of a fire.[218]

f) To generally do all things necessary to carry out the extinguishing and prevention of the spread of fire.[219]

3.3.7.3 Enforcement Of Laws For The Regulation And Control Of Fire

Powers for the enforcement of laws enacted for the regulation and control of fire include:

a) Every person who disobeys a lawful order or command of a fireward shall for each such offence be liable upon summary conviction to the penalty prescribed by the *Summary Proceedings Act*.[220] The *Summary Proceedings Act* provides as follows:

> 4. Every one who, without lawful excuse, contravenes an enactment by wilfully doing anything that it forbids or by wilfully omitting to do anything that it requires to be done is, unless some penalty or punishment is expressly provided by law, guilty of an offence punishable on summary conviction and liable to a fine of not more than five hundred dollars or to imprisonment for six months or to both.[221]

3.3.8 Ontario

3.3.8.1 Establishment And Operation Of Fire And Emergency Services

There is no general legislative requirement that Ontario municipalities provide fire

---

214 *Ibid.*, at s. 129(1)(b).
215 *Ibid.*, at s. 129(1)(c).
216 *Ibid.*, at s. 129(1)(d).
217 *Ibid.*, at ss. 129 (1)(d), 130(1). It should be noted that pursuant to section 130(2), a municipality may be liable to compensate the owner of any building pulled down or destroyed pursuant to section 130(1).
218 *Ibid.*, at s. 129(e).
219 *Ibid.*, at s. 129(f).
220 *Ibid.*, at s. 129(2).
221 R.S.N.S. 1989, c. 450, s. 4.

and emergency services. However, every Ontario municipality located within a fire region must extinguish grass, brush and forest fires located within its municipal boundaries.[222] Provincial legislation delegates to Ontario municipalities a variety of powers for the establishment and operation of fire and emergency services, which include the power to enact bylaws for:

a) The provision of fire fighting and fire protection services and for establishing, operating, promoting and regulating life and property saving companies.[223]

b) The establishment, maintenance and operation of a fire department to serve only a defined area of the municipality, and for the levying of a special annual rate on all rateable property in the defined area to cover costs associated with the establishment, maintenance and operation of the fire department.[224]

c) The entering into of agreements with other municipalities for the provision or sharing of fire and emergency services and for the levying of a special annual rate on all rateable property to cover costs associated with the agreement.[225]

d) Adopting and participating in an emergency fore service plan or program established by the fire co-ordinator of a regional, district or metropolitan municipality, or by a county or district fire co-ordinator, upon such terms and conditions as the municipal council considers appropriate.[226]

e) Secure against accident by fire the inmates and employees and others in factories, hotels, boarding houses, warehouses, theatres, music halls, opera houses and other buildings used as places of public resort or amusement.[227]

3.3.8.2 Regulation And Control Of Fire

Powers for the regulation and control of fire include the power to enact by-laws for:

a) Regulating or prohibiting smoking in retail stores where ten or more persons are employed.[228]

b) Prescribing the times during which fires may be set in the open air, and the precautions to be observed by persons setting the fire.[229]

c) Regulating or prohibiting the sale of fireworks.[230]

---

222 *Forest Fires Prevention Act*, R.S.O. 1990, c. F.24, s.21.
223 *Municipal Act*, R.S.O. 1990, c. M.45, s. 207(31).
224 *Ibid.*, at s. 207(31)(a) (b).
225 *Ibid.*, at s. 207(31)(c) (d).
226 *Ibid.*, at s. 207(32).
227 *Ibid.*, at s. 207(33).
228 *Ibid.*, at s. 207(34).
229 *Ibid.*, at s. 207(35).
230 *Ibid.*, at s. 207 (37).

d) Prohibiting the erection or the removal to another location within the municipality of wooden buildings, additions and fences.[231]

e) Regulating or prohibiting the use of fire or lights in factories, stables, cabinet makers' shops, carpenters' shops, paint shops, dye and cleaning works, and places where their use may cause or promote fire.[232]

f) Regulating or prohibiting the carrying on of manufacturing or trades that may be considered dangerous in causing or spreading fire.[233]

g) Regulating and enforcing the proper cleaning of chimneys.[234]

h) Regulating the mode of removal and safekeeping of ashes.[235]

i) Requiring buildings and yards to be put in a safe condition to guard against fire or other dangerous risk or accident.[236]

j) Requiring each inhabitant to provide as many fire buckets as may be prescribed and for inspection of such fire buckets.[237]

k) The making of such other regulations for the prevention of fire that the municipal council considers necessary.[238]

l) Requiring inhabitants of the municipality to fight and put out timber or forest fires.[239]

3.3.8.3 Enforcement Of Laws For The Regulation And Control Of Fire

Powers for the enforcement of laws enacted for the regulation and control of fire include the power to enact by-laws for:

a) Authorizing appointed officers to enter at all reasonable times upon property in order to ascertain whether a by-law is being obeyed, and to enforce or carry out the by-law.[240]

b) Providing that any person who contravenes any by-law is guilty of an offence.[241]

---

231 *Ibid.*, at s. 207(39).
232 *Ibid.*, at s. 207(40).
233 *Ibid.*, at s. 207(41).
234 *Ibid.*, at s. 207(42).
235 *Ibid.*, at s. 207(43).
236 *Ibid.*, at s. 207(44).
237 *Ibid.*, at s. 207(45).
238 *Ibid.*, at s. 207(49).
239 *Ibid.*, at s. 207(50).
240 *Ibid.*, at s. 207(46).
241 *Ibid.*, at s. 320.

3.3.9 Prince Edward Island

3.3.9.1 Establishment And Operation Of Fire And Emergency Services

There is no legislative requirement that Prince Edward Island municipalities provide fire and emergency services. However, Provincial legislation delegates to existing towns and villages a broad general power for the establishment and operation of fire and emergency services.[242] Similar powers are granted to municipalities for which a community improvement committee has been established.[243] New municipalities may receive the power to establish and operate fire and emergency services from the legislation incorporating the municipality.[244]

3.3.9.2 Regulation And Control Of Fire

Powers for the regulation and control of fire are not specifically provided for in Provincial legislation. However, such powers may exist in the general power given to municipalities to enact by-laws "... that are considered expedient and are not contrary to this or any other Act or regulations for the peace, order and good government of the municipality...".[245]

3.3.9.3 Enforcement Of Laws For The Regulation And Control Of Fire

Powers for the enforcement of laws enacted for the regulation and control of fire include the power to enact by-laws for:

a) Creating offences for violation of by-laws and prescribing penalties in an amount not exceeding $500.00.[246]

b) Prescribing means of enforcement of by-laws.[247]

3.3.10 Saskatchewan

Rural Municipalities

3.3.10.1 Establishment And Operation Of Fire And Emergency Services

There is no legislative requirement that rural Saskatchewan municipalities provide fire and emergency services. However, Provincial legislation delegates to rural municipalities a variety of powers for the establishment and operation of fire and emergency services, which include the power to enact by-laws for:

---

242 *Municipalities Act,* R.S.P.E.I. 1988, c. M-13, s. 30(b).
243 *Ibid.,* at s. 3(b).
244 *Ibid.,* at s. 32.
245 *Ibid.,* at s. 57.
246 *Ibid.,* at s. 58(1).
247 *Ibid.,* at s. 58(2).

a) Prevention and extinguishing of fires by means of a municipal force, contract or otherwise, including the acquisition of fire fighting equipment throughout the municipality or in any specified area of the municipality.[248]

b) Assessing and levying the cost of fire prevention and extinguishing services:

- throughout the entire municipality; or

- partly throughout the entire municipality and partly directly to those persons who receive the service; or

- directly on persons who receive the service.[249]

3.3.10.2 Regulation And Control Of Fire

Powers for the regulation and control of fire include the power to enact by-laws:

a) Prohibiting, regulating or controlling the storage of flammable liquids in and about improvements.[250]

b) Prohibiting, regulating or controlling the use, possession or storage of combustible, explosive or dangerous materials.[251]

c) Requiring buildings and yards to be kept in a safe condition to guard against fire or other dangerous risk or accident.[252]

d) Regulating the conduct and enforcing the assistance of persons present for the preservation of property at fires.[253]

e) Pulling down or demolishing improvements when considered necessary to prevent the spread of fire.[254]

f) Prohibiting the burning of straw within the municipality or any portion of it during a period to be stated in the by-law.[255]

3.3.10.3 Enforcement Of Laws For The Regulation And Control Of Fire

Powers for the enforcement of laws enacted for the regulation and control of fire include the power to enact by-laws for:

---

248 *Rural Municipality Act,* R.S.S. 1978, c. R-26.1, s. 215(1)(a).
249 *Ibid.*
250 *Ibid.,* at s. 215(1)(b)(i).
251 *Ibid.,* at s. 215(1)(b)(ii).
252 *Ibid.,* at s. 215(1)(b)(iii).
253 *Ibid.,* at s. 215(1)(b)(iv).
254 *Ibid.,* at s. 215(1)(b)(v).
255 *Ibid.,* at s. 215(1)(c).

a) Recovery of costs of fire prevention and extinguishing services remaining unpaid at the end of the year in which the service was provided by adding such costs to and forming part of the taxes on any land, improvement or business owned by the person owing the costs.[256]

Urban Municipalities

3.3.10.1 Establishment And Operation Of Fire And Emergency Services

There is no legislative requirement that urban Saskatchewan municipalities provide fire and emergency services. However, Provincial legislation delegates to urban municipalities a variety of powers for the establishment and operation of fire and emergency services, which include the power to:

a) Purchase, lease or otherwise acquire fire fighting vehicles, equipment and other apparatus.[257]

b) Establish a fire department or one or more fire brigades.[258]

c) Appoint a fire chief and as many fire fighters and other assistants that the council may consider necessary, and fix their salary or remuneration.[259]

3.3.10.2 Regulation And Control Of Fire

In addition, Provincial legislation delegates to urban municipalities the power to enact by-laws for:

a) Constructing, operating and maintaining fire halls.[260]

b) Entering into agreements with any other municipality, the Government of Saskatchewan or any person for the furnishing of fire fighting services or the use of the fire fighting equipment of the urban municipality in extinguishing fires outside the urban municipality on any terms that may be agreed on.[261]

c) Providing fire fighting services or the use of equipment in extinguishing fires outside the urban municipality and charge for those services if no contract has been entered into and a request for those services is made by a municipality or any person.[262]

---

256 *Ibid.,* at s. 215(2).
257 *Urban Municipality Act,* R.S.S. 1978, c. U-11, s. 136(1)(a).
258 *Ibid.,* as s. 136(1)(b).
259 *Ibid.*
260 *Ibid.,* at s. 136(2)(a).
261 *Ibid.,* at s. 136(2)(b).
262 *Ibid.,* at s. 136(2)(c).

d) Providing for the prevention and extinguishing of fires and for the preservation of life and property from destruction by fire.[263]

e) Prohibiting, regulating or controlling the storage of inflammable liquids in or about any buildings or class of buildings.[264]

f) Regulating the use, possession, storage or handling of any class of explosives or other highly inflammable matter, and prohibiting the use, possession, storage or handling of such matter except by permit authorized by a resolution of the council.[265]

g) Regulating the installation of fireplaces, stoves and stove pipes or other apparatus that may be dangerous in causing or promoting fires, and enforcing the proper cleaning of chimneys, flues and stove pipes.[266]

h) Requiring buildings and yards to be kept in a safe condition to guard against fire or the risk of fire or other dangerous risk or accident.[267]

i) Compelling the building of fire walls.[268]

j) Regulating the manner of disposal of ashes or combustible refuse and requiring the placing or keeping of ashes and combustible refuse in fire-resistant containers.[269]

k) Regulating the conduct of persons at or near fires and compelling them to assist in the fighting of fires and in the prevention of the spread of fire.[270]

l) Pulling down or demolishing buildings or other erections when considered necessary to prevent the spread of fire and providing compensation for loss or damage sustained by reason of the pulling down or demolishing in any amount equal to the amount of insurance to which the owner would have been entitled had the building been burned.[271]

m) Preventing the obstruction of the halls, aisles, passageways, alleys or approaches in or to any church, theatre, hall or other place of public meeting while occupied for a public assemblage.[272]

---

263 *Ibid.*, at s. 136(3).
264 *Ibid.*, at s. 136(3)(a).
265 *Ibid.*, at s. 136(3)(b).
266 *Ibid.*, at s. 136(3)(c).
267 *Ibid.*, at s. 136(3)(d).
268 *Ibid.*
269 *Ibid.*, at s. 136(3)(c).
270 *Ibid.*, at s. 136(3)(f).
271 *Ibid.*, at s. 136(3)(g).
272 *Ibid.*, at s. 136(3)(h).

n) Declaring that all or any part of the *National Fire Code of Canada* or any other fire prevention code is in force in the urban municipality with any revisions, variations or modifications than may be specified in the by-law.[273]

3.3.10.3 Enforcement Of Laws For The Regulation And Control Of Fire

Powers for the enforcement of laws enacted for the regulation and control of fire include the power to enact by-laws for:

a) The imposition of penalties for the violation of by-laws to a maximum $2,000.00 fine in the case of an individual and a maximum $5,000.00 fine in the case of a corporation.[274]

3.3.11 Yukon Territory

3.3.11.1 Establishment And Operation Of Fire And Emergency Services

Yukon legislation requires that its municipalities provide fire and emergency services. The Municipal Act provides:

> 267(1) Subject to any other Act, council shall by by-law establish a fire department.[275]

Yukon legislation delegates to municipalities a variety of powers for the establishment of fire and emergency services, which include the power to enact by-laws for:

a) The purchase of fire fighting equipment and providing proper buildings therefor.[276]

b) Establishing fire districts.[277]

c) Entering into agreements with other municipalities or the Government of the Yukon Territory or the Government of Canada for the use within the municipality of fire fighting equipment and personnel upon such terms and conditions and for such remuneration as may be agreed upon.[278]

3.3.11.2 Regulation And Control Of Fire

Powers for the regulation and control of fire include the power to enact by-laws for:

273 *Ibid.*, at s. 136(4).
274 *Ibid.*, at s. 92(1). It should be noted that section 191(c) of the Act makes it an offence to wilfully open or close any hydrant or obstruct free access to any hydrant without the authorization of a council or its designate. Offenders are liable to a maximum fine of $5,000.00.
275 R.S.Y.T. 1986, c. 119, s. 267(1).
276 *Ibid.*, at s. 267(2)(a).
277 *Ibid.*, at s. 267(2)(b).
278 *Ibid.*, at s. 267(2)(d).

a) Regulating the construction of buildings within fire districts with respect to taking precautions against the danger of fire, which regulation includes discriminating and differentiating between the character of buildings permitted as between fire districts.[279]

b) The destruction, alteration or removal of any building, structure, weeds, grass, rubbish or other thing that in the opinion of the municipal council constitutes or is likely to constitute a fire hazard or that should be removed for the protection of life and property, and to charge the costs and expenses of the destruction, alteration or removal against the property concerned.[280]

c) Regulating the manufacturing, processing, storing, selling, transporting or use of combustibles, chemicals, explosives or other dangerous products.[281]

d) Regulating the construction, installation and operation of tanks, pumps and measuring devices used, or intended to be used for the sale, storage or other disposition of gasoline, oil or other inflammable liquid.[282]

e) Regulating the use of fires and lights in the open air or elsewhere.[283]

f) Prohibiting persons from standing, loitering or sitting in the aisles, passages and stairways of churches, theatres, halls, skating rinks and other public buildings.[284]

g) Inspecting premises for conditions which may cause of fire, incur the danger of fire or increase the danger to persons.[285]

h) Prevention and suppression of fires, including the demolition of buildings and structures.[286]

i) Inspection and supervision of electric wiring and the levying of fees for such inspections.[287]

j) Regulating the installation of stoves and stove pipes or other apparatus or things that may be dangerous in causing or promoting fires, and enforcing the proper cleaning of chimneys, flues and stove pipes.[288]

---

279 *Ibid.*, at s. 267(2)(b).
280 *Ibid.*, at s. 267(2)(c).
281 *Ibid.*, at s. 267(2)(e).
282 *Ibid.*, at s. 267(2)(f).
283 *Ibid.*, at s. 267(2)(g).
284 *Ibid.*, at s. 267(h).
285 *Ibid.*, at s. 267(i).
286 *Ibid.*, at s. 267(k).
287 *Ibid.*, at s. 267(k).
288 *Ibid.*, at s. 267(l).

k) Prohibiting or regulating the sale and setting off of fireworks.[289]

l) The operation of fire protection and fire fighting services and equipment outside the municipality.[290]

m) Prohibiting or regulating the use of any explosive agent for blasting.[291]

n) Any matter which the municipal council considers necessary or proper for adequate fore protection or the protection of life or property.[292]

3.3.11.3 Enforcement Of Laws For The Regulation And Control Of Fire

Powers for the enforcement of laws enacted for the regulation and control of fire include:

a) Recovery of expenses incurred by a municipality in carrying out any action which the municipality ordered another person to carry out, but which that other person failed to carry out, including the collection of expenses in like manner as municipal taxes.[293]

b) Authorizing any employee or enforcement officer of the municipality to order any person carrying out any work or doing anything contrary to a municipal by-law to cease carrying out such work and doing such things, and providing that failure to obey such an order constitutes an offence.[294]

c) The imposition of penalties for the violation of by-laws, which penalties include fine, imprisonment or fine and imprisonment.[295]

4.0 ALTERNATIVE APPROACHES TO THE PROVISION OF FIRE AND EMERGENCY SERVICES

As we have seen, federal, provincial, territorial and municipal governments may and in some cases must provide fire and emergency services within the limits of their constitutional or delegated jurisdiction. These services may be provided in a variety of ways, including:

289 *Ibid.,* at ss. 267(m), 292(1),(2).
290 *Ibid.,* at s. 267(3).
291 *Ibid.,* at s. 292(1)(3).
292 *Ibid.,* at s. 267(4).
293 *Ibid.,* at s. 384(1). It should be noted that approval of the Executive Council must be given to collect expenses in like manner as municipal taxes.
294 *Ibid.,* at s. 383(1)(a),(b).
295 *Ibid.,* at s. 382. While the *Municipal Act* does not provide maximum penalties for the violation of municipal by-laws, the *Summary Convictions Act,* R.S.Y.T. 1986, c.164, s. 3(2) provides maximum penalties of a $500.,00 fine and 16 months imprisonment.

a) Establishment and operation of fire and emergency services.

b) Entering into agreements with other governments to provide or to share in the establishment and operation of fire and emergency services.

c) Entering into agreements with private contractors for the provision of fire and emergency services.

Each of these alternatives will be examined in turn.

4.1 Establishment And Operation Of Government Fire And Emergency Services

Many governments at the federal, provincial and municipal levels have established and operated their own fire and emergency services. Common examples of this practice include federal fire and emergency services at airports and military installations, provincial forest fire services and municipal fire departments. The primary advantage of this approach is that it allows the government providing the service to exercise complete control over the establishment and operation of the fire and emergency service, including such key elements as:

a) Development and implementation of risk management strategies.

b) Creation of a command structure.

c) Commitment to and allocation of financial resources.

d) Establishment of proficiency standards and training programs for personnel.

e) Acquisition and maintenance of facilities and equipment.

However, these advantages often come at a high cost, and are often difficult to obtain in an era of budgetary constraint. Consequently governments at all levels are seeking alternatives to the traditional approach of establishing and operating fire and emergency services. A number of these alternatives are considered below.

4.2 Inter-Governmental Agreements For Fire And Emergency Services

One alternative approach is for governments to enter into agreements with each other for the provision of fire and emergency services. Inter-governmental agreements may occur both between different levels of governments (such as between the federal and provincial governments for the provision of forest fire services by the provinces in national parks), and between the same level of government (a common example of which are inter-municipal agreements).

Inter-governmental agreements for the provision of fire and emergency services generally fall within one of the following three categories, as discussed below.

4.2.1 Agreement For The Provision Of Fire And Emergency Services

A government may elect to limit its involvement in the provision of fire and emergency services to only entering into an agreement with another government to provide the required services in exchange for financial or other payment. The obvious advantage to the government receiving the fire and emergency services is that it need not undertake the costs associated with establishing and maintaining fire and emergency services. This alternative is attractive to senior levels of government which may require fire and emergency services in a large number of locations. It is also attractive to small municipalities which may not receive sufficient funding to establish and operate fire and emergency services. However, the primary disadvantage is that the government receiving the services has no control over those services apart from the terms and conditions of the agreement. An example of an agreement for the provision of fire and emergency services is set out at Appendix B.2.

4.2.2 Joint Fire And Emergency Services Agreements

Governments may also choose to establish and operate fire and emergency services in partnership with each other. This approach is particularly popular with municipal governments located within the same geographic area, which frequently establish a "Joint Municipal Fire and Emergency Service" or a "Regional Fire and Emergency Service".

While legislation authorizing the establishment of joint fire and emergency services varies from jurisdiction to jurisdiction, most legislation simply authorizes the entering into of agreements with other governments for the joint use, control and management of fire extinguishing personnel and equipment.

The advantages to be derived from participation in a joint fire and emergency services arrangement include the following:

a) It allows participating governments to share capital and operating costs.

b) It may reduce redundancy in fire and emergency services facilities, equipment and personnel, thereby enabling a joint fire and emergency service to acquire specialized equipment and specially trained personnel which might otherwise be unattainable.

c) It may provide an increased level of fire and emergency services within a geographic area. For example, difficulties faced by rural municipalities in providing fire and emergency services to geographically distant areas may be reduced by the provision of these services by nearby urban municipalities which are participants in the joint fire and emergency service.

d) It allows governments to maintain a degree of control over the establishment and operation of the fire and emergency service at a reduced costs.

An example of an agreement for the establishment and operation of joint fire and emergency services is set out at Appendix B.3.

4.2.3 Mutual Assistance Agreements

Governments which choose to establish and operate their own fire and emergency services may enter into agreements with each other for providing mutual assistance when requested. Such agreements are often referred to as "mutual assistance" or "mutual aid" agreements.

The advantages associated with mutual assistance agreements include the following:

a) They may provide an increased level of fire and emergency services within a geographic area. They may, for example, allow a government to provide a basic level of fire and emergency services in the knowledge that in the event of a conflagration or other large scale emergency, assistance will be available from other participating governments.

b) They allow governments to maintain total control over the establishment and operation of the fire and emergency service at a reduced cost.

An example of a mutual assistance agreement is set out in Appendix B.4.

4.3 Private Fire And Emergency Services Agreements

A third option available to governments for the provision of fire and emergency services is to enter into agreements with private contractors for the provision of these services. In recent years the private sector has begun to offer a wide variety of fire and emergency services to government clients. These services include both general and specialized fire and emergency services.

Some private contractors have specialized in the provision of general fire prevention and emergency services. However, such services are most commonly provided by private sector corporations which have established and operate fire and emergency services to meet their own needs. These services may be offered to governments.[296]

In recent years the private sector has begun to offer a broad range of specialized fire and emergency services such as natural gas and oil well fire suppression, search and rescue, and the clean-up of hazardous materials. The advantages to a government which acquires private fire and emergency services include:

---

296 This practice is particularly common between large industrial facilities which store or produce flammable, combustible or otherwise dangerous substances and the municipalities in which such industries are located.

a) A possible reduction in the costs associated with establishing and operating those services which can be provided by private contractors on those occasions when the need arises.

b) A possible reduction of government exposure to civil liability for negligently performed services.[297]

5.0 ADMINISTRATIVE LAW

Administrative law plays an important role with respect to fire, emergency and safety services across Canada. Administrative law has been defined as follows:

> Administrative law deals with the legal limitations on the actions of governmental officials, and on the remedies which are available to anyone affected by a transgression of these limits. The subject invariably involves the question of the lawful authority of an official to do a particular act which, in the absence of such authority, might well be illegal (or ultra vires) and give rise to an actionable wrong.[298]

Thus, in many ways administrative law is similar to constitutional law. The relationship between administrative law and constitutional law may be summarized as follows:

> This need for governmental officials to be able to point to the lawful authority permitting their actions makes Administrative Law a close cousin to Constitutional Law.
>
> In its broadest sense, Constitutional Law comprises all of the fundamental rules for determining who and which institutions have to right to make laws for the government of our society; it is "a law for the making of laws". Administrative Law, on the other hand, deals with the actions of administrators to whom powers have been granted by laws which have been validly enacted under the constitution.[299]

5.1 Delegation Of Powers

The Province of Alberta has delegated to Alberta municipalities a wide range of powers with respect to fire, emergency and safety services. However, such delegation is not limited to municipal governments. The federal government and the Province of Alberta have also delegated a wide variety of powers relating to fire, emergency and safety services to other entities. Recipients of such delegated powers are referred to in legal terminology as "statutory delegates".

297 See discussion, section 6.6.6 *infra*.
298 D.P. Jones and A.S. de Villars, *Principles of Administrative Law*, Toronto: Carswell, 1985 at p. 3.
299 *Ibid.*, at p. 4.

The rationale for such delegation may include the following factors:[300]

a) The sheer magnitude of the business of government means that not everything can be dealt with by the federal Parliament or the provincial Legislatures.

b) Many government activities are technical in nature, and only broad principles should be contained in legislation.

c) The delegation of power to an administrator allows greater flexibility in applying broad statutory provisions to changing circumstances.

d) It may not be possible to devise a general rule to deal with all cases, which may be more conveniently determined in the discretion of a delegate.

e) The need for rapid governmental action may require faster administrative response than can be accommodated by the necessity of legislative amendment.

f) Innovation and experimentation in solving social problems may not be possible if legislation is required.

g) Someone actually has to apply legislation, and that person has to have authority to do so.

h) Emergencies may require broad delegation of powers with respect to a wide range of matters which would normally be dealt with by legislation.

There are three types of functions pertaining to fire and emergency services which the federal and provincial/territorial governments have delegated. They are legislative, judicial and administrative.

5.1.1 Legislative

Delegated legislative functions refer to the power to enact subordinate legislation, including the enactment of regulations by the federal and provincial/territorial governments, and the enactment of by-laws by municipal governments.

5.1.2 Judicial

Delegated judicial functions are those powers which have been given to the courts by the federal and provincial/territorial governments. A related function is what is commonly referred to as "quasi-judicial", which is a function which is essentially judicial in nature but which is exercised by an appointed official or administrative tribunal.

300 *Supra,* note 1 at p. 5.

5.1.3 Administrative

Delegated administrative functions, often referred to as executive functions, describe those functions involving the application and enforcement of the legislation.

In addition, the powers delegated by the federal or provincial governments may be either "mandatory" or "discretionary" in nature. Delegated powers which are mandatory in nature may be described as "duties" imposed on the statutory delegate.[301] For example, section 13 of the Alberta Safety Codes Act places a mandatory requirement upon accredited municipalities and corporations to administer the Act:

> 13(1) The Minister administers this Act but an accredited municipality and an accredited corporation shall provide for the administration of this Act in accordance with the order that designated it as an accredited municipality or corporation.

Discretionary powers, as the term suggests, allow statutory delegates to use their discretion in the exercise of the delegated powers. For example, the *Safety Codes Act* allows Safety Codes Officers to exercise their discretion to take such action as they consider necessary to remove or reduce imminent serious dangers to persons or property with respect to anything to which the Act applies or due to a fire hazard or risk of explosion. Specifically, section 43(1) of the Act states:

> 43(1) If a safety codes officer is, on reasonable and probable grounds, of the opinion that there is an imminent serious danger to persons or property because of any thing, process or activity to which this Act applies or because of a fire hazard or risk of an explosion, the officer may take any action that the officer considers necessary to remove or reduce the danger.

5.2 Statutory Delegates

There are numerous statutory delegates at both the federal and provincial/territorial levels whose powers relate to fire and emergency services. These are considered below.

5.2.1 Federal Statutory Delegates

There are a number of federal statutory delegates with powers relating to fire and emergency services across Canada. These delegates include:

a) Canadian Transportation Accident Investigation and Safety Board;[302]
b) National Energy Board;[303] and
c) Regional Safety Officers.[304]

301 *Supra,* note 1 at p. 51.
302 *Canadian Transportation Accident Investigation and Safety Board Act,* R.S.C. 1985, c. C-23.4.
303 *National Energy Board Act,* R.S.C. 1985, c. N-7.
304 *Occupational Health and Safety Act,* R.S.C. 1985, c. L-2.

5.2.2 Provincial/Territorial Statutory Delegates

Similarly, there are a number of provincial/territorial statutory delegates whose powers apply to fire and emergency services. They include:

a) Planning bodies;
b) Energy tribunals;
c) Environmental and Natural Resources Boards;
d) Fire Commissioners;
e) Fire Marshals;
f) Public Health Boards; and
g) Safety tribunals.

5.3 Judicial Review/Appeal Of Statutory Delegate's Decision

The primary advantage of having a dispute brought before a statutory delegate (such as an administrative tribunal) rather than before a court is that the member or members of a tribunal will usually have special expertise in the area of fire and emergency services which a court may not have. However, the disadvantages to this approach are twofold:

a) Most legislation authorizing a statutory delegate also provides for an appeal of the delegate's decision to either another statutory delegate or to a court, which second decision may itself be subsequently appealed to a higher court. This may make an administrative tribunal little more than a "stepping stone" along a long path of appeals.

b) In other situations where legislation does not provide for an appeal of the statutory delegate's decision, the legality of a decision of the delegate rather than the decision itself may be reviewed by the courts through a procedure known as "judicial review".

The distinction between an appeal and judicial review is summarized in *Principles of Administrative Law* as follows:

> "Judicial review" is not the same as an appeal. In general, the superior courts do not have the right to substitute their appraisal of the merits for any lawful action taken by an administrator. On the contrary, one of the consequences of the doctrine of Parliamentary Sovereignty is the right of the legislative branch to delegate powers to administrators without any right of appeal, whether to another administrator or to a court. Of course, legislation frequently does provide one or more levels of appeal, but there is no obligation for it to do so.
>
> Judicial review, therefore, is generally limited to the power of the superior courts to determine whether the administrator has acted strictly within the powers which have been statutorily delegated to him. Judicial review concentrates almost com-

> pletely on jurisdictional questions, and on the application of the ultra vires doctrine to the particular fact pattern surrounding the impugned administrative action.[305]

Thus, Canadian law provides three possible remedies to a party who is aggrieved by a decision or action of a statutory delegate. These remedies are an appeal to a statutory delegate, and appeal to a court, and a judicial review by a court. Each of these remedies are discussed below.

5.3.1 Appeal To Statutory Delegate

Legislation may provide for the appeal of a statutory delegate's decision to another statutory delegate, such as an administrative tribunal. For example, the Alberta *Safety Codes Act* provides:

> 46(1) A person to whom an order is issued may, if the person objects to the contents of the order, appeal the order to the Council in accordance with the Council's by-laws within 30 days of the date the order was served on the person.[306]

5.3.2 Appeal To Court

Alternatively, legislation may provide for the appeal of a statutory delegate's decision to a court.[307] Such legislative rights of appeal to a court generally fall into one of two categories. First, there are general rights of appeal, which do not contain any limitations, and second, appeals which are restricted to questions of law and jurisdiction.[308] In Alberta, the *Safety Codes Act* takes the second approach, providing that an order of the Safety Codes Council may be appealed to the Alberta Court of Queen's Bench, but only "... on a question of law or jurisdiction".[309]

---

305 *Supra,* note 1 at pp. 6-7.
306 *Supra,* note 76 at s. 46(1).

307 Most jurisdictions have included within their fire, emergency and safety services legislation the requirement that appeals from a statutory delegate be made to a court by way of a statutory appeal procedure rather than by of a judicial review. See for example the British Columbia *Fire Services Act*, R.S.B.C. 1979, c.133, ss. 27-28; Manitoba *Fires Prevention Act*, R.S.M. 1987, c. F-80, s. 57; New Brunswick *Fire Prevention Act,* R.S.N.B. 1973, c. F-13, s. 20; Newfoundland *Fire Prevention Act*, R.S.N. 1990, c. F-11, ss. 19-20; Northwest Territories *Fire Prevention Act*, R.S.N.W.T. 1988, c.F-6, ss.12-15; Prince Edward Island *Fire Prevention Act*, R.S.P.E.I. 1988, c.F-11, s.16; Saskatchewan *Fire Prevention Act*, R.S.S. 1978, c. F-15.01, ss.18-20; Yukon *Fire Prevention Act*, R.S.Y.T. 1986, c. 67, ss. 14-16. A notable exception is the federal *Occupational Health and Safety Act*, R.S.C. 1985, c. .L-2, s. 146, which does not provide a statutory appeal procedure from a decision of a Regional Safety Officer, thereby leaving the door open to an application for judicial review.

308 Some authorities suggest a third category, that of an appeal solely on matters of law. However, since it appears that the courts are willing to accept that "questions of law" includes "questions of jurisdiction", there is likely no real difference between the two terms. See for example, *King v. University of Saskatchewan*, [1969] S.C.R. 678 (S.C.C.) and *Re Clark and Ontario Securities Commission*, [1966] 2 O.R. 277 (Ont. C.A.).
309 *Supra,* note 76 at s. 49(1).

5.3.3 Judicial Review By Court

In the absence of a statutory appeal procedure as outlined above, an aggrieved party may bring an application to a court for judicial review of a statutory delegate's decision or action. For example, the federal *Occupational Health and Safety Act*[310] provides for the appeal of a decision of a Safety Officer, but does not provide a statutory appeal procedure from a decision of a Regional Safety Officer. Therefore, the only remedy available to a person aggrieved by a decision of a Regional Safety Officer is to bring an application for judicial review. In an application for judicial review, the jurisdiction of the court is restricted to determining whether the statutory delegate has either acted outside of its jurisdiction, or committed an error of law while acting within its jurisdiction. In the event that the court finds that the statutory delegate has in fact acted outside of its jurisdiction or committed an error of law while acting within its jurisdiction, the court may issue an order in the nature of *certiorari* quashing the decision and an order of *mandamus* compelling the statutory delegate to re-decide the matter. However, unlike a statutory appeal to a court, in a judicial review a court cannot substitute its own decision for the decision of the statutory delegate. It can only send the matter back to the delegate for reconsideration.

Therefore, from a practical perspective, in providing a statutory appeal to the Court of Queen's Bench of decisions of the Safety Codes Council, the Alberta *Safety Codes Act* provides those aggrieved with decisions of the Council with a broader remedy than would be available under judicial review of that same decision, in that the courts may substitute their decision for that of the Council. However, since the limitations on the scope of the statutory appeal under that Act are limited to a consideration of matters of law or jurisdiction, the scope of those matters which are appealable are similar to those available under judicial review - that is, errors of law and fact affecting the ability of the Council to acquire jurisdiction, and errors of law committed by the Council which cause it to lose jurisdiction, such as failure to follow the rules of natural justice.[311]

6.0 CIVIL LAW

Civil law is a general term used to denote a broad spectrum of law which is concerned with the private affairs of individuals, corporations and governments. Of particular interest to fire and emergency services is the branch of civil law concerned with civil liability. This branch of civil law is commonly referred to in legal terminology as tort law, and will form the focus of this section.

6.1 Definition Of Tort Law

By definition, a "tort" is a "civil wrong", which is comprised of 3 components:

310 R.S.C. 1985, c. L-2, ss. 145-146.

311 For example, see *Re North Coast Air Services Ltd.*, [1972] F.C. 390 (F.C.C.A.D.); Nanda v. Public Service Commission, [1972] F.C. 277 (F.C.C.A.D.]; and *Moshos v. Minister of Manpower & Immigration*, [1969] S.C.R. 886 (S.C.C.).

a) Act or omission which is not a breach of a contractual obligation alone;

b) Act or omission must not be authorized by law; and

c) Act or omission must inflict injury or damage which is:

   i) special, private and peculiar to the person injured as distinct from the public in general; and

   ii) the injury must be remediable by an action for damages.

6.2 Purpose of Tort Law

The primary purpose of tort law is to adjust losses and afford compensation for injuries sustained by one person as a result of the conduct of another. One author has described this purpose in the following terms:

> The study of the law of torts is, therefore, a study of the extent to which the law will shift the losses sustained in modern society from the person affected to the shoulders of him who caused the loss or, more realistically in many fields, to the insurance companies who are increasing covering the many risks involved in the conduct of business and individual activities.[312]

6.3 Types Of Torts

There are a significant number of torts, and the courts are willing to allow new torts as they arise. Those torts which are of particular interest to fire and emergency services include nuisance, the rule in *Rylands v. Fletcher* and negligence. Each of these is discussed below.

6.3.1 Nuisance

In legal terms a nuisance may be defined as "the unreasonable interference with the use and enjoyment of property". There are two primary types of nuisance - pulic and private. Public nuisance may be defined as "anything which unreasonably affects the comfort or convenience of a class of people". The remedy is criminal prosecution. Private nuisance is anything which unreasonably affects the comfort or convenience of an individual as distinct from a group, and includes interference with use and enjoyment of land. The remedy is civil action in nuisance.

6.3.2 Rule In *Rylands v. Fletcher*

If a person brings, or accumulates on his land anything which, if it should escape, may cause damage to his neighbour, he does so at his peril. If it does escape, and causes damage, he is responsible, however careful he may have been, and whatever precautions he may have taken to prevent the damage.

---

312 Wright, C.A. and A.M. Linden, *The Law of Torts* (5th edition) 1970 at 1.

6.3.3 Negligence

By far the most common tort affecting fire and emergency services in Canada is the tort of negligence. Negligence may be defined as:

> The omission to do something which a reasonable man, guided by those ordinary considerations which regulate human affairs, would do, or the doing of something which a reasonable and prudent man would not do.

6.3.3.1 Elements of Tort Negligence

There are four basic elements of tort negligence, each of which must be proven by a plaintiff on the balance of probabilities for a civil action in negligence to succeed. These elements are:

1) duty of care;
2) standard of care;
3) causation; and
4) remoteness.

Each of these elements is discussed below.

6.3.3.1.1 Duty of Care

A plaintiff must prove that a defendant owed a "duty of care". In order to determine if a duty of care is owed, the courts use the test of "reasonable foreseeability". This test provides that the courts will find that a duty of care is owed by one person to another if it is reasonably foreseeable that the actions of one may cause injury to the other, unless there is a policy reason why the duty should not exist.

It follows that if a defendant does not owe a plaintiff a duty of care, the defendant can be as careless toward the plaintiff as he wishes. Thus, for fire and emergency services the question becomes in what situations does the law impose a positive duty on someone to rescue someone?

The simple answer appears to be that there is no general duty to assist anyone in peril. As one judge put it, "... it appears presently the law that one can, with immunity, smoke a cigarette on the beach while one's neighbour drowns and, without a word of warning, watch a child or blind person walk into certain danger ...".[313]

In Canada, there are currently only three circumstances in which the law will impose a duty of affirmative action upon a person to undertake a rescue:

---

313 *Horsely et al v. McLaren et al., sub nom* "The Ogopogo", [1969] 2 O.R. 137, revd., [1970] 2 O.R. 487 at 489 (per Jessup, J.A.) (Ont. C.A.) affd. (1972), 22 D.L.R. (3d) 545 (S.C.C.).

1) Where there is a "special relationship" between the would-be rescuer and the imperilled person. This "special relationship" arises in a number of contexts, both by operation of statute and at common law:

   (i) Section 233(2) of the Criminal Code (R.S.C. 1970, c. C-34) requires, amongst other things, that "... every one who, having the care, charge or control of a vehicle that is involved in an accident ... [must] ... where any person has been injured, offer assistance ...". Failure to do so may result in a criminal conviction and the additional possibility of civil liability.

   (ii) Certain types of pre-existing relationships as between the would-be rescuer and the person in peril may place a duty on that would-be rescuer to attempt a rescue.

   These relationships may include, but are not limited to a parent - child relationship and teachers, or others acting "*in loco parentis*" (in the place of a parent) to a child.

   It should be noted, however, that Canadian courts have not yet given much recognition to the existence of "special relationships" as the basis for imposing affirmative duties of rescue. For example, in *Vanvalkenburg v. Northern Navigation Co.*[314] the parents of a seaman who fell overboard as a result of his own negligence were unable to recover from the ship's owner, whose employee - the captain - made an inadequate rescue attempt. The parents' action was dismissed because the captain owed the seaman no legal duty to go to his rescue.

2) It is a long established principle that a person who negligently places another person in peril has a duty to go to his rescue. *Connolly v. Grenier.*[315] However, even if a person is not negligent, but nonetheless due to their actions either:

   (i) caused danger, or

   (ii) created a situation where it is reasonably foreseeable that someone would be endangered.

   then that person is under a duty to rescue.[316]

   Thus, in a municipal context, it is possible that a municipality which negligently or without negligence fails to replace a traffic control sign which has become displaced might be under a duty to attempt to rescue any persons injured in a motor vehicle accident resulting from failure to replace the sign.

---

314 (1913), 30 O.L.R. 142 (S.C.A.D.).
315 (1909), 42 S.C.R. 424 (S.C.C.).
316 *Oke v. Weide Transport Ltd.* (1963), 41 D.L.R. (2d) 53 (Man. C.A.).

3) If a perilous situation arises, and a person who is under no legal duty to attempt a rescue (see above) undertakes that rescue anyway, and the victim relies on that undertaking, then there arises a duty on the part of the would-be rescuer to attempt to complete that rescue.[317]

   It is in these circumstance that a government (federal, provincial/territorial or municipal) which holds itself out to the public as providing emergency rescue services may be seen by the courts to be under a duty to the public relying on those services to attempt to complete such rescue.

6.3.3.1.2 Standard of Care

A plaintiff must prove that a defendant breached its duty of care. This is generally accomplished by establishing that the defendant failed to meet a required "standard of care". Thus, the standard of care is a minimum level of care below which a breach of the duty of care occurs. In order to determine whether such a breach has occurred the courts will employ the test of the "reasonable man".

The standard of care which must be exercised is different in every set of circumstances. The factors which may be taken into consideration by the courts in determining the standard of care which would be exercised by the reasonable man include:

1) Degree and magnitude of risk;
2) Degree of harm which could result versus Cost of taking precautions;
3) Degree of risk and harm versus the social utility of the action;
4) Special skills;
5) Physical characteristics; and
6) Age.

Assuming that, for whatever reason, a would-be rescuer has a duty to attempt a rescue, the law is clear that he is liable if he fails to attempt the rescue at all. It is also clear that if the rescuer performs the rescue in a non-negligent manner the rescuer will not be liable. However, what is not presently clear in Canadian law is whether the rescuer is liable if the rescue attempt fails as a result of the rescuer's negligence in attempting the rescue.

The law presently appears to be that the rescuer can be held liable if he negligently makes things worse.[318] It is suggested that this rule would apply to both volunteer and professional rescuers alike. Further, a person who is under a pre-existing duty to rescue will in all likelihood be liable if, as a result of his negligence, he fails to improve the situation. Finally, a government authority (federal, provincial/territorial or municipal) which is normally under no pre-existing duty to rescue can be held liable if that authority negligently fails to make things better after having undertaken to do so.[319]

---

317 Baxter v. Jones (1903), 6 O.L.R. 360; 2 O.W.R. 573 (Ont. C.A.); *Mercer v. S.E. & C. Railway Co.*, [1971] S.C.R. 849 (S.C.C.).
318 *Zelenko v. Gimbel Bros.* (1935), 287 N.Y.S. 134; affd. (1936), 287 N.Y.S. 136).
319 *Anns v. Merton Landon Borough Council*, [1977] 2 W.L.R. 1024; *Neilson v. City of Kamloops*, 31 B.C.L.R. 311, [1982] 1 W.W.R. 461, 12 D.L.R. (3d) 111, 16 M.P.L.R. 221 (B.C.C.A.).

Since the courts are very likely to find that a senior level of government or a municipality offering emergency rescue services (such as a fire department, ambulance service or paramedics) to have undertaken to effect a rescue by providing these services, both the individual fire and emergency services personnel and the government authority employing these personnel could be civilly liable if, through the negligence of the personnel a perilous situation is either not improved or actually worsened.

The question at this point thus becomes “what constitutes a negligently performed rescue?” In legal terms, a negligent rescue is one which falls below a certain "standard of care". That is, the law has set a standard minimum below which a breach of the duty of care (above) occurs.

The "reasonable man test" is difficult to define with any precision. It is a sliding scale of what is considered to be "reasonable conduct" in a given set of circumstances. These circumstances may include, but are not limited to, the physical characteristics and special skills of the rescuer. As a result, the standard which the law expects from a visually impaired person may be less than what it expects from a person with normal vision. Similarly, because of their special expertise in medicine, there is a higher standard in medical related matters for doctors than for untrained citizens. Thus, the test becomes that of the "reasonable doctor", the "reasonable paramedic", the "reasonable fireman", or the "reasonable first-aider", with different levels of expertise expected from each.

It is at this point that a distinction may be drawn between the "volunteer" and the "professional" rescuer. Both may be under a duty (for whatever reason) to rescue. However, it is the professional, (who in most cases possesses a higher level of expertise in rescue operations), who the courts will likely see as owing a higher standard of care to the rescuee. Put another way, a professional rescuer may be held liable for a negligent mistake that an inexperienced volunteer rescuer would not be liable for.

6.3.3.1.3 Causation

A plaintiff must also establish that the plaintiff caused the injury or damage. In legal terminology this means that the plaintiff must prove that there is "factual causation", meaning that the breach of the duty of care actually caused the injury or damage. In making this determination the courts apply the causation test, better known as the “but for” test, which requires that a plaintiff establish that "but for" a defendant's negligence, the plaintiff would not have been injured.[320] Thus, if the injury would have happened irrespective of the actions of the defendant, the plaintiff has not proven causation.

In addition, it must be established by the plaintiff that the cause of the injury was the "dominant" or "substantial" cause of the injury. That is, there is no negligence if the injury did not result from a dominant or substantial cause, even though the injury was

320 *Supra,* note 313.

caused by a breach of the duty of care. However, there may be more than one dominant cause of an injury, in which case it is necessary for the plaintiff to establish that the negligence of the defendant made a "material contribution" to the injury. This is a relaxation of the "but for..." test.

6.3.3.1.4 Remoteness

A plaintiff must prove that the actions causing the injury were not too remote. A defendant will not be liable in a situation where an injury or damage is caused by the defendant, but where it would be unfair or unjust to award damages as the cause of the injury is too remote from the occurrence of the injury itself. In considering the issue of remoteness the courts will find a defendant liable for all of the consequences of its acts which are "reasonably foreseeable" as a "real possibility". That is, a defendant will be held to be liable for all of the consequences of his acts which are "reasonably foreseeable".[321] However, the courts have modified this general rule to require that the defendant will only be liable for those consequences which were reasonably foreseeable as a "real possibility".[322] In addition, it should be noted that the courts do not require that the defendant be able to foresee the entire chain of events which leads up to the injury. Rather, the defendant need only have reasonably foreseen the nature of the injury itself.[323]

6.3.3.2 Liability Of Employer

While a rescuer may be held personally liable for a negligently performed rescue, the employer of the rescuer may also be held responsible. This may occur as a result of vicarious liability or inadequate training.

6.3.3.2.1 Vicarious Liability

In the situation where an employer such as a government actually "employs" a rescuer, there are three requirements which must be met for an employer to be vicariously liable for the actions of its employee:

1) There must be an "employer-employee" relationship.

2) The employee must have been acting in the course of his employment, and not "off on a frolic of his own".

3) That employee must have committed a tortious act.

---

321 *The Wagonmound (No. 1) Oversees Tankship (U.K.) Ltd. v. Morts Dock & Engineering Co. Ltd.*, [1961] A.C. 388, 1 All E.R. 404 (P.C.).
322 *The Wagonmound (No. 2) Oversees Tankship (U.K.) Ltd. v. The Miller Steamship Co. Pty. Ltd.*, [1966] 2 All E.R. 709 (P.C.).
323 *Hughes v. Lord Advocate*, [1963] A.C. 837, 1 All E.R. 705 (H.L.).

6.3.3.2.2 Inadequate Training

An employer may also be directly liable for a negligently performed rescue operation if that operation was performed by someone (representing the employer as a rescuer), who, because of inadequate training by that employer, did not have the skill and expertise to conduct the rescue in a non-negligent manner.

It is in this category that operators of fire and emergency services may find themselves incurring liability for the actions of volunteer rescuers representing these operators. Thus, a heavy onus is placed on the operator to ensure that its volunteer rescue personnel are trained to a level where they are able to undertake those rescue activities which they are asked to perform in a non-negligent manner.

6.3.3.3 Intervening Forces

As noted above, the general rules are that an individual rescuer may be held liable for a negligently performed rescue, and that the employer or sponsor of that rescuer may be vicariously liable. However, there is some authority for the proposition that if a third party was negligently responsible for creating the situation of peril which injured the victim, that third party is also responsible for any complications, misadventure or *bona fide* medical error occurring during the course of treatment.[324] The possibility exists that this principle may relieve the negligent rescuer of liability, and may place it instead squarely on the shoulders of the third party tortfeasor (person who committed the tort). However, the issue is still open as to whether an intervening forces defence would allow a medical professional (or rescuer) to avoid liability in the event that their actions constitute actionable negligence.

6.3.3.4 Liability to the Rescuer

The issue of civil liability for negligence in a rescue situation is a two-edged sword. Not only can a rescuer be liable to a victim for a negligently performed rescue, but a victim can also be liable to the rescuer if that rescuer is injured in the rescue attempt. As one famous British jurist stated in setting out the general rule in this area:

> It seems to me that, if a person by his fault creates a situation of peril, he must answer for it to any person who attempts to rescue the person who is in danger. He owes a duty to such a person above all others. The rescuer may act instinctively out of humanity or deliberately out of courage. But whichever it is, so long as it is not wanton interference, if the rescuer is killed or injured in the attempt, he can recover damages from the one whose fault has been the cause of it.[325]

324 *Katzman v. Yaeck* (1982), 37 O.R. (2d) 500, 136 D.L.R. (3d) 536 (Ont. C.A.).
325 *Videan v. British Transport Commission*, [1963] 2 Q.B. 650 at 669 (per Lord Denning M.R.).

Thus, if a rescuer is killed or injured in the rescue attempt he (or his estate) can recover damages from the party who created the situation of peril,[326] whether the rescue and subsequent injury to the rescuer are "reasonably foreseeable" consequences of the negligent act or not.[327]

It should be noted, however, that the above noted general rule does not apply if the rescue attempt is "wanton". Just what is considered "wanton" is something which must be decided by the courts in each particular case, taking into consideration all relevant factors in that case. These factors may include, but are not limited to the following:

1) Danger to victim.
2) Chances of success.
3) Qualifications of rescuer.
4) Relationship of the parties.
5) Panic of the moment. (The courts are less likely to find that a particular rescue attempt is wanton if the rescuer acted upon impulse rather than after careful consideration of the matter).

If the rescue attempt is found to be wanton, there is no liability if the rescuer is injured.

Finally, the courts have held that the above-noted "rescuer test" may also be applied to property. That is, persons injured while seeking to prevent property damage are seen by the courts as "rescuers", and may, in the right circumstances, be entitled to recover from the person whose negligence imperilled the property.[328] However, there is a difference between rescue cases involving "property" and those involving "life". The difference, of course, is in the value of what one is trying to save. While nothing is certain at this point, indications are that the courts will be more likely to see the attempted rescue of an item of property (such as a car) as being "wanton interference" than they will the rescue of a human life.[329]

6.3.3.5 Liability For Decision-Making

In addition to exposure to civil liability for their actions, public authorities providing fire and emergency services may also be liable for their decisions.[330] Following a trend that began in England in the 1970's,[331] the Supreme Court of Canada is

---

326 *Supra,* note 313.
327 *Urbanski v. Patel* (1978), 84 D.L.R. (3d) 650 (Man. Q.B.).
328 Toy v. Argenti, [1980] 3 W.W.R. 276 (B.C.S.C.).
329 *Ibid.*
330 For a full discussion of this subject see L.A. Reynolds and D.A. Hicks, "New Directions For The Civil Liability Of Public Authorities In Canada", *Canadian Bar Review* Vol. 71, No. 1, (March, 1992) at p.1.
331 See in particular the decision of the House of Lords in *Anns and others v. London Borough of Merton,*[1978] A.C. 728, [1977] 2 All E.R. 492.

demonstrating an increasing willingness to expand the limits of civil liability for decisions made by local public authorities.[332] As a result, public authorities may increasingly find themselves exposed to civil liability for their decisions or failure to make decisions with respect to the provision of fire and emergency services.

Historically, the only liability to which local public authorities in Canada were exposed as a result of decisions made in good faith and in the absence of bias or malice was the censure of a discontented electorate. The philosophy which underlies this approach is that decisions made by elected officials are in essence "political" decisions, and as such are properly reviewed through the political process. This philosophy was summarized by Lord Wilberforce in *Anns v. Merton (London Borough)*:

> As was well said, public authorities have to strike a balance between the claims of efficiency and thrift (du Parc LJ in *Kent and Porter v. East Suffolk Rivers Catchment Board*): whether they get the balance right can only be decided through the ballot box, not in the courts.[333]

The reasoning behind this approach has been summarized as follows:

> There are several reasons why the courts traditionally have been unwilling to expose the political activities of government to ordinary tort law scrutiny. The first relates to the separation of functions between the judicial, legislative, and executive branches of government. It is felt that those who engage in political decision-making ought to have the quality of their decisions judged by their electorate, and not "second-guessed" by the judiciary. Officials are elected to assess what is in the best interests of the collective, and in this process decisions may cause harm to private individuals. It is not that the judiciary cannot assess these decisions based on their own standards of "reasonableness" which is the point, but that they ought not to.
>
> The second concern is more pragmatic and administrative. Since policy formulation by public bodies involves difficult decision making, the balancing of conflicting interests, the weighing of competing claims of efficiency and thrift, which in turn demand access to and the analysis of information by those with special backgrounds and expertise, courts are naturally reluctant to "get involved". Judges do not want to spend their time acting like city councillors, examining "impact studies", listening to lobby groups, and pouring through financial reports. Finally,

---

332 The trend began with *Barratt v. North Vancouver (District)*, [1980] 2 S.C.R. 418, 114 D.L.R. (3d) 577, 33 N.R. 293 (S.C.C.); and continued with *City of Kamloops v. Nielsen et al.*, [1984] 2 S.C.R. 2, 10 D.L.R. (4th) 641, 54 N.R. 1 (S.C.C.); *Laurentide Motels v. Beauport* (Ville), [1989] 1 S.C.R. 705, 94 N.R. 1 (S.C.C.); *Just v. British Columbia*, [1989] 2 S.C.R. 1228, 103 N.R. 1 (S.C.C.), and *Manolakos v. Gohmann*, (sub nom. Rothfield v. Monolakos), [1989] 2 S.C.R. 1259, 102 N.R. 249 (S.C.C.).

333 *Supra*, note 331, at p.501. Lord Wilberforce's reference to *Kent and Porter v. East Suffolk Rivers Catchment Board* is found at [1940] 1 K.B. 319 at p.338, [1939] 4 All E.R. 174 at 184 (C.A.).

> if tort law review of political decisions were possible, there is the fear that this would lead to a flood of suits, intimidate decision-makers, and impede progress.[334]

However, in recent years Canadian courts appear to be experiencing increasing difficulty in rationalizing a "hands off" approach with respect to decisions made by local public authorities. At the root of this difficulty is the view that local public authorities should not be immune from the operation of the underlying philosophy of tort law which holds that the burden of loss should be shifted from the victim to the tortfeasor. This is especially true when the tortfeasor is a local public authority which may distribute the burden of loss to its ratepayers or to society as a whole by way of insurance. Indicative of the courts' increasing willingness to see the burden of losses arising from decisions made by local public authorities absorbed by these authorities is the view expressed by LaForest, J. in *Tock v. St. John's Metropolitan Area Board*,[335] where in a minority opinion he stated:

> Constraints of time and money will always mitigate against the building of absolutely failsafe systems (on the assumption that such systems are possible) and the maintaining of the best conceivable inspection system. Accordingly, a public authority charged with operating any service will inevitably have to strike a balance between the need to give due consideration to factors bearing on efficiency and thrift, and the need to protect persons and property from damage that the system in question is likely to cause. In a word, it will be necessary to make compromises, and I have no reason to doubt that these compromises will take into account the possibility of a certain amount of inevitable damage.
>
> ...if the legislature wishes to shift the risk from a public authority to the individual, it can do so in express terms. I see no reason why it should be presumed to be authorizing a serious nuisance. Nor do I accept that any weight should accorded a showing by the public body that damage was inevitable. The determination that damage was inevitable, in the sense in which that term was defined earlier, does not provide a rationale for concluding that it is reasonable to demand of the person whom misfortune has singled out that he or she pay for the damage concerned. The costs of damage that is an inevitable consequence of the provision of services that benefit the public at large should be borne equally by all those who profit from the service.[336]

In an attempt to reconcile these two competing legal philosophies Canadian courts have adopted the approach taken in *Anns*[337] whereby decisions made by local public authorities which are characterized as "policy" decisions are immune from exposure

---

334 L.N. Klar, "The Supreme Court of Canada: Extending the Tort Liability of Public Authorities", *Alberta Law Review* Vol. 28, No. 3 (1990) 648 at p.650.
335 [1989] 2 S.C.R. 1181, (1989), 64 D.L.R. (4th) 620 (S.C.C.).
336 *Ibid.*, at 1200-1201 (S.C.R.).
337 *Supra*, note 331 at p.500.

to civil liability, and where decisions which are "operational" in nature are subject to the tort law process.[338] While this approach may be appealing from a philosophical perspective, its practical application is proving to be difficult. As Madam Justice Wilson observed in attempting to determine whether the enforcement of building inspection by-laws constituted "policy" or "operational" decisions:

> It may be, for example, that although the building inspector had a duty to enforce the by-law, the lengths to which he should go in doing so involved policy considerations. The making of inspections, the issuance of stop orders and the withholding of occupancy permits may be one thing; resort to litigation if this became necessary, may be quite another. Must the City enforce infractions by legal proceedings or does there come a point at which economic considerations, for example, enter in? And if so, how do you measure the "operational" against the "policy" or vice versa? Clearly this is a matter of very fine distinction.[339]

In addition, it is suggested that the policy versus operational decision approach is not so much an objective test as it is a framework within which the courts may choose to emphasize either of the competing philosophies through manipulation of the definition of the terms "policy" and "operational":

> This already difficult distinction between policy and operational decisions is becoming even further blurred by the courts as they struggle with the philosophical issue of which decisions of local public authorities should be properly reviewed by the electorate through the political process and which should be reviewed by the courts through application of tort law. It is submitted that the courts' continuing attempts to define and re-define what constitutes policy and operational decisions is more a reflection of the courts' attempts to apply the legal philosophy to which they subscribe at any given point in time than an attempt to determine what constitutes policy and operational decisions in the empirical sense. Thus, it may be argued that the distinction between policy and operational decisions may be little more than a legal fiction given life by the competing legal philosophies.[340]

In recent decisions the Supreme Court of Canada has significantly narrowed the scope of those decisions which may be characterized as "policy" in nature and has correspondingly widened the definition of "operational" decisions. The law in this area as it presently stands may be summarized as follows:

> Following the Supreme Court of Canada's decision in *Just,* several conclusions can be drawn regarding the liability exposure of a public authority within the con-

---

338 This approach was first adopted by the Supreme Court of Canada in *Barratt v. North Vancouver*, and has continued in the cases which followed. See supra, note 332.
339 *City of Kamloops v. Nielsen* et al., supra, note 332 at p.23 (S.C.R.).
340 *Supra,* note 330 at 4-5.

> text of the policy/operational dichotomy. First, it would appear that the "pure policy" decisions of public authorities will continue to be immune from review by the courts, provided that these decisions constitute a bona fide exercise of discretion. While there maybe some doubt about this conclusion in light of statements contained in *Just* which indicate that decisions on pure policy matters must be reasonable in all the circumstances, it is submitted that the better view is that these decisions will not be reviewed by the courts on the basis of ordinary principles of negligence. *Just* also held that decisions will be characterized as falling within the pure policy sphere if motivated by economic or political factors. As a result, it was held that generally, pure policy decisions are made only at the highest levels of the public authority.
>
> Second, all decisions and actions which cannot be labelled "pure policy" will be characterized as falling within the operational sphere, including those matters which were formerly classified as "secondary policy decisions". These matters will be subject to the review of the courts on the basis of a private law duty of care. It would appear, given the general statements by Cory J. in *Just*, that all aspects of a system of inspection and maintenance will fall within the operational sphere. Some of Mr. Justice Cory J.'s comments, however, indicate that notwithstanding these general statements there may be decisions made regarding the system of inspection which are governed by budgetary considerations. It would appear that in these circumstances the courts will classify the decision as being within the pure policy sphere.
>
> Finally, notwithstanding the recent position taken by the House of Lords in *Murphy*, the proper starting point when determining whether a public body owes a duty of care is to use the two-step approach from Anns. If the pubic authority ought reasonably to foresee the infliction of loss or damage upon a person, then it will owe a prima facie duty of care to that person. A public authority may be exempted from this duty of care if an exemption exists in legislation or the common law. A common law exemption will apply if the decision in question can be characterized as falling within the "pure policy" sphere and constitutes a *bona fide* exercise of discretion.[341]

In choosing to narrow the scope of "policy" decisions while widening the ambit of "operational" decisions made by public authorities the Supreme Court of Canada appears prepared to institute a philosophical shift in the accountability of public authorities for their decisions from that of political process to one of judicial review. In so doing, the decision as to whether and to what extent local public authorities will undertake the regulation and management of the environment appears to have been removed to some extent from the hands of local public authorities and placed within the domain of the courts.

---

341 *Supra*, note 330 at 21-22.

As a result, in the absence of statutory exemption provisions in enabling legislation,[342] public authorities will now be required to make most of their decisions with respect to the provision of fire and emergency services within their boundaries in accordance with the tort law standard of "reasonability" rather than the political standard of "expediency". Further, if in its decision in *Just* the Supreme Court of Canada intended that pure policy decisions must themselves meet the test of reasonability, then public authorities which fail to meet the expected standard of care in the the provision of fire and emergency services should be prepared to defend that failure by demonstrating to the satisfaction of the courts that their failure was the result of "reasonable" decision-making.

6.4 Responding To The Spectre Of Tort Liability

The preceding discussion on the subject of the law of torts leads to the inevitable conclusion that fire and emergency services personnel are often involved in situations which have the potential of resulting in exposure to tort liability. Unfortunately, the discussion often ends at this point. A working knowledge of the fundamentals of tort law should provide fire and emergency services personnel with the ability to recognize situations where tort liability may arise and to react to these situations in a way which will minimize and perhaps even eliminate their exposure to liability.

In response to the possibility of tort liability it is recommended that fire and emergency services personnel consider the following suggestions.

1) Training

   Adopt training programs which ensure that personnel are trained to the highest standard possible. As a minimum, personnel should be trained to the level of the "industry standard".

2) Standardized Procedures

   Recognize that standardized procedures such as "Standard Operating Procedures" or "Standard Operating Guidelines" are a valuable tool in ensuring that all personnel react in a pre-determined manner to an anticipated series of events. Recognize also that these standardized procedures must be designed to specifically address the individual and often unique needs of each operator of fire and emergency services. Following standard "off the shelf" operating procedures or guidelines from other fire and emergency services organizations which may not be applicable to an organization's particular situation may do little to avoid tort liability if it can be established by a claimant that the standard procedures were inappropriate in the circumstances. Further, standardized operating procedures should

342 There are indications that provincial and territorial governments may be prepared to incorporate provisions into enabling legislation which would expressly provide immunity to civil liability for the decisions of local public authorities with respect to the environment. See for example in Alberta the *Safety Codes Act*, S.A. 1991, c. S-0.5, at s. 12 and the *Environmental Protection and Enhancement Act*, S.A. 1992, c. E-13.3, at s. 206.

be updated regularly to respond to changing circumstances such as new hazards, increased fire and emergency service responsibilities, updated equipment, and new operating techniques.

3) Contracting Out Of Liability

Fire and emergency services organizations may take a variety of proactive steps to reduce their exposure to tort liability. For example, fire and emergency services organizations which carry out inspections on private property[343] may reduce their exposure by entering into liability waiver and indemnity agreements with those for whom the inspection is being carried out. These agreements may provide, *inter alia*, that in exchange for carrying out the inspection the party requesting the inspection agrees not to bring a civil lawsuit against the fire and emergency services organization or its personnel for damage or injury caused by the organization or its personnel during the inspection, and may further provide that the party requiring the inspection will indemnify the organization and its personnel against any lawsuit brought by a third party as a result of the inspection. An example of a liability waiver and indemnity agreement in the context of an application for a burning permit is found in the "Fire Permit Application Agreement" set out in Appendix B.1.

The liability waiver and indemnity agreement may also be used in other applications, such as in reducing exposure to tort liability resulting from the issuance of a burning permit. An example "Fire Permit Agreement" which addresses this issue is set out in Appendix B.1.

4) Liability Insurance Coverage

An area which is often overlooked, particularly by individual fire and emergency services personnel, is liability insurance coverage. Many fire and emergency services personnel wrongly assume that their employer or the fire and emergency services organization with whom they are otherwise affilitated provides them with liability insurance coverage which will provide them with a legal defence in the event that they are named in a civil lawsuit and will indemnify them against the claim if they are found to be liable. In actual fact, many fire and emergency services personnel, particularly volunteers, may not be covered by any insurance policy, or if they are covered, the coverage type and limit may be inadequate. It is suggested that fire and emergency services personnel investigate what if any coverage is provided, and consider obtaining or upgrading such coverage if necessary.

---

344 Inspections may be carried out in a variety of contexts, including general fire prevention, private hydrants and other extinguishment apparatus, and even as a pre-condition to the granting of a burning permit.

5) Legal Advice

Finally, a working knowledge of the fundamentals of tort law should provide fire and emergency services personnel with the ability to recognize situations where tort liability may arise or may have already arisen. Upon recognizing these vulnerable areas, it is recommended that professional legal advice be sought from legal counsel who have knowledge and experience in the field of fire and emergency services law.

7.0 CONCLUSIONS

Clearly, the relationship between fire and emergency services and the legal context within which these services are delivered is an important one. In order for fire and emergency services in Canada to meet the challenge of providing effective and efficient services which satisfy the objectives of the employers and operators of such services, while also meeting the requirements of society as reflected in the legal system, it is necessary for fire and emergency services professionals to develop a sound understanding of those facets of the legal system which impact upon those services.

As a minimum, it is hoped that this chapter has served to eliminate some of the mystique which often pervades the operation of the legal system for fire and emergency services personnel and the organizations they represent. It is also hoped that the information presented here will provide fire and emergency services personnel with a bais from which to address many of the issues which they face which have legal implications. Finally, it is also hoped that this chapter will create a desire to learn more about the legal system and the role of fire and emergency services within it.

What Is Emergency Planning?

Chief Laird Burton
County of Strathcona Fire Department, Alberta

Photo Courtesy of Fort Saskatchewan Fire Department.

This Chapter addresses key issues in emergency planning. It briefly discusses the steps of planning and provides a broad view of both the process and its content – the Emergency Plan. The content of this chapter is equally applicable at municipal level as it is at Departmental level in the Fire Services.

"What plagues and what portents, what mutiny, what raging of the sea, shaking of the earth, common in the winds, frights, changes, horrors, divert and crack, rend and deracinate, the unity and married calm of states."

– William Shakespeare

A CONCEPTUAL VIEW

Emergency Plans are road maps designed to guide the response effort of one or more agencies during disaster periods. If performed effectively, these plans are invaluable for the success of the emergency response effort. However, as important as they are, these plans are only a by–product of a planning process and it is that process which gives them meaning and value.

The two most common features of disasters are that no one can believe they have happened, and two, only those who have planned will really succeed in their recovery effort on behalf of both their department and citizens. The social and psychological balance that is achieved with good planning has profound productivity implications. We must stop looking at disaster and emergency planning as a waste of resources but rather view these as productivity opportunities. Business enterprises are now investing more and more resources into disaster planning and recovery. At the same time, enlightened municipal corporations are starting to realize that their disaster plans enhance their competitive edge and provide real economic and social advantages.

As noted in Chapter 1, one of the main challenges to effective emergency planning is to identify the requirements which are similar to all disasters and those which are unique to one's own community or organization. The truly effective planners will not make the error of simply adopting someone else's plan or using a fill–in–the–blank program. Both of these approaches may lead to plans which do not align with the risks and may even deepen the impact of the disaster. A municipality's emergency planning process must strike a balance between the use of common hazard analysis (see chapter 4) and planning tools on the one hand and the individual nature of the municipality on the other.

Consider this question: "How large is your municipality?" This is not a Socratic question. The size of a municipality plays a key role in defining its emergency planning requirements and capability. It is important to realize that there is a resource: event ratio that dictates whether a disaster will be declared or if the event will be handled as an emergency within the scope of the Fire Department's control. In general Emergency Services can handle the majority of incidents and emergencies which occur in their municipality. Effective planning guides Fire officers and assists them with the categorization of these incidents.

Many methods exist to help rank incidents. The following four categories help, at a conceptual level, to better understand the type of planning which is required.

Top To Bottom Disaster. The first category relates to events which are obviously disastrous. They include such events as tornadoes, floods, multiple casualty incidents, and aircraft crashes. The 'top to bottom' notion refers to the power structure which exists during the response period to these disasters. This power structure involves high level decision makers at very early stages of the disaster response period. Consequently, Incident Commanders and service sector officers should expect simultaneous pressure from both the event and those in power (i.e., government, industry or other officials).

Bottom to Top. This category of planning relates to incidents which may grow to become disasters. These are far more difficult situations to manage for Fire commanders whose natural tendency is to try and handle incidents by themselves and not involve others, even when the risks begin to multiply. Asking for help is not always easy for these commanders, especially when the situation demands the involvement of non–traditional aid partners (e.g. managers from other levels of government).

Some incidents in this category may become "Apprehended Disasters." In other words, the impact of the incident is reduced to the reality that it did not escalate into a full–blown disaster. Transportation incidents often fall into this description. Examples would be the train derailments which occurred in Mississauga, Ontario (1979) and in Oakville, Manitoba (1994).

Inside Out. This category of planning is often used in the corporate world to describe companies that have one line of business to which they add only other related lines. One such company is the 3M® (Minnesota Mining and Manufacturing).

This is an important concept for disaster planners. It suggests the formation of a core of plans which say: in a disaster you do what you normally would do, but in more rushed circumstances. For example, assessors perform assessments as they usually do, but under disaster conditions. Therefore, when developing plans for emergency responders, this horizontal line of business format can clarify a refill service level versus the typical 'we can do anything' disorder that often gets us in difficulty.

Outside In. This planning concept includes situations when others come to you with ideas for inclusion in the overall disaster plan. This type of planning is especially useful for Fire Departments which are involved with a local industry. Often, these Departments are unlikely to have the resident expertise to do proper hazard analysis of these complex industrial operations. The 'Outside In' concept allows Fire Departments to gain from the local industry's knowledge and resource base. The concept also allows Fire Departments to gain from the knowledge and expertise of other jurisdictions. Their programs or technologies could be evaluated for inclusion within your plans.

A current example of this type of planning may involve the "In Place Sheltering" model. It states that evacuation during a toxic gas release may be more dangerous than holding people in defendable buildings. Would this line of reasoning fit with the industries and transportation risks in your area? If so, this form of outside in planning may be of value to your municipality.

One key tenant of emergency planning is that all four concepts (or forms) of planning should be reflected and balanced in the overall approach. The use of only one or two forms of planning may make the overall Emergency Plan far less flexible and effective. Another general tenant of planning is the shift towards continuous improvement. This is very different from the approach common to the 1980s when one established long term plans (e.g., five to ten years) that were left untouched until their sunset date. Emergency plans in the late 1990s may (and should) be reviewed on a daily basis if issues arise that will improve the plan. In fact, the whole function of planning is now seen in terms of daily activity cycles and no longer in terms of months or years.

The above may have a radical and positive impact on disaster planning. Therefore, the rest of this chapter will focus on methods for establishing up–to–day plans. However, before proceeding to the process of planning, it would be wise to briefly describe the current direction of disaster or emergency planning in Canada.

> "Government must plan for the predictable and prepare for the unpredictable".
> —Polybiub 150 B.C.

THE ROLE OF GOVERNANCE IN DISASTER PLANNING

The main impact of disaster research, here in Canada and abroad, has been the acceptance of "community based" planning as the most efficient level for quality results. The planning process may be coordinated by one 'lead' agency. However, if the planning process is left to only one agency, the plan will be less than comprehensive and effective. Effective planning requires the direct involvement of the entire community!

Disaster or emergency management identifies four phases, each of which with its own unique but overlapping planning requirements:

Mitigation. This phase involves any activity that will eliminate or reduce the probability of occurrence of a disaster. It also involves activities designed to postpone, dissipate or lessen the effects of an emergency/disaster event. Examples include such elements as building and fire codes, zoning laws (e.g., buffer zones, restricted development areas, flood plains), transportation of dangerous goods regulations and dangerous goods routing by-laws.

Preparedness. This is the most commonly utilized element of planning because mitigation efforts are never completely successful at eliminating disasters. The preparedness phase involves planning how one will respond to emergencies or disasters should they occur, increasing local resources and developing their ability to respond effectively. Preparedness activities are designed to help save lives and minimize damage by preparing people to respond appropriately during disaster situations.

Proper response requires updated plans, trained people, appropriate resources, communication systems and emergency public warning systems. The Preparedness phase includes activities which are designed: to ensure the most effective and efficient response; to minimize damage through such systems as forecasting (e.g., plume dispersal models) and warning; and to establish the groundwork for response operations (e.g., stockpiling supplies).

Response. The activities of the Response phase immediately follow the occurrence of a disaster and are designed to save life and property, in that order. The Response phase activities include:

1. Emergency assistance to those injured by the disaster event.
2. Search and rescue.
3. Shelter and medical care.
4. Reduction of secondary damage (e.g., sand bagging against further flood waters or security patrols to control looting).
5. Establishment of a system to ensure that responders are able to have a positive impact and that they are not making the situation worse or becoming potential victims themselves.

Recovery. This is the fourth phase of the emergency management cycle. The Recovery stage attempts to return life in the community to normal. It involves two stages: Short– and long–term. Short–term recovery returns vital life support systems to minimum operating levels. Long–term recovery from a disaster may go on for years with complete re–development of the disaster area.

The Recovery stage presents opportunities to mitigate against the arising of future events. An effective recovery planning system should include a mechanism for avoiding future emergencies or better respond to them.

THE ROLE OF BUSINESS AND INDUSTRY IN DISASTER PLANNING

The entire field of emergency management is undergoing major changes. One of the greatest shifts has been the inclusion of industry–based assessment in the emergency planning of governments. It reflects a move away from the more traditional wartime emergency planning towards a practical risk analysis process. The following are examples of the applied planning process:

1. The establishment of land use regulations and buffer zones.
2. The development of emergency response agreements (i.e., CAER groups).
3. The establishment of hazardous material routes.
4. The siting of hazardous facilities within an area plan.

5. The use of process safety management as a control to avoid disasters.
6. The implementation of inspection programs oriented to overall community safety.

At the international level, planning for disasters has become an issue of global competitiveness with the European community leading the way to reduced risk through aggressive planning. Both the Europeans and Pacific Rim countries see North Americas lax attitude toward industrial losses as an effective competitive advantage. With the advent of the North American Free Trade Agreement, Canada, the United States and Mexico have started to work towards improving the level of disaster planning. This increased level of awareness can be tracked in the introduction of numerous regulations aimed at reducing our risk through effective planning. Canadian examples include the following:

1. Environment Canada's Green Plan resulted in a Hazardous Spills Prevention and Response Program (1991).
2. Emergency Preparedness Canada's Emergency Preparedness Act (1988).
3. Environment Canada's Canadian Environmental Protection Act (CEPA) (1988), the Hazardous Products Act (1988) and the Transportation of Dangerous Goods Act (1985).

There have also been a number of major non–regulatory advances directed toward improved disaster planning. These include the following:

1. The 1986 Bhopal Aftermath Review. It was a Federal review of the Canadian situation after Bhopal and resulted in 22 recommendations.
2. The creation in 1986 of the Major Industrial Accident Council of Canada. This was an initiative of the Federal Government in response to the Bhopal aftermath review. A dozen working groups (WG) were formed based on voluntary participation by representatives from government and various industries.
3. The establishment in 1991 of the Emergency Planning for Industry CAN/CSA–2731– M91 standard by the Canadian National Standards.
4. The establishment of the Joint Emergency Preparedness Program (JEPP) by Emergency Preparedness Canada (EPC). This program helps funds Provincial and Municipal emergency preparedness programs and helps purchase select items (i.e., communications equipment and response vehicles).

Of all of the above regulations and initiatives, the one with the greatest impact for the emergency services in Canada is the formation of the Major Industrial Accident Council of Canada (MIACC). This body involves representatives of various orders of government, Industry representatives. It determines the broad direction of much of the technical risk analysis and planning for disasters.

As mentioned above, MIACC has a dozen working groups (WG) each with its own objective. These are identified below to provide a flavour of the type of activities in which MIACC is involved.

WG1: Assessment Guidelines for Municipalities and Industry

Objective: Public protection from the effects of major industrial accidents through enhancing the capability of municipalities and industry to perform effective risk assessments.

WG2: Qualification and Training Standards for Emergency Response Personnel

Objective: To establish an effective and consistent level of response to major industrial accidents involving dangerous substances through the enhancement of the capability of emergency response personnel.

WG3: Joint Municipal and Industry Emergency Preparedness

Objective: To provide consistent levels of protection for municipalities and industry against major industrial accidents through the coordination of effective emergency planning.

WG4: Accident Reviews

Objective: To prevent or reduce the probability of a recurrence of major industrial accidents involving dangerous substances, through the identification and dissemination of lessons learned from past experiences.

WG5: Buffer Zones and Land Use Planning and Control Guidelines

Objective: To establish appropriate techniques for land use planning and control in order to achieve public protection from the effects of major industrial accidents.

WG6: Coordination of Chemical Information Systems

Objective: To reduce the impact and severity of major industrial accidents involving dangerous substances, through the collection and provision of comprehensive information regarding prevention, control, emergency medical treatment, mitigation and emergency response.

WG7: Emergency Planning for Industry

Objective: To establish a consistent level of public protection from major industrial accidents through effective contingency planning by private and public facilities.

WG8: Lifecycle Management of Hazardous Substances

Objective: To create a high level of safety consciousness in the handling of hazardous substances, particularly by downstream small and medium–sized enterprises through lifecycle management of these substances.

WG9: Chemical Process Safety

Objective: To establish a high level of safety in facilities handling hazardous substances through the implementation of adequate chemical process safety programs.

W10: Legislation

Objective: To develop harmonization and simplification of prevention, preparedness and response legislation in Canada.

W11: Environmental Health and Safety Audits

Objective: To enhance the quality of prevention, preparedness and response programs through the use of appropriate safety audits.

WG12: Social and Psychological Impacts of Major Industrial Accidents

Objective: To promote adequate social and psychological recovery of victims, volunteers, workers and authorities from the impact of a major industrial accident.

Other initiatives. There are a number of other initiatives which can assist disaster planners and responders. These include the following:

1. The Canadian Petroleum Association (CPA).
   a. In 1989 it established the Environmental Codes of Practice
   b. Developed public consultation guidelines for the petroleum industry (Community Awareness component)
2. The Canadian Chemical Producers' Association (CCPA).
   a. Codes of Practice (Life Cycle)
   b. Established, in 1992, the Community Awareness and Emergency Response (CAER) program
   c. Involved in research and development in manufacturing
   d. Involved in transportation concerns through Transcaer, Transportation Emergency Assistance Plan (TEAP) and distribution
   e. Involved in Hazardous Waste Management
3. Canadian Manufacturers Association has been instrumental in the development of the Simplified Guide to Emergency Planning (1996).
4. Mutual Aid Programs (MAP).
5. CHLOREP. It involves response teams and advice for planning to deal with chlorine spills.

Given the above list of associations and agencies, the most valuable resource to disaster planners at community level will be the actual contact with the industries and businesses which exist within the community. These are the engines of a growing municipality and are absolutely vital in all phases of emergency management, especially the planning phase. Business and industry will also bring decision making and risk management tools to the plan and can contribute significantly to the process of working together.

THE COMMUNITY-BASED DISASTER PROGRAM

"How can one achieve a community based program without bogging it down?" The answer must include both goal setting and involvement levels.

The success of community emergency management programs depends upon smooth and effective interactions among the many members of the community. This is not easy but is a critical requirement. Each community is extremely diverse and encompasses a wide range of people. Their involvement and concerns with the functions of emergency management may be full time, temporary, mild, intense or any combination of these. Each individual and organization in the community has a distinct point of view, set of priorities and way of operating. When emergency protection is at stake—whether for mitigation, preparedness, response, or recovery—the overall goal of the community's safety must take precedence over separate interests.

THE STEPS OF EMERGENCY PLANNING

There is no one way to effectively conduct emergency planning. However, a number of requirements stand out as critical to the process. These steps are outlined below.

Step 1: Develop an action plan (i.e., define the planning team, its mandate, schedule of activities, review process).

Step 2: Complete a Hazard/Vulnerability Analysis (HVA) for the community.

a) Use personnel who would represent the community and its various organizations. Their goal is to identify the community's potential and actual hazards and produce a 'risk map.'
b) Each agency and organization must decide how it will contribute to the hazard identification and the plotting of the risk map.
c) The team must identify agency and organizational responsibilities as they relate to each of the four emergency management phases.
d) Existing programs which help the community to mitigate and prepare for each potential hazard must be identified. Responsibilities of the various agencies and organizations to respond to specific hazards must also be identified. Roles during the recovery process will vary in accordance to the specific hazard.
e) The team's work should be integrated into the overall community emergency management program. This team should remain active and serve as a vital part of the comprehensive emergency management agency of the community.

Step 3: Decide who can help and/or respond. This step should include members of the Hazard Analysis Team (above) but go beyond them.

Step 4: Obtain political/executive support. This level of support should be sought actively and regularly. It should be formalized so that all key decisions have a high level of buy in.
Step 5: Team formation for the development of the Plan.
Step 6: Draft the basic Plan and Appendices
a) Mission, vision, situation
b) Organization structure and responsibilities
c) Execution
d) Administration
e) Audit quality control
Appendix
a) Purpose
b) Operational guidelines
c) Responsibilities
d) Functions by time phase
e) Organizational chart, S.O.P.s and attachments
Step 7: Write S.O.P.s .
Step 8: Develop second draft of Plan.
Step 9: Exercise the Plan.
Step 10: Critique the Plan.
Step 11: Revise the Plan.
Step 12: Establish audit and quality control measures to ensure continuous improvement of the Plan.

PLANNING CHECKLIST

The following planning checklist is not all inclusive. However, it should help to identify key points relating to the various components of an Emergency Plan.

Hazard Analysis

1. Has a hazard vulnerability analysis (HVA) for the community been completed?
   a. If so, when?
   b. If not, are there plans and time lines to complete it?
2. Is the HVA in writing? (If so, where is it located?)
3. Has the HVA been distributed to agencies and people who need it (i.e., executive, planning organizations, nearby entities, fire, police)?
4. Does the HVA contain:
   a. All hazards existing or affecting the jurisdiction?
   b. Introduction explaining why HVA was done?
   c. Demographics?
   d. Jurisdiction geography?
   e. Descriptions of hazards?
   f. Historical occurrences of incidents?
   g. People, property or facilities vulnerable to hazards?

   h. Hazardous structures or hazards shown on maps?
5. What is the schedule for updating the HVA?

Mitigation

1. Is the HVA being distributed to elected officials, planning, zoning and operational agencies for use in mitigation as well as planning purposes?
2. Have any mitigation options (i.e., rules, enforcement, research/assessment) been identified?
3. Has your office or Emergency Management been involved with other agencies to provide hazard mitigation input and information (i.e., planning, zoning, building code, hazard insurance, ecology)?
4. Has mitigation input and information been provided in writing to other agencies?
5. Are files, records or copies of mitigation related correspondence available?
6. Does the community's Emergency Management agency review Environmental Impact Statements and provide hazard mitigation information?
7. Has mitigation been added to the local operations plan? Are there plans to do so? When?
8. Is any other local agency more appropriate to coordinate mitigation efforts? If so, which agency? Why?

Disaster Planning and SOP Development

The following questions should be considered when developing your emergency plans and Standard Operating Procedures (SOPs):

1. Is there an ordinance for the local emergency management organization? Dated when?
2. Is there a joint organization agreement?
3. Does your emergency management organization have a basic plan?
4. Is the plan signed by the municipality's elected officials?
5. Does organization's basic plan follow a prescribed format?
6. Does your emergency management organization have a table of annexes to the basic plan which matches provincial requirements?
7. What, if any, is the schedule for updating annexes?
8. Does your emergency management organization have copies of relevant agencies' written S.O.P.s or checklists?
9. Does your emergency management organization have written S.O.P.s or checklists for each of the following contingencies (as appropriate):
   a. Flood Watch/Warning?
   b. Dangerous Goods?
   c. Earthquake?
   d. Water shortage?
   e. Dam failure?
   f. Severe weather warning?
   g. Search And Rescue (SAR)?

Resource Identification

The following questions should help identify the key resources needed by a community for its response effort:

1. Does your emergency management organization have lists of local government personnel and equipment?
2. Does your emergency management organization have lists of private sector personnel and equipment?
3. Are the written agreements for use of private sector resources available to the appropriate response personnel?
4. Does your emergency management organization have mutual aid agreements with neighbouring jurisdictions? (List these jurisdictions.)
5. Does your organization have procedures for the activation of these resources?
6. Are volunteer personnel being specifically registered by emergency assignment classifications?
7. Are volunteer personnel trained to carry out the responsibilities for which they are registered?
8. How often are resource lists updated? (Should be at least annually.)

Training and Education

Training and Education are equally important to the development of an effective plan. These questions should help to enhance the plan.

1. Does your local emergency management organization have a designated training officer?
2. Has the director or coordinator received training in the past year? What type and when?
3. What is the basis of the local emergency program? (i.e., Emergency Site Management, Incident Command, Comprehensive Emergency Management.)
4. Have local elected officials received briefings or training on the local Emergency Management program during the last year?
5. Have heads of other local agencies received briefings or training on the local Emergency Management program during the past year?
6. Has training been conducted for EOC staff in the past year?
7. Has volunteer training been provided in the past year? What type and when?
8. Does your emergency management organization have records of training dates and personnel trained?
9. Are these training records maintained by type of training conducted?

Tests and Exercises

1. Have tests and/or exercises been conducted in the past year for:
   a. Response (on–scene) agencies? When?
   b. Warning system? When?
   c. Emergency Broadcast System? When?
   d. Emergency staff alert? When?

   e. EOC activities? When?
   f. Individual annex(es) to plan(s)? When? What annex(es)?
2. What tests and/or exercises are planned and for when?

External Influences

1. Does your emergency management organization maintain contact with the following external influences?
   a. Elected officials?
      (1) Are meetings held routinely? How often?
      (2) Is written information provided regularly? How often?
   b. Other agency heads?
      (1) Are meetings held routinely? How often?
      (2) Is written information provided regularly? How often?
   c. Media?
      (1) Are meetings held routinely? How often?
      (2) Is written information provided regularly? How often?
   d. Local business and industry?
      (1) Are meetings held routinely? How often?
      (2) Is written information provided regularly? How often?
   e. School officials?
      (1) Are meetings held routinely? How often?
      (2) Is written information provided regularly? How often?
2. Have family emergency preparedness plans been prepared for emergency responders and EOC personnel?
3. Are there procedures for recording and releasing casualty figures?

Public Education

1. Are emergency preparedness handouts and other information available for public distribution?
2. Have handouts and programs been prepared locally for local hazards? Comments.
3. Have appropriate Public Service Announcements been provided to local media?
4. Have newspaper articles been written by local media on the local emergency services program or activities?
5. Is regular contact regarding Emergency Public Education made with:
   a. Elected officials?
   b. Other local agencies?
   c. The media?
   d. Business and industry?
   e. Schools?
6. Is Emergency Public Education made available at community events?

Public Information

1. Has an Emergency Public Information Officer (EPIO) been designated by your

local emergency management organization? Who?
2. Have written EPIO procedures been prepared?
3. Has the EPIO been trained for his/her role and responsibilities?
4. Is the activation authority list of your Emergency Broadcast System (EBS) plan current?
5. Are the procedures for activating the local EBS current?
6. Have Public Service Announcement (PSA) scripts been prepared and provided to the media?
7. Are PSAs based on hazards identified in the Hazard Vulnerability Analysis?
8. Do PSAs reflect information the public needs to know for each hazard?
9. Have agreements been made to provide emergency public information with:
   a. Local radio stations?
   b. Local TV stations?
   c. Local newspapers?
   d. Local cable TV?
   e. Chamber of Commerce?
10. Is there a communication link, other than by telephone, to provide information to the media?
11. Are there procedures for alternate methods (i.e., couriers) of providing information to the media?

Communications

1. Does your community have an EOC or a designated EOC area?
2. Does the EOC contain a communication facility?
3. Is the EOC also a Central Dispatch/911?
4. Does the EOC have sufficient telephones for incoming and outgoing calls commensurate with expected EOC staffing? How many lines are there? How many instruments?
5. What are the telecommunications (phone or radio) links between the EOC and:
   a. Law enforcement?
   b. Emergency medical?
   c. Fire?
   d. Search And Rescue (SAR)?
   e. Ham radio operators?
   f. Mutual Aid EOC?
   g. The Provincial EOC?
   h. Public Works?
6. Are there designated staff assigned to operate key equipment?
7. Are assigned personnel trained in the use of the equipment?
8. Is there a test and maintenance schedule?
9. Is a volunteer Ham radio officer appointed and active?
10. Is back–up power available to all communications equipment?

Public Warning System

1. Does your community have a 24–hour–a–day public warning capability?
2. Are there warning procedures?
3. Are procedures posted at the warning point?
4. Is there an established warning fan–out? To whom? By what method?
5. Does the warning system include:
   a. Sirens? What percentage of the population is covered?
   b. Pagers?
   c. Emergency Broadcast System?
6. Are rural areas covered by the warning system? How?
7. Are there procedures for providing warning if telephones or electric power is unavailable? What are they?

Municipal Emergency Operations Centre (EOC)

1. Does your community have a designated EOC? If so, where is it located?
2. Does the EOC have protection from external explosions?
3. Is the EOC located in a designated flood plain?
4. Is the EOC located in any other known or designated hazard area?
5. Is the EOC occupied on a day–to–day basis by local emergency services or other associated emergency function(s)? If yes, by which organization, for how many people, how often and for how long?
6. Is the EOC supplied with food? If yes, for how many people and for how long?
7. Does the EOC have an independent water supply? What is its capability?
8. Does the EOC have cooking facilities? What sort of fuel does it require?
9. Does the EOC have sleeping facilities? For how many people? What degree of privacy/isolation does it have?
10. Does the EOC have rest rooms and shower facilities? For both genders?
11. What is the square footage of the operations area? Is it adequate for its current mandate?
12. Are there written security procedures for the EOC? Where are they held? How current are they?
13. Is the EOC in the basement, at ground level or on an upper floor of the building?
14. Is there a mobile EOC capability? What is it? Where is it located?
15. Is there an alternate EOC site or sites? If yes, where is it located and what are its specifications?
16. Does the EOC have emergency power? If yes, what type (watts and voltage capacity)?
17. Is the fuel supply for the generator protected? For how long? What type of fuel?
18. Are maps, charts, forms, plans and procedures readily available?

EOC Activation and Management

1. Can your local emergency management director/coordinator be contacted on a 24–hour–a–day basis? How? By whom?

2. If the director is unavailable is an 'alternate' designated in writing?
3. Is any other responsible official designated as available (on–call) 24–hours–a–day? Who? When? How are they reached?
4. What is the established call–out/notification list?
5. Do EOC procedures include:
   a. Who is in charge?
   b. EOC staffing pattern/schedule?
6. Are there any other written EOC procedures? (List procedures.)

Direction and Control Organization

1. Is there an EOC organization chart?
2. Are there lists of people who are assigned to the various EOC functions?
3. Are successors to the chief elected officials designated in writing?
4. Are there written departmental succession lists?
5. Have functional appointees been provided with copies of plans and procedures?
6. Have appointees received training in their functions?
7. Have successors been trained in their functions?

Declaration of State of Local Emergency

1. Are your local elected officials aware of their disaster responsibilities?
2. Are there written procedures for declaring a 'state of local emergency'?
3. Are all appropriate jurisdictions aware that they must make their own proclamation of emergency for extraordinary expenditures?
4. Are there written procedures for requesting provincial assistance?
5. Are there procedures for transmitting the Declaration and the Request for Assistance to the Province?

Disaster Records and Documentation

1. Is responsibility assigned for maintaining records of emergency disaster costs? To whom?
2. Are there procedures for recording emergency/disaster costs?
3. In a case of a joint organization, do procedures indicate whether the other political jurisdiction(s) will maintain their own records?
4. Are there procedures to prepare for the establishment, coordination and conduct of:
   a. Public damage assessment or survey?
   b. Private damage assessment or survey?

Evacuation Strategies

1. Are major evacuation routes identified within the community?
2. Are traffic control points identified?
3. Are predesignated shelter/destinations identified?

4. Do certain agencies have specific evacuation functions? Who does what?
5. Have any community educational efforts been accomplished?
6. Do plans/SOPs identify who is responsible for carrying out evacuation?
7. Are there procedures for rapidly carrying out evacuation? (i.e., is a sample declaration prepared)

Mass Care Strategies

1. Are local facilities identified and listed for mass (congregate) care?

On–site Management of Incidents (Feedback/reporting system)

1. Are there written requirements for responding agencies and other jurisdictions in the community to provide situation updates to the municipal EOC?
2. Are there procedures for requesting additional assistance from:
   a. The responding agencies to the municipal EOC?
   b. The municipal EOC to Provincial EOC?

Assessment, Recovery and Restoration

1. Is the Federal Disaster Assistance Guide for Local Government readily available?
2. Have facilities for use as Disaster Assistance Centres been identified?
3. Are there procedures for local government in these centres?
4. Are there procedures to indicate:
   a. Who establishes these centres?
   b. Who operates them?
   c. Who performs other related responsibilities?

Deactivation Considerations

1. Are there local written procedures for deactivating:
   a. Volunteers?
   b. Municipal resources?
   c. EOC staff?
   d. The EOC?
2. Are there procedures for notifying the county or Province of deactivation?

Post Incident Activities and Follow–up

1. Are there procedures for post–emergency reports? (i.e., what went right, what went wrong, lessons learned.)
2. Are there procedures for conducting post–emergency critiques and de–briefings?

3. Are there procedures for modifying emergency plans and programs based on lessons learned?

THE NEED TO OVERCOME MISCONCEPTIONS

Emergency Plans, and their related procedures, should be checked to ensure that they are realistic. A significant part of this reality check is satisfied by verifying that those who are designated to perform an activity or provide a resource can in fact do so, given the disaster situation. Another part relates to the assumptions which are made regarding the disaster environment. Failure to plan for the real disaster situation can result in a somewhat misguided plan which addresses the wrong needs of the time.

The following are but some of the more prevalent myths about disasters and their outcome.

1. **Warnings will produce panic responses.** People panic when faced with a great threat or danger.

The most common response initially is denial. Panic is defined as a sudden, unreasoning, hysterical fear which spreads to other people rapidly. In terms of disasters it would imply behaviour such as irrational flight to escape.

In general, panic requires three conditions which rarely exist:

a) seeing the threat with a perception of possible entrapment (escape route blocked).
b) feeling of powerlessness or impotency.
c) feeling of social isolation or sole dependency on oneself.

In fact, people often stay in potentially threatening situations rather than move out.

2. **People won't listen to official advice.**

The warning period of most disasters is usually marked with multiple information sources, which are typically inconsistent. According to Perry et. al. (1981) there is a distinct effort made by most people to confirm the situation and its magnitude. Conflicting and vague message content can entirely neutralize the desired response. Uniformed personnel, with specific information and advice as to adaptive actions is the most effective and believed source for warning.

There are seven key functions which must be addressed in any effective warning system. They are:

a. Detection
b. Measurement of magnitude
c. Collation/integration of all warning inputs
d. Interpretation

e. Decision to warn
f. Message content
g. Dissemination

3. Evacuation of communities will produce substantial numbers of automobile accidents.

Studies of several hurricane and flood evacuations have refuted this. Most evacuations tend to be relatively well orchestrated and organized (Quarantelli, 1980).

4. Typically, most people will go to public shelters during disaster evacuations.

In actuality, few will go to shelters. Studies indicate (Perry, et al., 1981) that somewhere between three and 30% will seek shelter in publicly established facilities. Their stay is usually short. Most will go to a relative's or a friend's home.

5. Most victims are dazed and relatively non–functional due to the shock of the event. Most victims wait for public officials to organize and undertake the response effort.

Typical response is rational and directed toward helping others. Disaster victims react in an active manner and do not wait for assistance from outsiders. They demonstrate an ability to cope with the immediate problems of the situation. Typical response is self help and immediate aid to others (Drabek et. al., 1981).

Rare cases of "disaster syndrome" (a variety of responses such as hyperactivity or shock) exist but are the exception. People continue to perform their traditional behaviour in the presence of danger. In general, disasters do not cause disabling emotional consequences or leave numbing mental health problems among their victims. Moreover, depending on the event, only a very small percentage of the population will evidence intense shock.

Planning implications are that few victims will get to the hospital via official transportation.

6. Anti–social behaviour, especially looting and other forms of crime increases after most natural disasters.

While rumours of looting are high and cause great concern, actual cases are rare. However, because of the public fear of this activity, local officials must present an image of control and security. By contract, the most common response reflects altruism and heroic acts.

7. Media coverage provides an accurate and balanced portrait of the disaster scene.

In general, the atypical and exceptional responses are focused upon by the media in hopes of stimulating readership and attracting viewers. The competition among the media heightens the emphasis on the unusual or unique. Three fairly distinct phases are discernable in the coverage of major events such as emergencies and disasters:

a. Stunned by the tragedy or impact – this involves genuine concern for people.
b. Accusation – this stage follows after the initial impact has worn off. If something went wrong, then there will be a hunt for the one responsible for it.
c. The story behind the news – this stage involves a search for controversy and the story behind the news. What really happened and why?

8. Disaster exercises and other planning tools allow emergency organizational responses to be integrated and predetermined.

Despite the prevalence of exercising and other planning tools, excessive fragmentation of the organizational response continues to be documented. The complexities and scope of the emergency multi–organizational networks are at times overwhelming! (Drabek et. al., 1981).

9. Disaster victims receive most help from relief agencies.

Informal aid networks are the rule with nearly a utopian mood prevailing (see points #5 and #6 above). In short, people depend on family and friends first. However, relief agencies do provide valuable assistance during disaster response. They often address the needs of special–needs groups and those who are most vulnerable.

10. Psychological scars remain with disaster victims – they never fully recover.

Very little evidence in the research points to long term effects of disaster impact. The exception to that is the Buffalo Creek Disaster (Erickson, 1976). By contrast, Drabek and Quarantelli have not substantiated findings in the Buffalo Creek disaster. Buffalo Creek was a unique situation, with community differences and only a small amount of participation in therapeutic community programs. By contrast, there is much evidence that responders are suffering many long term psychological problems as a result of exposure to traumatic disaster situations.

11. Following disasters, local community leaders typically initiate many forms of disaster mitigation.

While some instances of rather successful mitigation can be cited (i.e., Rapid City, South Dakota), overall patterns suggest minimal mitigation planning in the restoration process. This is due primarily to the intense pressure from family units and businesses to quickly rebuild rather than relocate.

12. Local authorities always know who is in charge.

Quite the contrary! In most cases studied, there seems to be a problem with ambiguity of authority. After reviewing the response to 27 disasters, researchers concluded that "Search and/or rescue takes place in loosely structured situations with uncertain exercise of authority" (Quarantelli, 1980). Additional research and social mapping have now provided substantial verification that organizational perceptions of "who is in charge" varies dramatically during a disaster situation (Drabek et. al., 1981).

13. More communication means better communication.

Too often what is perceived as poor communication really reflects a lack of inter–agency coordination. In most cases, the problem has been too much communication, or the inadequate regulation of the flow and volume of information.

SUMMARY

This chapter addressed the issue of emergency planning. It acknowledged the fact that emergency plans are imperative for effective disaster response. However, it also noted that it the planning process is far more significant than its outcome, the Emergency Plan.

There are a number of ways to look at the planning process. Whatever steps are taken, it ultimately must involve those who are expected to put the Plan into action. More often than not, these people will represent a variety of individuals and organizations.

Another 'truth' about emergency plans is that they must guide action at a critical and chaotic period. As such, these plans should be as comprehensive as possible and yet remain user friendly. They should be easy to understand and follow. They should be treated as an adaptable tool which needs frequent oiling and refinement. It is only then that they will meet their intended objective.

"So, What Have We Got Here?"

Chief Gary Richardson
City of Ottawa Fire Department

Photo Courtesy of Gerry Emas, Edmonton Emergency Response Department.

This chapter outlines in broad terms the key issues, steps and tools of hazard analysis at community and at site levels. It is founded on the principal that effective emergency planning must be based on meaningful hazard analysis.

The chapter was not meant to provide a guide for hazard analysis. Rather, it was intended to provide a prospective on the issue, which would stimulate your imagination and encourage you to perform the hazard analysis process.

In an ideal world Emergency Site Managers would never have to ask the all too frequent question: "So, what have we got here?" Instead, they would know well ahead of the disaster the risks confronted by their community and would have the plans necessary to deal with these hazards. However, ours is a less than an ideal world.

Emergency Services have traditionally been predominately reactive. They often stood by and waited until they were called out and then responded as quickly as possible. Efficient and effective service demands today can no longer afford this approach. Service to the public today involves the prevention of these events from occurring in the first place, reduction of their consequences when they do occur and the mitigation of emergencies after the fact. One could argue that the truly effective Emergency Service would experience no emergency calls at all.

The reality is that disasters often catch response personnel by surprise. That element of surprise further aggravates the chaotic and dangerous conditions which are often present at disaster sites. One of the most successful ways to overcome these conditions (and the element of surprise) is through effective emergency planning, starting with an analysis of local hazards.

Timely, thorough and accurate hazard analysis can enhance a community's emergency planning efforts, its response activities and ultimately, its recovery process. It can also facilitate efforts to mitigate the disaster and its effect. In other words, effective hazard analysis may lead to actions which would either prevent disasters from taking place, or reduce their impact should they occur. However, none of that can happen without meaningful information about the hazards within the community.

Technology is one of the greatest tools in the conduct of hazard analysis. It facilitates the collection, tabulation and analysis of information necessary for meaningful hazard analysis. It also makes that information instantly available to site managers, scene commanders and their team of disaster responders. This allows for more effective planning and response efforts on behalf of the community.

This chapter examines how the Fire and Emergency Services can enhance their ability to meet its emergency management challenge through effective hazard analysis. Several key questions are answered through the hazard analysis process. They include:

1. What is a hazard?
2. What are we trying to determine about it?
3. Whom or what are we trying to protect?
4. What can we accomplish by analyzing each hazard?
5. What do we need to know about it?
6. Who will conduct the analysis?
7. How will we use the information attained?

The answers to some of these and other related questions may challenge the way we currently see the world. Some of the answers may confirm what we suspected all along to be the truth. Regardless, as you read this chapter I urge you to keep an open mind and remain flexible in your analysis of this issue.

DEFINITIONS

Appendix A contains a host of definitions for terms and abbreviations. Some of these are duplicate here to facilitate the discussion on this specialized topic of 'hazard analysis.' The following definitions should help establish a common understanding of the terms involved in the process and facilitate its communication and application.

B.L.E.V.E. It stands for Boiling Liquid Expanding Vapour Explosion. This occurs when a vessel containing a liquid under pressure is heated causing the liquid inside to boil. The resulting expansion inside the tank causes the tank to rupture explosively.

Hazard. The Webster dictionary defines 'hazard' as a "fortuitous event; chance; danger; peril; risk." Kasperson and Pijawka (1985) are more specific. They noted that "hazards may be broadly defined as threats to humans and what they value—life, well- being, material goods, and environment."[1]

This definition contains all of the components of planning that should be considered by emergency managers. The more specific the focus the more able we would be to do a better job. Rather than relying on a broad and generic framework, we could instead relate to real and specific hazards in our environment.

The term 'hazard' can be divided into two categories which can themselves be defined in broad terms. They are natural and technological hazards.

Natural Hazards. These refer to what has previously been labelled in insurance terms as "Acts of God" and include floods, storms, draughts, famines, epidemics, earthquakes and many more. These hazards are readily identified in many cases and planning for them is made easier because they have "readily well understood hazard–chains."[2]

The implication here is that we have more experience upon which to assess these hazards. Being somewhat common, natural hazards are more visible and familiar to us than technological hazard. We also have substantial experience and knowledge upon which to base our analysis of them. There also exists a "limited potential for preventing events."[3] This makes the analysis of natural hazards somewhat easier than the analysis of technological hazards.

1. Kasperson and Pijawka (1985), p. 6.
2. Kasperson and Pijawka (1985), p. 8.
3. Kasperson and Pijawka (1985), p. 8.

Technological Hazards. As their name implies these hazards occur as a result of human activities. As Chapter 1 indicated, the presence of these hazards is high and their numbers are growing exponentially as technology explodes around us. They are often unfamiliar to us and contain tremendous risk. Kasperson and Pijawka (1985) emphasized the point by observing that "technology has emerged as the major source of hazard for modern society."[4]

Obviously, their number, complexity and the fear associated with these hazards pose major obstacles for their analysis. Moreover, because these technology driven events do not fit our normal view of the world we, therefore, can not respond to them using traditional mitigation techniques. This limitation may create serious problems for Emergency Site Managers.

Risk. Kasperson and Pijawka observed that "risk, as differentiated from hazard, may be thought of as the probability that a particular technology, or activity, will lead to a specified consequence over time or activity."[5] Stated differently, *risk* is the combined outcome of the *probability* that a particular event will take place and the *consequence* of that event.

Using the above terms and definitions, let us look at the issues related to the process of hazard analysis, its key principals and its process.

WHY BOTHER?

Anyone embarking on identifying a comprehensive analysis of the "hazards" in their jurisdiction must first develop a clear understanding of the reasons for that analysis. While this sounds like common sense, it is all too often forgotten, or worse yet, ignored by those doing the analysis. The first step in establishing any process is asking the question "Why?"

The need for hazard analysis may be viewed from two general and somewhat related perspectives. One is the needs of effective emergency preparedness; the other serves the requirements of effective response. The former demands a clear and accurate picture of the operational environment so that systems, resources and training can be made available to handle it appropriately. The latter demands that relevant information be rapidly available to those who need it.

One obvious reason for identifying hazards is to ensure the safety of responders. The response to emergency situations requires that decisions be made quickly and be based on as much relevant and accurate information as possible. The knowledge gained about the environment and its hazards can then enhance the ability of responders to make effective decisions during periods of crisis and disaster.

4. Kasperson and Pijawka (1985), p. 7.
5. Kasperson and Pijawka (1985), p. 10.

When responders are surprised by the hazards in their operational area the result may contain serious consequences. However, these situations are avoidable when responders are made aware of the hazards before they confront them. The following analogy should make the point clearer. Fire fighters can perform their tasks much more effectively when they are aware of building logistics such as exits, standpipes, as well as fire hose locations and contents. That awareness can save valuable time on the scene and make the incident commander much more effective. This has been a long accepted concept and crews routinely conduct "building familiarization" tours in their respective districts.

The same attitude must be created and maintained with respect to hazard analysis. As noted above, this is particularly difficult when dealing with technological hazards. Natural hazards, on the other hand, are relatively well understood by virtue of past experience with them. The tornadoes that struck Barrie, Ontario in 1985 and Edmonton, Alberta in 1987, brought home the message that tornadoes are a reality. That went a long way to end the complacency held by some communities at the time that "it will not happen here."

Cyclical occurrences of natural events can foster this type of ambivalence. Floods are a prime example of this situation. Consider this. At the time of this writing, Medicine Hat, Alberta, was undergoing its worst flood in 100 years. The event highlighted a number of general issues. Two of particular significance to hazard analysis are: the influence of experience (or lack of it) with such a disaster, and the credibility of hazard information.

In many disaster situations few, if any, disaster responders and members of the public have actual experience with the disaster (i.e., a one–in–one hundred year flood). Consequently, hazard predictions, without valid analysis, often fall on deaf ears. This is not because people do not believe the experts. It is because they often base their values and beliefs on knowledge gained through experience.

Additionally, many technological hazards are a relatively new phenomenon. New chemicals are developed everyday with the potential to cause harm in some as yet undiscovered way. Our failure to recognize the danger because we have never seen it before, can cause staggering consequences to disaster responders and the general public. Moreover, the lack of acceptance of the hazards involved may result from both familiarity with the hazard as much as unfamiliarity with it. Mazur (n.d.) noted that "public attitudes toward hazards are formed in a manner similar to the way attitudes toward politics, religion, or any other topic are formed... People tend to agree with those they like and associate with and to disagree with those whom they dislike or disapprove of."[6]

6. Mazur (1987), p. 43.

To find salient examples of this is not difficult. One of the most feared hazards encountered by Fire Services personnel is the Boiling Liquid Expanding Vapour Explosion (BLEVE). The devastation that can result from BLEVE explosions and the limitations of traditional approaches to fire fighting are well known today. Unfortunately, this was not always the case.

Two incidents in the late sixties and early seventies, demonstrate the importance of hazard identification. As noted below, this is not just for the sake of the general public, but also serves fire fighters and other disaster response personnel.

On June 21, 1970 at 6:30 a.m., Crescent City, Illinois experienced a fifteen–car derailment on a set of tracks that ran through the centre of the community's business district. Nine of the cars contained liquefied petroleum gas. They ignited and the resulting fire quickly spread to neighbouring buildings. Once it was determined that the cars contained propane an immediate evacuation order was put into effect. Forty three minutes after the initial derailment the first car BLEVE'd. A second car BLEVE'd two hours later followed by a third only five minutes later. The remaining cars burned for fifty–six hours!

The immediate evacuation at this scene occurred because the responsible people knew the danger associated with L.P.G. containers. Miraculously, there were no fatalities, despite the fact that 90 percent of the business district was destroyed. Sixty–six people were injured. (The NFPA video on this incident is quite informative.)

By contrast consider the tragedy that befell Kingman, Arizona on July 5, 1973. In this case a fire resulted when workers were pumping off the contents of a single L.P.G. tanker at a distribution centre on the outskirts of town. Upon their arrival responding fire fighters found flames impinging on the tank car. The nearest water supply was twelve hundred feet away. Ten minutes after the arrival of emergency crews the tank car exploded. In the resulting ground flash, twelve of the thirteen fire fighters on the scene were killed instantly and ninety–five spectators who had stopped on the highway over one thousand feet away to watch the fire were injured.

What made this incident particularly tragic was the fact that the distribution centre in question was in an isolated area and the lack of sufficient water supply made cooling the tank impossible. The responders lost their lives through a failure to react in time to the potential hazard!

Preplanning of this fixed site would have likely highlighted the hazards inherent to the site and would have established a course of action. The lack of a water supply and the inherent dangers of the commodities handled on site would then have been made clear and recognized at the receipt of the call. The dispatch would have provided a warning to all responders. As it turned out, no lives were in danger except those placed in proximity to this incident by traditional reactive scene management and a lack of understanding of hazard analysis as a key component of comprehensive preplanning.

Today the B.L.E.V.E hazard is widely recognized by Fire Departments throughout the world. Events which impact in such dramatic ways quickly change the way we look at the world. The role that "vicarious knowledge in developing Disaster Plans"[7] plays is significant. We should all learn from our mistakes and those of others. The tragedy is that these mistakes are made in the first place.

To stop this cycle of events and help prevent future events we must begin to realize that effective emergency preparation begins with effective hazard analysis. In this way lives and property are not placed in jeopardy in the first place. Responder's tunnel vision, which often creates fatalities, is the result of the failure to learn from the lessons of others. While the responders to the Kingman, Arizona incident epitomized this behaviour, they are not alone. I am sure that all of us can look back at examples from our own careers where good luck rather than good management prevented tragedy. We can not rely on luck to always be there.

It may well be argued that we can never prevent all of the possible disasters that may befall us. Perrow (1984) observed that many disasters are caused because of the complexity of our technologies and the tight inter–linking of their various parts. He coined the term 'normal accidents' to describe these disasters. Erikson (1991) noted that as human systems become more and more elaborate accidents are simply inevitable. My first Training Officer told me that the three main causes of fires are men, women and children. After a twenty–four–year career in the fire services I cannot dispute his reasoning. However, that does not imply that a stoic acceptance of these facts, and the removal of the responsibility for emergency preparation, are credible solutions. Any preparation is better than no preparation.

We must overcome complacency. Something is not "not dangerous" because it is common. Yet we regularly assume this to be the case. The classic example is the propane tank often found in backyard bar–b–ques. These tanks are often taken for granted by many, including emergency personnel. And, many lack the necessary knowledge of this L.P.G. (and its properties) to make informed decisions on its use and hazards. A forty–pound tank can BLEVE with surprising force!

Human blood is another example. Before the advent of AIDS, how many of us thought of human blood as a dangerous product. Today, all health care workers regularly guard against contact with blood products. Responders are regularly taught to recognize the hazards and prepare for them.

The answer to the question "why bother?" lies in an observation made by Kasperson and Pijawka (1985). They observed that "equipped with a hazard assessment and a control analysis, the manager is positioned to select a hazard management strategy."[8] It is worth noting that strategic planning should not be unique to business. It needs to be a part of the Fire Services regular operations. Without such a strategy we unnecessarily risk our personnel and the public at large.

7. Kartez and Lindell (1987).
8. Kasperson and Pijawka (1985), p. 9.

WHERE DO WE BEGIN?

Hazard analysis needs to be conducted at two levels during two separate phases of emergency management. The first should be conducted during the emergency planning (or preparedness) phase. It should include an analysis of the hazards inherent to the community. This is a global analysis involving many facets and criteria.

The second hazard analysis is more specific and should be undertaken at disaster scenes during the response phase. It is often conducted by the first–on–scene responder and may be conducted by subsequent arrivals, as needed. The focus of this analysis is more site–specific and time–immediate.

Hazard analysis at community level

The first question that must be answered before any attempt to identify specific hazards is "what should the analysis achieve?" In other words, why do we want to identify the hazards inherent to the community? The most obvious and significant answer is, of course, to ensure the safety of response personnel and the public. Another reason is to avoid or reduce property damage. A third reason is to enhance the productivity of the Fire Services. It can be well argued that any organization that establishes a culture of emergency preparedness and learning cannot help but become more effective in achieving its public protection mandate.

It should be readily apparent, therefore, that there is a need for a taxonomy of hazards. This is a list of hazards categorized according to a variety of factors (i.e., their hazard). The creation of such a taxonomy is demanding, particularly where technological hazards are concerned. The question that must then be answered is "What hazards are we going to focus on?"

Crocker (1993) noted that "the risk a particular hazardous event represents can be quantified using a measure defined by: Risk = Frequency x Consequences."[9] Several factors enter that equation. One, hazards must be placed on a continuum that ranges from low impact and consequence to extreme impact and consequence. This is a relatively easier task for natural hazards where past experience and readily available knowledge assist greatly in labelling or listing hazards and their consequences.

Additional factors to be considered are the probability of occurrence of each event and its likely duration once it has occurred. Further exacerbating the task of hazard analysis are the differences which such factors as quantity and location of the hazard play in the hazard mitigation effort.

It is important to note that these and many other factors affect our perceptions about the hazards, their potential impact on us, the degree of risk which we are prepared to live with and the actions which we must take for our protection. Ultimately, we and the public make subjective choices as to what action we should and should not undertake.

9. Crocker and Alp (1993), p. 37.

Regardless, a comprehensive (and qualified) list of hazards for the area, municipality or jurisdiction is a solid basis for the next crucial task – resource allocation. The question to be answered then is "how much of our resources do we wish to commit to each category of hazard?" The term 'category' is used purposely because it is perhaps the only logical way to preplan for the myriad of potential technological hazards that will likely materialize through the hazard analysis.

In this regard, as in many other activities, what is unintentionally ignored or neglected may turn around to cause the greatest problems. Recognition of individual hazards will, for example, be a tremendously difficult job in large urban environments. On the other hand, small communities with static industrial bases and limited occupancy types may find it easier to list everything that might constitute a hazard in their micro environment. In any case, the process of hazard analysis must be undertaken and be completed as comprehensively as possible.

Complacency in this area can be dangerous. Consider the fact that many hazards are not stationary but 'mobile.' For example, trucks, buses, trains and automobiles can carry unpleasant surprises to and through all communities. And, just because a building is deemed to be residential or nonindustrial in nature, it does not mean that its owners or tenants have not made it a high hazard occupancy.

One of my experiences illustrates the above point. As a Fire Inspector, a few years ago, I was conducting a routine license inspection of a small Dry Cleaning depot in a strip mall on a residential street. Much to my dismay I discovered over one hundred five–gallon pails of perchlorethylene piled to the ceiling in a back room. A fire in this building would have created many problems for both unsuspecting responders and the public. This example should demonstrate that no amount of planning can totally prepare us for all situations that may arise. However, we can be better prepared by understanding the hazard and being prepared to respond to it regardless of its location. This knowledge enhances our flexibility to handle surprises of this nature. Moreover, it is the knowledge of the hazard not necessarily the location that is important. This is the key point.

Resource allocation to hazard analysis must follow guidelines that are location specific. Cities such as Edmonton and Hamilton with many petroleum processing sites will have different hazard– related response priorities than service oriented cities such as Victoria, Ottawa or Fredericton.

As noted above, the efficient allocation of emergency resources requires both the knowledge of the hazards as well as the probability of their occurrence. Both of these factors must be considered when prioritizing hazards. For example, it would make little sense for a community to commit their precious resources to prepare for air plane crashes if the community has no airport and is no where near a flight path. While responders from Locherbee Scotland may disagree, reality is that we can not prepare for every eventuality. And, perhaps because of this limitation, it is particularly important to perform the hazard analysis. It facilitates a better understanding of the hazards and risks and the procedures resulting from this knowledge, can be applied in a variety of situations as appropriate. Moreover, the commonplace practice of these techniques in organizations can help managers to better manage their organizations.

The last component of developing a hazard analysis process involves the logistics of the process. As noted earlier, the identification of hazard categories and the establishment of risk priorities are followed by the allocation of resources. However, the actual location of the hazards still remains a problem. It is one thing to know that propane presents a danger to responding emergency personnel and quite another to find out the hard way that the fire you are fighting involves propane. The issue here is one of education. This is not just a matter of the education of emergency responders. That is crucial! But equally important is the education of the public at large, corporate citizens and politicians. As noted earlier in this chapter, any one may fail to recognize potential hazards and in doing so cause harm. A variety of sources are available and should be used to deliver the necessary educational programs.

As in all aspects of life, we learn first and foremost from experience. This experience can come from our own personal involvement in events, or through the experiences of others. One can only hope that these experiences did not involve fatalities. Some situations, although highly risky and potentially disastrous, do not develop to their full potential and remain manageable. Many reasons may avert a full–blown disaster. The advantage of this situation is that we do not undergo the disaster experience. One disadvantage is that we may miss an opportunity to learn from the experience because its impact was insignificant. Kartez and Lindell (1987) cite the "failure to learn from one's own experience as a major impediment to better preparedness."[10] This impediment can be fatal.

Experience alone does not imply knowledge. If experience is to be beneficial, mistakes should never be repeated, and actions that have proven effective should be explained to others so that they too can learn. While this sounds simple and should be common sense, it is not.

Those of us in the emergency services often attempt to minimize the impact of our actions, particularly if the consequences of these actions are in any way undesirable. By doing so we are in fact perpetuating the problem and impeding the learning process that is so crucial to avoid repeating these mistakes.

Consider, for example, technological hazard incidents. These are relatively new hazards and continue to result in unpleasant surprises for unsuspecting scene managers and the public. If we do not share information about these incidents we are doomed to repeat them time and again. The trouble is that we need to share our mistakes! On the other hand, by sharing them we can prevent other Fire Services personnel from enduring tragic consequences by making the same mistakes.

10. Kartez and Lindell (1985), p. 47.

Sharing information should be commonplace. We need to maintain regular and ongoing communications with other emergency services. When an incident occurs in one jurisdiction its members should quickly relay relevant information to Fire Departments in other jurisdictions. In case of concern over litigation relevant information should be released as soon as possible. It is never too late to learn.

Admittedly, learning from experience, while effective, is not the desirable way to achieve knowledge about hazards and their potential impact. There is a wealth of materials, in all forms, available from a wide variety of sources that we could and must access to make our job easier and safer. Increasingly, computer software programs are becoming available to make needed information readily available. Printed materials are available from manufacturers, researchers, emergency service providers and various trade journals. They provide a valuable source of data regarding various hazards and their consequences. A wide range of videos are also available.

Fire Departments should create and maintain a comprehensive database utilizing all of these sources of information. The down side is that this data base should be upgraded constantly. The up side is that the knowledge inherent to the database can literally save lives.

To be effective the data must be used properly. We must never lose sight of the fact that "for knowledge to be meaningful it must be correlated with the power to act preventively."[11] If we fail to do this we are guilty of the worst kind of negligence. Better data on their own is of little benefit unless we also understand their use.

Hazard analysis at site level

The second type of hazard analysis is often conducted at Site level during the response phase of the disaster. This is typically the responsibility of the first–on–scene emergency responder whose task it is to "size–up" the situation. Decisions must then be made quickly with potential consequences on the health and safety of others at the site. These decisions should be approached in a systematic way that allows for consistency regardless of the situation. This approach will have a bearing on the activities of others at the scene including the Emergency Site Manager.

Therefore, responders and Emergency Site Managers alike must understand the importance of effective size–up. All incidents should be approached in the same way. Decisions should be based on conclusions arrived at through determination of the facts, probabilities, needed resources, desired strategy and an action plan. This approach is an integral component of all incident command systems.

Facts consist of such information as weather and scene conditions upon arrival. Probabilities are any changes that may occur with respect to the facts. Resources needed are considered in terms of immediate needs and future requirements. The

11. Jasanoff (1988) p. 11.

strategy is situation specific and is based on a variety of factors which include command experience, preplanning, the facts and the probability of changes to them. The resource requirements of the situation should also be considered. The action plan which is then developed must be flexible enough to allow for changes in conditions or unforseen circumstances.

Decision making techniques like this are prevalent in Emergency Services, large or small. Through techniques which are common and understood by all, we are more likely to achieve order in otherwise chaotic circumstances. We deal daily with "uncertain future events,"[1] and must begin to plan for them more than ever before, because by doing so we can "increase opportunities to prepare effectively"[2] for them.

Decision making involving conditions of risk and uncertainty creates unique challenges for the decision maker. Add to that the potential, in disasters, for tragic consequences and you quickly realize that the more information one has upon which to base those decisions, the more effective the decision can be. Effective hazard analysis helps to provide meaningful and useful information.

THE LOGISTICS OF HAZARD ANALYSIS

Once we have realized the benefits of the hazard analysis process, and have asked the appropriate questions, we can begin the logistical work of the actual analysis. Sociologists and other planning professionals refer to 'hazard chains' as a frame of reference for analysis. Understanding these chains is crucial before analysis begins.

As an example let us use a chain of hazard evolution which was described by Kasperson and Pijawka (1985) as it relates to technological hazards. The chain begins with '*human needs*' (e.g., shelter, transportation) which are translated into '*human wants*' (e.g., high rise towers and automobiles). These wants are satisfied through a '*choice of technology*' (e.g., petrochemical processing). There is an '*initiating event*' which causes this technology to '*release of materials or energy*' which creates situations of '*exposure to materials and energy*' ultimately leading to '*human/biological consequences.*'

The intervention of emergency responders in the chain has traditionally occurred *after* the initiating event. That is not early enough to influence the hazard environment in the community. Hazard analysis techniques should change this.

Building codes today mandate the involvement of various departments at the 'choice of technology' stage. In this way, future potential for risk can be recognized early and choices can be made to modify or minimize the hazards involved. This involvement actually increases the data base as information is added prior to the existence of the hazards. However, to perform this task effectively one requires the knowledge generated by the hazard analysis process.

To be effective, the hazard chain should be related to the hazard management process. This linkage must be understood by everyone involved in the process and utilized each time a hazard is considered. The process is explained below.

The process should be based on information gleamed through research, primarily on the available choices of technology (i.e., their strengths and limitations) as well as the human and biological consequences of exposure to materials and energy. This research should serve as a basis for the hazard assessment.

The hazard assessment component should achieve the following:

1. Identify the hazards inherent to the technology or the community.
2. Help assign priorities to action and resources.
3. Assist in the estimation of risk.
4. Help evaluate social values.

Once completed the hazard analysis should lead into 'control analysis.' This process, in turn, should help:

1. Judge tolerability of the technology and its consequence of failure.
2. Identify means of controlling technological failures.
3. Assess modes of implementation of these controls.
4. Evaluate the distribution of costs related to the control of technological incidents.

The control analysis is followed by a selection of an implementation strategy. Four options are available, each with its own consequence.

1. Complete acceptance of the risk.
2. Spread of the risk (i.e., through insurance or other partnerships).
3. Reduction of the risk (e.g., reduction in scale).
4. Mitigating the risk (e.g., buffer zones).

Once a strategy is accepted it must then be implemented and the implementation should be evaluated. This then completes the cycle and begins it anew as the lessons learned from the evaluation are fed into the next hazard analysis.

All the steps of the hazard analysis process are interdependent. This suggests that action(s) taken at any point in the process can and will impact the rest of the process. This also reinforces the need to include, in the planning process, all responders that may be involved in the mitigation of related incidents.

Many small communities tend to rely on outside resources for assistance in the response to chemical incidents. Such reliance may be necessary due to lack of expertise or resources. That reliance is healthy as long as it does not cause the community to abandon its own hazard analysis efforts.

And, while all sources of information should be considered, when it comes to local planning, there is no substitute for first hand knowledge gained through personal involvement in the process. This takes time and effort and should be done well before the disaster occurs. An emergency scene is no place to start learning about the hazard you are confronting.

Using the above mentioned processes and the information they generate, we are now ready to establish our own list of hazards and to prioritise them. Depending on the size and nature of our community, this may result in an extensive and ever growing list. And, as the list of hazards grows the priorities we set for dealing with each hazard may change. Consequently, the information must be regularly communicated to those responders who may find themselves at a disaster scene.

While it may not be possible to have an encyclopedic knowledge of all hazards, it is possible to have the information quickly made available when required. Agencies such as Canutech, with twenty– four hour access, have already proven this concept workable. Moreover, to be truly effective the information must be shared by all agencies involved in the incident. Kartez and Lindell (1987) observed that "problems frequently arise during emergencies because each discipline (fire, police, etc.) sees problems only in terms of its own capabilities."[12] This type of scene management can have catastrophic results. Hazard identification and analysis cannot occur in a vacuum. There is no advantage to the planning process if any responder at the scene is left unaware of the dangers posed by the hazard.

HAZARD CHECKLISTS

One of the main tools available to emergency planners is the hazard checklist. This list facilitates the process of hazard identification and also provides greater consistency in the process. This is because such lists provide a higher level of objectivity.

There are many types of lists each with its own advantages and disadvantages. Three such checklists are already in widespread use. They will be discussed below. It is worth noting, however, that organizations should not feel bound to use any of these check lists and may develop their own version to meet their unique needs.

The first check list is the Hazard Evaluation Form (Figure 4.1) which was developed at the Canadian Emergency Preparedness College at Arnprior, Ontario. It is illustrated (in modified form) to show how one can identify and then prioritise hazards.

This method requires that all hazards of concern be listed as 'potential' hazards. Each hazard is then rated or quantified in terms of its historical occurrence, change in its hazard condition, impact from other factors and degree of effect. The rating factors are totalled for each hazard and compared with the totals of the other hazard on the

12. Kartez and Lindell (1985), p. 487.

list. The comparison of these totals (i.e., largest sum to smallest) can help in establishing the prioritization of the hazards on the list.

This system is workable and valuable. It does, however, have one significant flaw. The use of numbers to indicate the degree of hazard may be misunderstood by some to imply that this is a 'scientific' measure of hazard. It is not. It is still based on some degree of subjective analysis.

Figure 4.1 – Hazard Evaluation Form

Municipality ______________________ Date ____________

Potential Hazard	Rating for Potential*				Sum of (1) to (4) (5)	Planning Priority (6)
	Historical (1)	Change in conditions (2)	Effects from Other Areas (3)	Lack of Ability to Cope (4)		

Rating Guide:

* Column (1) is on a scale ranging from '0' (no potential) to 5 (high potential) based on historical evidence.
* Columns (2) and (3) is on a scale ranging from –3 (great improvement) through to '0' (no improvement) to +3 (deterioration from historical records).
* Column (4) is on a scale ranging from '0' (no change) to 3 (high effect) on hazard potential.

The completed form (Figure 4.2), for example, shows how all hazards, whether natural or technological can be listed and compared by using the same list during the same process. This completed analysis, with its prioritised list, can then form the basis for action by all key response organizations during their planning effort.

Once completed, the Hazard Evaluation Form would look something like Figure 4.2 below. This hazard evaluation form should be reviewed regularly, especially following any significant changes to the hazard composition of the community. As new hazards are identified, they should be rated in the same manner as those already on the list and added to the hazards' data base under the appropriate heading. This should help to maintain the Hazard List both complete and current.

Figure 4.2 – Hazard Evaluation Form

Municipality ***City of Winnipeg*** Date June 24, 199

Potential Hazard	Rating For Potential*				Sum of (1) to (4) (5)	Planning Priority (6)
	Historical (1)	Change in conditions (2)	Effects from Other Areas (3)	Lack of Ability to Cope (4)		
River Flood	**5**	***–3***	***0***	***0***	***2***	***4***
Flash Flood	**5**	***2***	***0***	***2***	***9***	***1***
Tornado	***4***	***1***	***0***	***1***	***6***	***3***
Haz Mat Incident	**5**	***0***	***1***	***1***	***7***	***2***

Another commonly used hazard list is the one developed and used by Federal Emergency Management Agency (FEMA). The weighting here is more comprehensive and allows for the prioritization of the criteria through separate values. The check list is also more detailed. However, the principles remain the same.

The FEMA model looks at four factors. They are: the history of the event, the vulnerability of people to it, vulnerability of property to damage and the probability of the event occurring. Each of these four factors is weighted and together they represent a sum which allows for ranking of the hazard against the other hazards on the list.

FEMA Model criteria.

History	**Evaluation**
0–1 Times in 100 years	Low
2–3 Times in 100 years	Medium
4 + Times in 100 years	High

Vulnerability of people	**Evaluation**
1%	Low
2–10%	Medium
11+%	High

Vulnerability of property	**Evaluation**
1%	Low
2–10%	Medium
11+%	High

Maximum threa (area of the community impacted?	**Evaluation**
5%	Low
6–25%	Medium
26 +%	High

Probability (chances per year)	**Evaluation**
Less than 1 in 100	Low
BT. 1 in 100 and 1 in 10	Medium
Greater than 1 in 10	High

Low = 1 point Medium = 5 points High = 10 points

Total risk = History (X2) + Vulnerability (X5) + Maximum threat (X10) + Probability (X7)

Listed below (Figure 4.3) is a sample of an application of the FEMA model.

Figure 4.3 – FEMA Model (example)

Hazard	History	Vulnerability People	Vulnerability Property	Maximum Threat	Probability	Score	Rank
River Flood	HIGH 2x10=20	LOW 5x1=5	MED 5x5=25	MED 10x5=50	MED 7x5=35	135	4
Flash Flood	MED 2x5=10	HIGH 5x10=50	HIGH 5x10=50	HIGH 10x10=100	MED 7x5=35	245	1
Tornado	MED 2x5=10	LOW 5x1=5	LOW 5x1=5	HIGH 10x10=100	MED 7x5=35	155	3
Haz–mat	HIGH 2x10=20	MED 5x5=25	MED 5x5=25	MED 10x5=50	HIGH 7x10=70	190	2

Please note that despite the differences in the two checklists the priority determined for the hazards is the same. This is because the weighting factors are similar. A third type of hazard check list, called the SMUG system, is discussed below.

SMUG HAZARD PRIORITY SYSTEM

This system is known by the acronym SMUG, which stands for Seriousness, Manageability, Urgency and Growth. It allows a direct comparison of a number of possible hazards (through ratings of high, medium or low) against four separate factors which are common to all hazards.

The system compares all hazards, using one factor at a time, and records the results in a table. The system works as follows:

1. All hazards are listed in no particular order.
2. Factors are assessed one at a time.
3. All hazards are rated (using H, M, or L) against one hazard. In other words the assessment is reached by relational comparison of one hazard against all others as it relate to one factor at the time. More than one 'High' may be given out. And, if the group cannot agree on a rating, the highest rating should be put down just to be on the safe side.
4. Step 3 is repeated for each of the remaining three factors.
5. A brief explanation is provided to support the rating.
6. The hazards are compared using factor analysis.

The four factors and the rationale for the High, Medium and Low ratings are detailed below.

Seriousness. Seriousness is the relative impact of a hazard in terms of dollars and/or people. Under this category, hazards would be rated a 'High' if they represent a threat to the largest number of people or would cause the greatest financial loss.

Manageability. Manageability means the degree of change we can impose on the hazard. If we can lessen the impact of the hazard, then the rating for manageability should be high. If it were manageable only after it had occurred, then the rating would be low.

Urgency. A 'High' in this category indicates that we need to do something about this hazard now. A 'Medium' rating indicates that we ought to do something about it in the near future. And, a 'Low' rating indicates that there is no urgency and that it would be appropriate to plan for action sometime in the future.

Growth. If we do nothing about the hazard will it grow worse or remain as it currently is? If the hazard would increase quickly it should be rated as a 'High.' If it would grow gradually, it should be rated 'Medium' and if it will stay static, then it is worth a 'Low' rating.

Having allocated a relative rating to all identified hazards on each of these factors, we can now review our list with the intent of prioritizing the hazards. Those with the most highly rated factors are those which warrant a high priority for attention.

As noted earlier, it is important to provide evidence in support of each rating. These 'justifications' could be most helpful to put order among hazards which seem to have the same number of High, Medium and Low ratings. These justifications can also serve as a basis for a narrative–based explanation regarding the prioritization of the hazards.

The checklist created using SMUG is somewhat different than the previous two models. The four criteria are not quantified by numbers. Instead they are rated as High, Medium and Low. This results in a more subjective listing. Figure 4.4 below, demonstrates the SMUG system using the same examples as used by the other checklists. The City of Winnipeg is again used as the venue.

Note that since the City of Winnipeg is protected by a floodway, the seriousness of the flood is minimized. Hence the low seriousness rating for the flood. As we can see, the resulting priority ratings are slightly different than with the previous two lists. In fact, according to the SMUG system the number one hazard priority for the City of Winnipeg relates to Hazardous Materials.

The above examples illustrate a few of the many ways through which hazards can be identified and prioritised. These tools are invaluable to planners because they provide structure and consistency to what can become a very convoluted process. Checklists can also be created which help responders, in actual incident mitigation, by creating a 'to do' list for scene managers. One of the key benefits of this type of 'to do' list is that it provides managers, especially novices, with a framework for handling the disaster scene.

The fundamental failing of checklists of any type is that they are very limiting and rigid. Therefore, too heavy a reliance on them can lead to problems as unforseen circumstances arise. Flexibility is crucial in emergency management and we cannot become too reliant on tools. To do so may prevent us from maintaining the ability to think on our feet, an activity which is crucial for success. We will always encounter situations that do not fit neatly into a category, or onto a list. And, we absolutely must have the capacity to handle these when they arise.

Figure 4.4 – SMUG Hazard Priority System

Hazard	Seriousness	Manageability	Urgency	Growth	
***River* Flood**	H M **L**	**H** M L	H M **L**	H M **L**	
	–floodway –ample warning	–mitigation measures	–medium term (Predictability)	–hazard potential will change little	4
Flash Flood	H **M** L	**H** M L	H **M** L	H **M** L	
	–vulnerability –lack of warning	–mitigation measures	–near term	–slow growth corresponding with urban growth	2
Tornado	**H** M L	H M **L**	H **M** L	H **M** L	
	–high death/damage	–sudden impact –very destructive	–near term	–same as flash flood	3
Haz–Mat	H **M** L	**H** M L	**H** M L	H M L	
	–great dislocation – historically low death and/or damage	–mitigation measures –regulatory controls	– immediate –threat/ predictability	–same as flash flood	1

Another shortfall of checklists is that they do not cover the likelihood of a number of hazards occurring in combination. The resulting danger can be magnified exponentially by these mixtures. When this occurs all of the ratings change and the priorities are no longer valid. Moreover, continued utilization of the information on the checklist can court further disaster. Also, failure to recognize the possible change in priority of a hazard places those close to the incident in danger.

Checklists, which are a valuable tool for planners must always be utilized with the knowledge that they are just that, a tool. They are not a substitute for common sense, education and experience. Used properly in the planning process they aid in effective incident management. Used improperly or inappropriately they can lead to serious and unexpected consequences giving the question "What have we got here?" a whole new meaning.

SUMMARY

Emergency services that wish to be progressive in the areas of safety and scene management must consider the hazard identification and prioritization process as a valuable tool. Accepting hazard analysis as part of doing business, as a philosophy, is the first step in the process. The next is to get the entire service on side and begin macro planning.

At this stage those members of the organization who will be directly involved in incident mitigation should begin to formulate the process. This planning should be locale specific. Factors to be considered should include: the size of the municipality, size and stability of the infrastructure, available resources, experience, disaster history, demographics, climate patterns, government presence and involvement, as well as prior knowledge with disaster response.

The actual establishment of a data base will begin at the onset of the process and continue throughout the life of the program. Today's technological expansion will mandate constant vigilance of the hazards. All sources of information must be considered and utilized as appropriate. Industry, government, private organizations, environmental groups, educational facilities, other emergency services and members of the general public may all have valuable information to offer.

Internally, your own people are a most valuable resource. You can and should create an organization that is constantly searching for hazards and examining their consequences. This cultural climate of learning is fostered through an acceptance and recognition of the contributions made by all of its members. Everyone, regardless of their position, is capable of significant input. And, the most innocuous bit of information may have devastating impact if ignored.

Once received, the information must be shared. We must, as emergency service providers, network as never before. Current information technologies make the synergy produced by talking to each other easier to achieve than ever before. I must emphasize that the most important information to share is the most difficult for most of us to talk about; our mistakes. However, as difficult as it is to admit, and despite litigation concerns, we simply can not allow others to repeat our mistakes; to fall victim to tragedy because of our silence or fear of reprisal. Experience is lost if we do not learn from it.

The sharing of information must occur at a micro level as well. Large urban services often have problems with internal communications. The various infrastructure locations, coupled with different shifts make it difficult to communicate. Information sharing begins at home! Informing your neighbouring emergency service providers of a dangerous situation while failing to inform your own people properly is ludicrous. And yet it happens.

Once collection of data begins, it must be manipulated in such a way as to facilitate the identification process. Whatever tools are used, they should be employed consistently throughout the process. It makes little sense to have different subunits of the organization use different checklists or systems for hazard priority. Unfortunately, in a large urban setting this is not only possible, but occurs on a regular basis.

Police and fire or ambulance services often plan in similar areas without any idea that they are doing so. Redundancy of this type can be eliminated through communication with the other response organizations. Therefore, one needs to assign a coordinator for all planning efforts who, regardless of his/her organization, should have a community–wide focus.

A well coordinated hazard identification process must be an integral component of the day–to–day operations of all emergency services. Actual incident management will still occur as per local protocols. And, regardless of who is in charge at the scene, all will benefit from access to the hazard–related data. The result is bound to be enhanced safety of response personnel as well as the public.

This chapter has taken a very generic look at what is a very complex issue. It was not meant to provide a guide for hazard analysis. Rather, it was intended to provide you with a new perspective on the issue, stimulate your imagination and encourage you to undertake a higher level of preparedness through the collection and sharing of hazard–related information.

Picture 4.1

A tire fire is more than a fire in a tire shop. What are the complications?
(Photo Courtesy of Gerry Emas, Edmonton Emergency Response Department.)

Picture 4.2

Is this a fire in a lumber store or is it more? Do you know?!
(Photo Courtesy of Gerry Emas, Edmonton Emergency Response Department.)

"Help! Is There Anyone (Else) There?"

Dave Worman
Director, Protective Services
City of Fort Saskatchewan

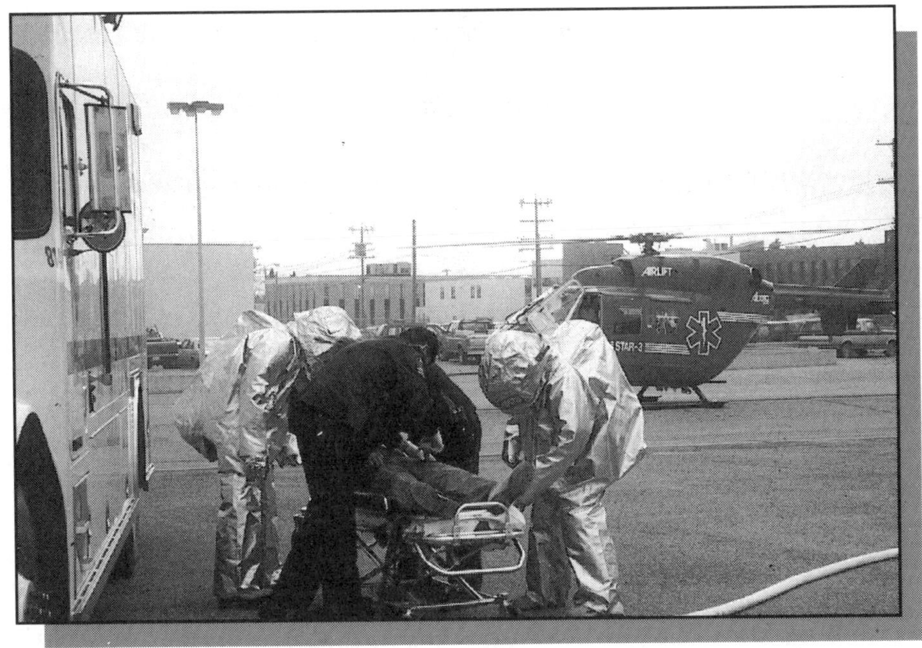

Photo Courtesy of Edmonton Emergency Response Department.

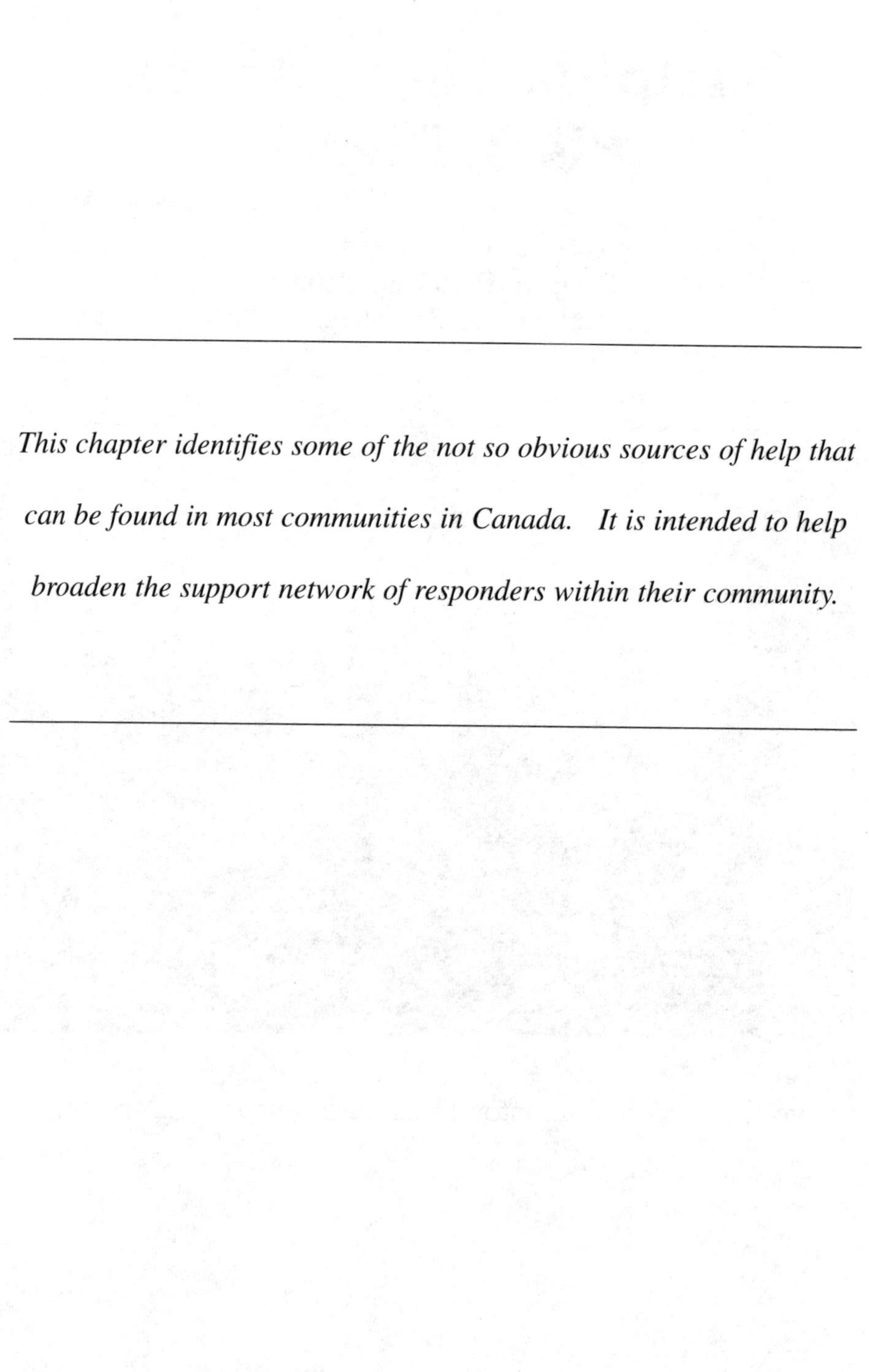

This chapter identifies some of the not so obvious sources of help that can be found in most communities in Canada. It is intended to help broaden the support network of responders within their community.

Why would we include a chapter entitled "HELP! Is There Anyone (Else) There?" Why do we need anyone else? Doesn't the municipality provide us with everything we need? What is wrong with our Fire, Police, and Ambulance services? They do all right; don't they? Isn't emergency planning my job? Why do I need anyone else?

Stop and think about it. Is it really practical or even possible for the municipality to provide everything that could be required to mitigate the effects of every possible major disaster? Can one individual, regardless of how knowledgeable and experienced he or she is really be expected to single handedly plan and prepare for the response to all possible scenarios? And, how likely is it that the only response needed during any major incident would be from the Fire, Police, and Ambulance Services?

Communities that experience major disaster will likely require all the resources they can muster plus outside resources in order to effectively respond to the incident. This is born by experience and is becoming more accepted by municipal emergency planners.

Two key elements in the previous statement are worth remembering. First, it does not say that it takes all the resources the MUNICIPALITY can muster; it clearly and deliberately says it takes all the resources the COMMUNITY can muster. The second thing worth remembering about this statement is that it clearly recognizes the need for resources from outside the community.

In one way or another, disasters impact everyone in the community. Injuries as well as loss of life and property are obvious impacts of a disaster and could effect everyone. But what happens to a community when it loses its supply of natural gas or electricity, or when there is no longer a safe supply of water and a healthy sanitation system? In many disasters, food and clothing supplies are diminished or lost entirely. What about schools, nursing homes, day care centres, churches and hospitals? What is the impact on a community when these facilities are lost or severely damaged? As well, businesses both large and small could suffer temporary or permanent loss of part or all of their market share. This could result in the loss of jobs as well as other economical impacts with far reaching and long lasting consequences.

When the physical, social, emotional, economical, and spiritual fabrics of a community are effected, then clearly everyone in the community is effected.

We should agree on three key issues. They are: everyone is likely to be effected by a disaster; it is not practical for the municipality to provide everything needed; and, no one individual can plan for everything that will be needed to be done. Given these three issues, then we can also agree that emergency preparedness and disaster response is truly a community wide responsibility.

So, do we need help? And, is there anyone (else) there? The answer on both counts is a definite "Yes!" And, given that, maybe the emergency planners job is not so much to know and to do everything that needs to be done. It is to know who else is in the community that can do what needs to be done.

All too often we emergency planners tend to isolate ourselves and attempt to do it all ourselves. Or, at best we try and include only some of the vast expertise and resources available in all communities.

Every community regardless of its size or location either has, or has access to, resources to effectively prepare for, respond to and recover from major emergencies. Having said this, it is very important to recognize that each community's degree or level of preparedness, response and recovery will vary depending on its available resources. However, the key is to recognize these resources and their limitations and plan accordingly. Communities differ one from the other just as each emergency is different from all other emergencies. So, not only is it important to ensure all available resources are included in the emergency plan, it is equally important to do realistic planning and only include those resources which are available.

Every emergency planner dreams of having unlimited resources, but in reality all communities are forced to make do in one way or another depending on the disaster situation. If forced to evacuate I am sure we would all prefer a fleet of modern transit buses. However, in reality a lot of us do not have any, or at best not enough buses. So let's plan to use what we do have, such as, school buses, private vehicles etc.

We need to ensure that we include all available resources. We also have to ensure that we include resources that are readily available. But that's not all. It's not good enough just to include them in the plan, it is imperative that they also be included in the planning process. Then, when the call for help does go out, everyone else who is out there comes prepared for the situation at hand.

So you ask "who else is out there?" You may be surprised! Help can come from least expected sources as well as from some very obvious and predictable ones. That is why we have a chapter called "HELP! Is There Anyone (Else) There?"

This chapter identifies some of the not so obvious sources of help that can be found in most communities in Canada. Remember we may not always have our first choice of everything we need readily available. But with help from others, a little innovation and some imagination we can make do and do the very best we can with what we have. So let's explore this further and see when the call does go out, just who else might be out there.

Before we rush out and attempt to identify all the possible sources of help available to us, we need to determine all the things we will need help doing. And, you guessed it, we will need help doing this. Few effective emergency plans are written in isolation by one individual without assistance and input from others. Emergency planning teams or committees seem to be the most effective approach. These teams require leadership, guidance and facilitation which is probably best provided by the individual responsible for emergency planning. However, that individual can not possibly perform the emergency planning process alone.

The makeup of emergency planning teams will vary from community to community depending on the size and diversity of the community and to some degree, the type of risk the community is subject to. Generally, the committee should include representatives from a cross section of community stakeholders including emergency response services, elected officials, business, industry, communication, transportation, social services, schools and many more.

Just as one individual should not attempt to perform emergency planning without input from others, neither should the planning committee. They should seek help and not rely entirely on the experiences and expertise available in their community. You see, the problem most of us have in the emergency field is, we haven't had first hand experience in dealing with major disasters. So why not take advantage of the experience and expertise of those who have?

There are excellent guidelines and standard manuals produced just for this purpose. Many safety associations, Provincial and Federal Government agencies, private consulting companies as well as industrial and municipal organizations have produced very high quality standards and guidelines for effective emergency planning. These manuals are readily available and if used effectively will assist emergency planners in the production of good emergency plans. I strongly recommend the use of these manuals as they have been developed by experts in the emergency preparedness field and include the experiences of many who have front line experience in dealing with the many aspects of emergency preparedness, response and recovery.

So, even at the early stages of the process there is someone else out there who can help. Seek them out and make use of this great resource even at this early stage of emergency preparedness.

Now that the emergency planning team has been formed, and the guidelines and standards manuals have been obtained, the emergency planning and response process can begin.

As identified and discussed in other chapters throughout this book, emergency planning and response is not a simple one or two step process. It is a fairly complex multi–faceted procedure, including hazard analysis, emergency medical, fire, police, communications, public warning, recovery, transportation, social services and others.

This chapter does not go into detail on effective methodologies or the philosophy of good hazard analysis or any other component of the emergency plan. It identifies agencies and other resources that may be of assistance in emergency preparedness and response. It also suggests roles, responsibilities and functions that may be assigned to these agencies. It is extremely important that this search for assistance takes place in the earliest stages of the planning process. Obviously it is too late to seek help during a major incident. It is also unreasonable to assume that the various agencies and organizations will respond to an emergency as a coordinated, synchronized team without some preplanning, communication and familiarization with each other. These points can not be stressed enough. Roles and responsibilities must be clearly defined and understood, not only by the tasked or designated agency but also by each of the other agencies.

Surprises, confusion or misunderstanding during disaster response should be kept to the bare minimum. Nothing should be assumed or taken for granted. Pre–planning, communication, training and practice go a long way to ensure the effectiveness of the plan and the response effort. We know that it is too late during an incident to do this, but it is also too late when the plan is completed or near completion. The greatest degree of commitment and ownership of the plan will occur during its earliest stages of development. Additionally, the plan will be much more thorough and effective, and your job will be much more manageable if the expertise, knowledge and experience of others is included in the process.

Determining the type and degree of risk your community is exposed to does not have to be an overly complicated exercise. However, it is an extremely important one and one that you will definitely require assistance with.

People who live and work in your community will know best what the risks are to their community. They will typically view hazards as belonging to one of two very general categories; those which are man made and those which are caused by nature. The size, diversity and location of your community will have a significant impact on the type and degree of risk confronted by the community.

Some examples of man made hazards include large transportation incidents involving land, water or air traffic, dangerous goods as well as large industrial or manufacturing processes. Natural disasters include tornadoes, hurricanes, earthquakes and floods. Some communities are confronted by some obvious risks. These are based on the geographical location of these communities. For example, they may be located near a large shipping harbour, a major airport or a busy highway system. They are obviously facing a higher risk of transportation incidents. Equally obvious are other hazards such as the presence of large industrial and manufacturing processes in close proximity to these communities.

Hazardous commodities can be transported through your community on a regular basis even though they are not produced or even used there. If you do not know what the volumes, frequencies and specific products are, then it is going to be very difficult, if not impossible, to develop an effective emergency plan to deal with an incident involving these products. You do not need to be near major transportation corridors or manufacturing facilities to be at risk from dangerous goods. Recreation and water treatment facilities use chemical products in large enough quantities that could, under certain conditions and circumstances, be very dangerous. Automotive fuel is transported and stored in all communities and many agricultural processes use dangerous goods in large quantities in even the most remote areas. These products are being transported, stored and used in all communities on a daily basis. You obviously need to know what these products are, how they react under certain conditions and what their effects are on people and property in order to better prepare for disasters involving these products.

Because most natural disasters are predictable, determining the risk associated with them is somewhat more manageable. For instance, if your community is not located near an earthquake zone or near a large body of water and historically precipitation amounts have not resulted in any flooding, then it seems reasonable that the risk of earthquakes and flooding would be described as low or nil and would not be a high priority in your emergency plan.

If done correctly, the risk analysis process (see Chapter 4) will identify and prioritize the hazards according to severity and frequency.

Assistance to complete the risk analysis for natural hazards can come from the weather bureau or environmental officials in the area. They should know what natural disasters are most likely to occur in your area. They also have statistics on the frequency of these events and, more often than not, can predict their occurrence . Have these people on board and get their help with this process. As they will be among the first to know when these events are about to happen, retain these experts as part of the emergency warning plan.

Information on man made hazards, and assistance in emergency planning and support in the response to dangerous goods incidents, are likely available throughout many communities. Do not assume anything or take anything for granted. Accurate, reliable information from a knowledgeable source at this stage of the process will contribute significantly to an effective response plan.

The people who use hazardous products or those who manufacture and transport them on a regular basis know what is needed to effectively manage an emergency incident involving them. Officials from harbours, airports, railways and other transportation systems know the travel patterns, frequency and volumes in their (and your) area. They also know the potential hazards associated with these routes. Industry and manufacturing personnel know the risks associated with their respective operations and products.

Include as many of these experts as possible in the planning process. They are the experts and are often willing partners. Where appropriate, they will help not only in determining the risk but also in undertaking appropriate emergency planning and response actions. They are an invaluable resource, so much so that we should question our ability to be successful without them.

We are finally ready to start writing the emergency plan. In it we should include many others in and around the community who can help. We have already included other organizations on the planning committee and have obtained copies of standards and guidelines produced by them. We also have received assistance from other sources to complete the risk analysis exercise.

The development of the emergency plan and the response procedures will really test our ability to be creative and innovative. Our ability to act quickly and effectively could save lives, suffering and property. Here is where we will need all the help we can get.

We now need to identify as many sources of help as possible. To do so, we should break the emergency plan into its main components and view each one separately. Emergency plans contain actions and procedures for all the components of an effective emergency response and are not limited to those of the Fire, Police and Ambulance Services. The groupings of activities may vary from plan to plan. However, they will generally fall into the following main categories: Fire, Police, Emergency Medical, Communications, Transportation, Social Services, Public Health, Public Works, Public Relations, recovery and warning.

Before we look at these individual areas and discuss alternative methods to provide some services, lets look at a more general and very common way of getting help during a major incident. What I am referring to is Mutual Aid Agreements.

Mutual Aid Agreements are generally defined as agreements made between two, often bordering, municipalities whereby each one agrees to assist the other in the event of a major incident.

A key difficulty with mutual aid agreements is that not everyone fully understands the intent of their specific agreement. Sometimes it is not clear how to access resources through mutual aid agreements, or, exactly what resources are available from a mutual aid partner, or under what conditions these resources may or may not be available. However, mutual aid agreements are clearly a valuable part of the emergency plan and remain one of the best sources of help during an emergency.

As stated earlier, in some scenarios we will need help from outside our own community and our mutual aid partners will surely be among the first we would turn to. Mutual aid partners need not only be our municipal neighbours. Any agency or institution within close proximity with resources suitable to assist in any part of the emergency response would make an excellent mutual aid partner. Groups of stakeholders in a region may wish to form a Mutual Aid Association whereby all members agree to assist each other and share resources in the event that any one member is unable to cope with an emergency of its own. Armed Forces bases, large industrial complexes, some educational institutions and other government departments (e.g., Forestry, Environment, Transportation and Utilities) all make excellent mutual aid partners.

When we enter into mutual aid agreements regardless of who the partner or partners are, we absolutely must ensure that:

1. The mutual aid agreements are in writing and authorized by those with the authority to do so (e.g., elected officials or appointed individuals).
2. The terms and conditions of the agreement are crystal clear and understood by both parties.
3. The method of activating the plan is identified and understood by both parties.
4. The agreement remains updated and current at all times.

In this manner, mutual aid agreements can be a tremendous asset to any emergency plan. Outdated and ambiguous agreements can have extremely negative impact on even the best of emergency plans. It serves no purpose, and can be very dangerous, to assume that your mutual aid partners are capable and willing to provide a level of service that for whatever reason, they are not. It can be equally dangerous to have a good understanding of what services can be provided by mutual aid partners but those who are responsible for activating the plan are not informed of how and when to do so. Mutual aid agreements of this type can provide a false sense of security and in fact may do more harm than good.

So yes, there are others out there who can help given the framework of mutual aid agreements and yes, they can provide some of the best help available; but only if enough time and effort is invested to ensure that what you think will happen actually happens. In other words, invest the necessary time to have a solid plan.

Approach your neighbours, and develop good written mutual aid agreements with those that are willing and able to assist during a major emergency. Ensure that every appropriate person and agency understands the contents of the agreement. Make doubly sure that those who may have to activate the agreement are informed of and are comfortable with the method to do so. Do not make the potentially dangerous mistake of signing these agreements, placing them on some shelf and then forgetting about them. Revisit these plans regularly, update them and make sure they remain current and ensure that everyone who needs to be, remains informed.

One last word on mutual aid agreements and associations. When you enter into one you do so as an equal partner. In other words, your mutual aid partners will be relying on you just as you will be relying on them. Do not commit to any terms and conditions that you cannot honour.

FIRE AND AMBULANCE SERVICES

Typically, it is the Fire and Ambulance Services which make use of and benefit the most from mutual aid agreements. It is impractical for most communities to have enough pumpers and ambulances to respond to every worse case scenario. As managers and operators of these services, we naturally depend on each other in these situations. However, mutual aid agreements can and usually do include far more. Mutual aid partners can agree to assist each other in many ways. All types of equipment, materials and services can be obtained this way.

In some disasters, a community may lose access to its emergency operations centre (EOC). The best alternative location may be located in a neighbouring municipality or inside a large locally–based industrial site which has space for this purpose.

When evacuation is necessary, there may not be a safe place in the community to evacuate to. Neighbouring communities can then provide this service and you can do the same for them. Communications systems and equipment, rescue equipment, vehicles, transportation equipment, hospital and other medical services, as well as manpower are only a few examples of the resources available through effective mutual aid agreements.

On a different note, during an all out response to a major disaster, your community may still require the services of your emergency departments to handle other day–to–day emergencies. Under some conditions mutual aid partners may agree to provide some or all of these day–to–day services while your department's resources are focused on the major emergency.

However, as we know, Fire Departments may require assistance in addition to that which is provided by their mutual aid partners. Much of this assistance does not have to come from trained professional fire fighters and their equipment. In fact, in most cases you are better off if it does not. If day–to–day or common tasks are done by others, then the trained and specialized members can be freed to do those things that require their expertise, training and specialized resources.

Sufficient manpower is always going to be difficult to obtain in any major emergency. The longer the incident lasts, the more manpower you are going to need. Physical exhaustion and mental stress will take its toll. In every community, there are folks who can help. Your support may come from the local hockey, baseball or rugby team, or students at the local high school, college or university. Or it may come from the personnel of the local armed forces base or the employees of a local factory or chemical plant. Also available are local chapters of service clubs like the Kinsmen and Rotarians or church members who are organized in active groups. They are out there somewhere and they will help. Your job is to find them, make the necessary arrangements and include them in your plan. These non–professionals can haul hose and other equipment, assist with sand bagging operations, haul air bottles, or assist with evacuation activities, crowd control and many other labour intensive tasks.

Depending on the location of the incident, an adequate water supply for fire fighting may not be close by. Many local contractors, trucking firms, farmers and municipal departments such as Parks and Public Works have tanks and tank trucks that could be used in an emergency for this purpose.

There are also organized search and rescue groups who train regularly in some areas. Groups like the Search and Rescue Dog Association, military SAR TECH and ski patrol groups. These groups would be very valuable because they are organized, trained and knowledgeable about adverse conditions. These groups are an extremely important part of a good emergency plan and are invaluable during disaster response.

Contractors, businesses, and other companies and agencies will have equipment necessary for salvage and recovery operations. Before any major incident make sure you are aware of who they are and how to access them. Also do not forget your friends and neighbours in the surrounding farming, ranching, forestry and mining communities. They have equipment, materials, manpower and expertise that could help.

Fire Departments need all kinds of help during a major emergency. Set it up ahead of time. It doesn't take a professionally trained fire fighter to haul hose, breathing air, drinking water or other materials and supplies to and from the site. Most people can do a lot of the things that need to be done to assist fire fighters in doing what they need to do. Help is out there, arrange for it in advance, and it will be there when you need it.

The same applies to emergency medical services. You will need as many trained professionals as you can possibly muster. But emergency medical services is not just transporting victims to the hospital in ambulances. Even with good mutual aid agreements in place, there are only so many ambulance attendants and ambulances around. At the hospital, there are only so many nurses and doctors. Volunteers can assist these trained professionals and free them to do the things that require specialized training and expertise. Here again, most people can be of assistance. You are going to need stretcher bearers, traffic and crowd control both at the site and at the hospital. Supplies and equipment will have to be transported. Pre–arrange volunteers to do this. Many active organizations would be glad to help out. Church groups, hospital auxiliaries, members of the local Legion, the Red Cross and Salvation Army are only a few of the resources available in nearly all communities.

Support and sponsor CPR and First Aid training in your community. Chances are that in a major disaster you will never have too many qualified first aiders!

During a major emergency, you will have an urgent need for a number of other emergency medical resources. At any given time, there could be hundreds of individuals involved in all the different components of the emergency response. Some of them could become injured, ill or overcome. Their needs too will have to be met.

If evacuation is necessary, evacuees who arrive at their destination will bring their medical problems with them. Expectant mothers, the old and frail, those with illnesses and previous injuries will require treatment. Some will arrive without their prescription drugs and others without medical aids. The emotional stress that comes from having to leave their homes or the loss of their homes and other property will cause medical problems for some. Others whose loved ones are missing, deceased or seriously injured may also require medical assistance and counselling.

Many victims, responders and others will experience critical incident stress. Arranging for counselling services in advance can minimize the pain and suffering in all these cases. You need to ensure that medical professionals, pharmaceutical distributors, community health nurses, the clergy and professional counsellors are included in the plan. The way to access these services should also be identified.

The local hospital or medical centre is a key component of the emergency medical response. Many major emergencies could result in more patients than these facilities would normally deal with at any given time and these resources could become overwhelmed. Again, just as is the case of fire fighters, EMT–As and paramedics at the emergency site, the nurses, doctors and other professionals at the hospital must be free to provide their professional expertise and leave other medical duties to others.

Stretchers bearers, traffic controllers, security personnel and media and public relations people will also be required. These arrangements must also be made in advance. In some communities, there are retired medical personnel, or practicing medical personnel who reside in your community but work elsewhere, who could be called upon to help. Public and media relations people from private companies and other organizations may volunteer to assist during an emergency. These people have training, skills and experiences that would be extremely valuable. The local Toastmasters Club may have some members who could assist.

In some emergencies involving multi–casualties, there just will not be enough ambulances to go around regardless of mutual aid agreements and the best of planning initiatives. Some injuries may require that the injured be transported immediately using any available means. These may mean public transport buses, privately–owned vehicles (i.e., station wagons or mini–vans) or even pick–up trucks.

You need, therefore, to develop an inventory of people and contact numbers for this purpose and keep it current. In major emergencies, this inventory could well save lives.

Just as the Fire and Ambulance services will require assistance during a major disaster, so will the Police Service. They will receive help from neighbouring police services, but even then, depending on the incident, they could still use additional help.

SECURITY AND PROTECTION OF PROPERTY

Security is invariably a major concern during most major emergencies. When people are forced to evacuate, they must usually do so in a hurry leaving many valuables behind. Unfortunately, the risk of vandalism and theft exists even during disasters. This may necessitate extensive security measures and planning effort. In some emergencies, for example, the incident may impact a very large area. In others, the impact could affect businesses and other institutions which, due to criminal or public safety reasons, must be restricted to public access. This can take far more resources than most police departments have. Police departments will still be responsible for law and order not only at the site but elsewhere in the community at the same time. There is help out there for this purpose, but it must be planned for in advance and built into the emergency plan.

Look for people with experience in giving and receiving direction, people with authority. In many cases, people who normally wear a uniform would make good candidates for consideration for security duties. Military and ex–military personnel living in and around the community, park and wildlife officers, employees of private security companies, retired members of police services and correctional officers are all examples of people who would make excellent security personnel for the response period. If these groups of professionals are not available, then by all means recruit others from the various service clubs and organizations in the community. Be creative. Local scout groups, police patrol volunteers, sports teams, the Fish and Game Association, environmental groups, dance companies, craft groups, the flying club, the ski club, the snowmobile club and others all have a group of people with an identity, a reasonable degree of organization and usually a willingness to support the community, especially in a time of need.

If these people are brought in at the early stages of the process and included in ongoing communications and training, they will be a great help. Make sure that they, and others, clearly understand their role and what is expected of them. Make sure it is understood by everyone just how they will go about providing help. Find out their needs and support them so they can do the best possible job for you, and the community, when called upon.

DISASTER SOCIAL SERVICES

As noted earlier in this chapter, when a community experiences a major emergency it is not only the Fire, Police and Ambulance services that will respond. Experience shows that the entire plan will likely be activated and involve many other jurisdictions.

The massive task of caring for the survivors is usually referred to as Disaster Social Services. Disaster Social Services usually provides food, clothing, shelter, inquiry and registration services for all survivors who are in need of these services.

In every disaster, there will be many people who will be able to look after their own needs. Most of them will gain help and shelter with friends and family. However, in all likelihood, there will be many who will require municipal assistance.

You will need a system to track both those to whom you provided aid as well as those who were assisted by family and friends. You will need a system of Registration and Inquiry. Such a system will assist you to respond to inquiries about specific individuals who were or are believed to have been in the area of the disaster. Moreover, it would help reduce duplication of efforts in trying to locate those who were evacuated or relocated.

The importance of the Disaster Social Services program cannot be understated. The well being of the survivors of a disaster is critical to the well being of the community as a whole. If a community is to rebound and provide a quality of life to its residents after a disaster, then it will do so through the survivors of the disaster. Caring for the needs of the survivors, both during as well as following a disaster, is critical to this process.

A brief summary of the roles of the Disaster Social Services Agency follows. It is not intended to go into much detail about these functions. What we will attempt to do is identify who else might be out there who can provide these services.

The Disaster Social Services Agency typically establishes and operates reception centres where evacuees are received and from which all Emergency Social Services are provided. These Centres are the place from which safe, immediate, temporary lodging for homeless people is provided along with clothing supplies and food services until regular sources of supplies become available. Registration and Inquiry (R&I) service is also provided at the Centre and assists in the reunification of families. Personal services such as the temporary care of unattended children and dependent adults, provision of information, financial aid, material assistance and counselling are also provided by Disaster Social Services.

Who in your community could best provide these disaster social services? The Canadian Red Cross Society provides these services in many communities and regions. Many people have been blessed with the caring, commitment and dedication of the people in this organization. They unselfishly respond anywhere in the world and provide these services to people in need. If it were not for them and organizations like them, many communities would have perhaps not recovered from the devastation of their disaster and the personal loss suffered by thousands of their citizens.

The Salvation Army, the Royal Canadian Legion, Church organizations and others have often assisted those in need following major emergencies. They are likely to continue their activities. Therefore, you need to support these local groups and organizations in your region. Help make them a viable component of your community. Include them in your emergency plan and assign them the roles of Disaster Social Services Agency.

Supplement these social agencies with other volunteers who have knowledge, skills and access to the other resources which they will need to provide the above mentioned basic services. The need to organize and maintain accurate registration and inquiry processes may be provided by people who do similar functions routinely. Secretaries and data processors who work at schools and other institutions are good at this. Shippers and receivers are good at matching incoming and outgoing information. Dispatchers, who regularly track large fleets of taxi cabs or transit busses, are good information managers. These people and others could contribute to an effective registration and inquiry system.

LODGING

Where can temporary lodging be found in your community? Hotels and motels are obvious places. However, most communities affected by large disasters would not have enough to accommodate everyone in need. If your community has hotels and motels, contact their managers in advance and arrange for them to accommodate as many people as possible on short notice. School gymnasiums and community halls can provide shelter for large numbers on a temporary or for an extended period of time. However, they must be set up and administered effectively. Residents, whose homes have not been impacted, could provide places to stay for others. Make sure that you also have a communications plan to access these additional resources, if and as necessary. Neighbouring communities could also be approached to provide temporary shelter for evacuees. Once again, any advance communication and planning will contribute greatly to the effectiveness of this effort.

FEEDING

The provision of food services during an emergency is an immense task and may be required to go on long after the immediate incident is over. In most communities and surrounding areas there are many people who can do this. Additionally, many organizations and groups are organized to provide food on a large scale (e.g., social or sport events). Most communities have catering companies who provide food services to large gatherings. Moreover, many institutions such as schools and jails, military facilities, hospitals and businesses have kitchen facilities on location and are capable of producing food in large volumes.

Contact these resources in advance and include them, local restaurants and grocery stores in the emergency plan so that when the need arises you can be assured that adequate food supplies and services would be available.

Remember that the evacuees will not be the only ones needing to be fed. There will be hundreds of volunteers and responders who will also need food and refreshment. At the same time, the disaster may result in the destruction or unavailability of all normal food supplies, water and other utilities necessary to prepare food. The residents of your community may require food, cooking fuel, supplies and assistance to prepare their meals.

Food services is indeed a large and critical part of the Disaster Social Services. And if providing the food is not a big enough challenge, then providing a safe and healthy food supply certainly is. The lack of safe and sufficient water supply, and the unavailability of utilities necessary for proper preparation and temperature control, truly complicates the task of providing a safe food supply. Many people suffer dietary disorders and food allergies and will require specialized assistance. Plans for this eventuality should be made in advance. You should ensure that dietitians, health officials and other experts are involved.

CLOTHING

The provision of sufficient clothing during an emergency is another huge task. Most man–made and some natural disasters provide very little warning and are often unpredictable. As a result, when a community is impacted the people are not prepared for evacuation. When an evacuation is called for, residents are often forced to flea with little of their belongings (e.g., clothes, extra food, living aids). Moreover, in some cases personal possessions such as clothing could be lost or destroyed by the disaster event. When that happens, survivors will likely arrive at the reception centre and other lodging facilities with only the clothes on their back.

The time of day and the current weather conditions will obviously have a large impact on the clothing requirements of survivors. Just the same, you should attempt to pre-arrange access to all types of clothing supplies prior to a disaster. Make sure people are assigned the responsibility of providing clothing in the event of an emergency. A drop–off centre for the gathering and distribution of donated clothing will be needed and extra space for it will have to be pre–arranged.

Your community may already have organizations which are providing clothing for the less fortunate and needy. Contact these organizations and include them in your plan. They have an existing network, procedures and trained volunteers for that task. They may also have access to supplies from all sources in the region.

Retail outlets and any wholesale suppliers can be contacted beforehand. Arrangements should be made to access their supplies in the event of an emergency. Again, the Salvation Army, Red Cross and other organizations do a wonderful job of this but your assistance will make their job easier and more effective.

SPECIALIZED SERVICES

The personal services supplied by the Disaster Social Services Agency during a major emergency can vary as much as the people who require them. All the special needs that people have before an emergency, plus other needs resulting from the emergency, will have to be addressed.

The age of your 'clients' will vary from the very young to the very old. You will have to provide services to people from all ages; people with hearing and vision impairment; those who can not walk; or, those who are not fluent in English (or French). There will be people with allergies. There will be those who have physical or mental disabilities. Some may be emotionally disturbed. Some may be sick.

The response will vary from person to person. Some people will require isolation, medication and counselling. Some will need living aids such as wheelchairs, walkers, crutches and cribs.

Who in your community can provide these items and services? Think about the daycare facilities, seniors' lodges, medical clinics and retail suppliers. These facilities and their staff members provide these services on a regular basis and would be an invaluable asset in an emergency.

COUNSELLING

The trauma and stress created by a disaster will cause emotional difficulty for survivors, victims, relatives and responders. Specialized care in the form of psychological counselling will be needed to deal effectively with these problems. At this time, I can only caution that this service must be provided by those who are fully trained and qualified/certified to do so. Some Social Workers, members of the Clergy, individuals trained in Critical Incident Stress Debriefing and mental health professionals in and around the area should, therefore, be included in your emergency plan.

It's important to remember that, in most cases, Disaster Social Services needs will extend well beyond the immediate emergency response time. It could be days, months or even years before the community is well again. Therefore, when planning for the provision of these services and when identifying people who will provide them, plan for a long sustainable program not a short fix.

TRANSPORTATION

Another main category where you will need help is in the area of transportation. Sometimes, when we think of transportation in an emergency we only think of our needs during evacuations. While evacuations certainly require a large amount of transportation resources, they are not the only activity for which you will require additional transportation resources.

Let's examine evacuation situations first. Your transportation needs will naturally vary greatly from one scenario to another. As in the case of Disaster Social Services activities, you could be providing transportation services for a huge diversity of people. If all evacuees are able to walk onto and sit upright unassisted in conventional vehicles, then the transportation requirements are not too challenging. Local transit systems, taxi cabs, private vehicles and school buses meet these needs quite easily.

Prior arrangements will make access to these resources quite accessible. Through prearranged mutual aid agreements and communication plans, enough of these resources can generally be made available in a timely manner. But what about all those other people who can not walk onto a bus and sit upright without assistance? Do you know where your resources are to transport them in a safe and efficient manner?

Here are just a few examples of very special transportation challenges. What about daycare centres full of infants and the very young? What of seniors' centres and nursing homes occupied by the very old and immobile? What if you had to evacuate the local hospital? What if an entire jail population had to be evacuated? In most cases, you will not have specialized transportation vehicles to meet your transportation needs.

Nursing homes, hospitals and children's nurseries are quite often evacuated by simply manually rolling the people in their beds or cribs down the street to a safe location. This will require a lot of manpower, blankets and clothing for protection from the elements. There really is no other way to safely evacuate these facilities in a timely manner. You should be talking to the managers of these facilities before an incident, arrange the necessary manpower and as much as possible predetermine evacuation locations so as to minimize the trauma and stress associated with the disruption of an evacuation.

If there are special transportation vans with hydraulic lifts in or around your community arrange for access to them in an emergency. Most of these accommodate wheelchairs, walkers, canes and crutches used by the less mobile residents. If there are not enough of these vehicles, then simple manpower may have to be used to carry people to a safe place or alternate transportation vehicles.

In any event, plan for it to happen quickly. In most cases there isn't much time to plan for evacuation once an emergency happens. Arrange for help from any transportation resources that are organized and especially those with a communication system. Taxi companies, courier services, transit companies, trucking firms and many supply companies all have vehicles equipped with radio communications. Many are suitable to transport a large number of people with varying needs during an emergency. Private citizens can also be organized to provide their vehicles for this purpose.

There will be other transportation needs during an emergency. For example, materials and equipment will have to be transported to the site or to other points in the community. These items could be delivered by others IF arrangements are made in advance.

Everything from half tons to large tractor trailer units will likely be needed. Trucking companies, rental companies, businesses and private individuals will need to be identified and included on your resource lists. Car dealers, especially those with used vehicles, could also be a valuable source. The military, forestry services, provincial and federal parks services and transportation and utilities services, all have access to suitable vehicles for this purpose. Specialized vehicles for the transportation of food such as refrigeration trucks may be also required. All terrain vehicles, four wheel drive units, snow machines and water tankers may be required.

Many communities have organized groups which participate in activities focused around the use of these vehicles (e.g., all terrain vehicle or skidoo clubs). Include them in the Emergency Plan. Helicopters, light aircraft or even large aircraft may be involved in some disaster responses. Make arrangements for them in advance. Emergency responders and all volunteers will need to be transported between work sites and rest sites. Pre–arrange for a comfortable means of transportation for them.

Prepared food will need to be delivered to various sites. Arrange for hot food to arrive hot and cool food to arrive cool. All of the transportation resources that can be mustered will be used in some fashion. Do not leave out any possibilities. What seems like an unusual source now (i.e., a bunch of dirt bikes) may, in some cases, be your only means of getting around.

UTILITIES

Emergency Public Works, in some emergency plans, is the organization identified with the responsibility to provide utility services including electrical power, natural gas, water and sanitation. Typically, this organization also supplies equipment and materials as well as the manpower to do the job. They often provide such things as barricades, flashers, pumps, sand bags, signs, heavy duty equipment and much more.

In most communities, the most obvious resource to supply this type of service are the municipal public works and engineering departments. However, most municipalities will not have enough resources in these departments and some may not have any at all. So, you will need help with this as well. But, where will help come from this time?

First of all, contact the electrical and natural gas utility supply companies in your community. They must be included in the Emergency Plan for the shut off and restoration of these services, as required. Pre–plan and arrange with them to ensure that their 24–hour emergency numbers are identified in your plan. This will facilitate a quick response when their services are needed.

Much of the materials and equipment required to provide public works functions during an emergency are the same as those required to deliver routine public works functions when there is no emergency. So they should not be too hard to find. The difficulty in a disaster might be in getting large enough quantities of these resources. Mutual aid agreements can be very helpful in this regard as unaffected neighbouring municipalities will have some of these resources.

Local contractors will definitely have some of the needed resources, and may even have some specialty items not found in the local municipal public works yards. Rental companies are another good resource. Farming operations, logging companies, mining companies and any other large operation or company doing work in the area should be contacted and included in the plan. Once again, provincial and federal departments (e.g., Transportation and Utilities), or national or provincial parks operations will also have equipment and materials that may be utilized in an emergency. Engineering or technical expertise regarding buildings, roadways and other infrastructure can be provided by private businesses, government agencies, consultants or companies which specialize in that field.

COMMUNICATIONS

Communications are almost always a problem regardless of the disaster. Telephone lines can become jammed. Physical damage can occur to communication lines and equipment. Equipment and channel incompatibility can exist between response agencies. All these can lead to significant communication difficulties resulting in a major breakdown of the communications process.

Even though the technology exists, it is impractical to simply buy enough alternate communications equipment and systems to cover all these possibilities. However, it is possible to minimize some communication difficulties in a cost–effective way. The need to do this will vary depending on the ability and flexibility of existing communications systems.

Let's look at ways to supplement our current communication capabilities. (The whole complex issue of alternate technical systems and resources, which are available on the market, is left for other publications.) Let us also assume that the equipment of choice is already in place and that we must now identify some sources of help which may be available during an emergency.

The first source that comes to mind is the amateur radio club, if it operates in the area. In some communities where an amateur radio club exists, it is housed in the Emergency Operations Centre (EOC) and is a permanent member of the Emergency Plan's Communications Group. This is an extremely effective arrangement. It is a win–win arrangement. You get the communications back–up and the expertise that you need; the club gets the space and support it needs to function.

Many members of amateur radio clubs have portable hand–held radios and can be dispatched as messengers to virtually anywhere. They are also able to communicate with other ham radio operators from across the world, who will likely have compatible equipment.

Ham radio operators who are dispatched outside the EOC will be able to communicate with the operations centre and, therefore, provide a valuable link to the field! Support these groups in any way you can and contribute to their ability to function in your community. They are an excellent source of help for many communications problems.

Most communities can rely on a variety of other sources to assist them with emergency communications. Almost anyone with communications equipment could help. Of course, it will not all be compatible and everyone will not be able to talk to everyone else. However, with a little imagination some of these problems can be minimized. Taxi cabs, utility companies, contractors and other businesses have vehicles and people who carry radios, cellular phones and other forms of communication on a regular basis. By strategically locating these people and their resources during an emergency, some communications difficulties can be made less difficult.

There are no perfect solutions to potential communications problems and you may never eliminate them altogether. However, steps can be taken to minimize them. Talk to your communications supply companies. Maybe, the local phone company can do something with land lines in an emergency that will help. Some telephone systems can provide a line load control program whereby pre–designated phone lines are protected in a planned shut down of the rest of the phone system. In some circumstances, this can protect dedicated lines from an unplanned crash of the system.

Local radio supply companies may be able to supplement your current communication capabilities during an emergency. Some recreation vehicle clubs and off road vehicle clubs have communication systems that could assist. Private citizen–band radios still exist and could be used. The military and other agencies in the area should be contacted. The emergency plan should then reflect all viable options and how to access them.

Another part of effective communications during an emergency is its public information component. It is a vital part of the overall emergency plan. It is also critical to the success of any emergency response effort. Those who require public information must receive it in an accurate and timely manner from a reliable source. Inaccurate and untimely information in any emergency can cause chaos and significantly impact the effectiveness and efficiency of the emergency response.

MEDIA

The reality is that the media will be present during disasters and your response effort to these events. You will have to work with them to get your message out accurately and at the right time.

You will definitely need help in providing quality public information during an emergency and for some time following the emergency. The media is your best source of help in the process. When the process is managed effectively, the media can provide instant and accurate information to the general population. You need to establish good working relationships with the media prior to a disaster to facilitate this process during a disaster. You also need to develop protocols and procedures that will assist you in providing good public information and that will also accommodate members of the media in doing their job.

In situations when enough time is available to provide warnings to the public, these warnings can be broadcasted over the electronic media outlets. In most areas, where multiple media outlets exist, arrangements must be made with them all. Otherwise, the public will have to be advised of the station(s) chosen to carry the warning message.

Instructions and update information during an emergency can also be delivered through the various media outlets. This service will also be valuable long after the emergency is over, when those impacted by the incident will need to be guided through the recovery process. The media can assist with this task which may also include providing notice for public meetings. Elected and other officials will need to be included in the communications plan. They should be included early on so that they are informed and prepared.

All components of the communications program will have to be recorded and filed for reference. Media personnel will require access to phones, faxes and photocopiers. Their information management system is a complex one. They will need your organizational skills. The availability of secretaries and other staff who manage information systems on a regular basis, can be a great help.

You should assign media liaison staff who have some comfort and experience in dealing with the media. Most communities have people who do this on a regular basis. If not, then find someone with effective communications skills, preferably someone with a reasonable degree of comfort around the media. Get assistance from the local media representatives. They will identify their needs and can guide you with your plans to deal with other media.

CONCLUSION

At the beginning of this chapter we asked the question "Is There Anyone (Else) There?" To answer this question completely is almost impossible. To a large degree, the answer depends on where you are and what is going on or available in your area. You may be in a large or small community, a rural or urban community, a remote isolated community or one in close proximity to a lot of resources. Regardless, every community has a wide range of resources within its boundary, and every community has access to extensive resources from outside its geographical area.

It is the Emergency Planner's job to include all available resources in the emergency plan and the emergency planning process. We, emergency planners, must be innovative and creative and do the best we possibly can with whatever we have. We cannot afford to leave out any possibility because someone's life may depend on it!

Emergency response and preparedness is truly a community project. Everyone can be impacted and almost everyone can contribute.

Ultimately, it must be well organized, pre–planned and clearly communicated. Expectations, roles, responsibilities and procedures must be clearly defined and understood. There simply can not be any surprises.

Once everything has been agreed upon and included in the plan, then it is practice, practice, practice. Don't expect or assume that things will go the way they should if the plan is completed, put on the shelf and never revisited. Through regular contact, communication, training and practice, the plan can be changed, and altered. It can then evolve into an effective tool which will enable the community to defend itself to the best of its ability against all threats.

There IS someone ELSE out there. In most cases you only need to ask and THEY WILL HELP!

Picture 5.1

The Red Cross Emergency Response Team at a scene.
(Photo Courtesy of Terry Chicoine, Canadian Red Cross Society, western Division.)

Picture 5.2

Mutual aid from a local airport Fire Department.
(Photo Courtesy of Gerry Emas, Edmonton Emergency Response Department.)

The Dangerous Goods Response Team

Deputy Chief B.E. Williams, Ph.D.
Battalion Chief G.A. Spratt
Edmonton's Emergency Response Department *

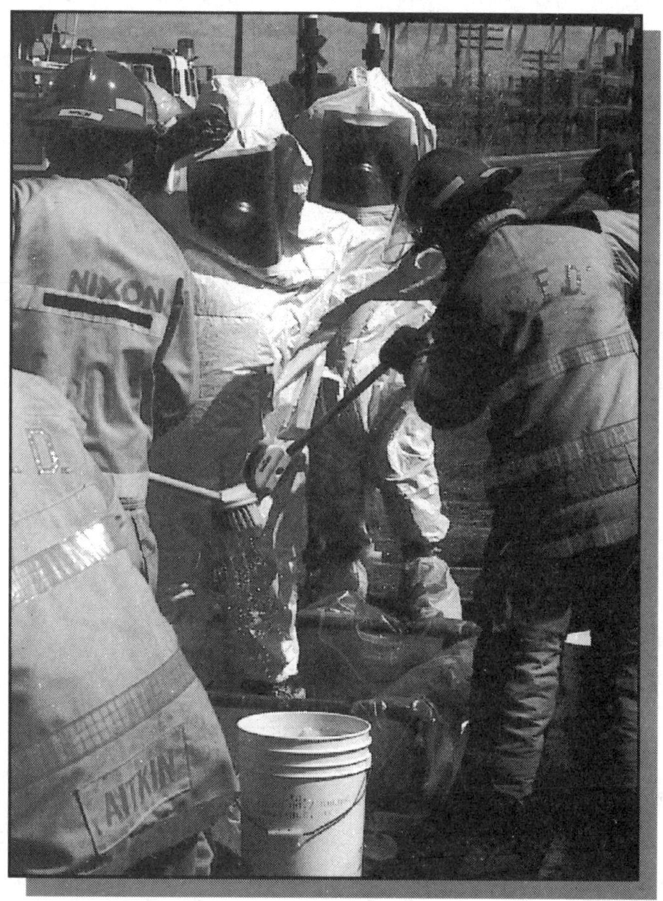

Photo Courtesy of Deb Erkes,
Edmonton Emergency Response Department.

This chapter discusses several issues surrounding the effective management of Dangerous Goods Incidents and answers the following questions relating to a Dangerous Goods Response Team (DGRT):

1) *Why is a DGRT needed?*
2) *What should a DGRT be able to do?*
3) *How is a DGRT established, maintained and trained?*
4) *What resources should a DGRT have?*
5) *How does one manage DGRT operations?*

* *The authors would like to thank Dr. Uwe Terner for his comments and suggestions. Specializing in chemistry, pharmacology and toxicology, Dr. Terner developed the Second Responder program now utilized by the Cities of Edmonton and Calgary, and adopted for use by the U.S. Coast Guard and the U.S. Marine Corp. He provides expert consultation on establishing a DGRT, product handling and risk analysis during DG incidents.*

The number of emergency incidents involving Hazardous Materials or Dangerous Goods has been steadily rising over the past ten years. Rapidly changing technology, increased awareness and concern for environmental contamination, as well as growing concerns regarding litigation are factors which have led many municipalities to consider establishing or contacting a Dangerous Goods Response Team. In this chapter we will discuss several issues surrounding the effective management of Dangerous Goods Incidents and answer the following questions relating to Dangerous Goods Response Teams (DGRTs):

1. Why is a DGRT needed?

2. What should a DGRT be able to do?

3. How is a DGRT established maintained and trained?

4. What resources should a DGRT have?

5. How does one manage DGRT operations?

WHY IS A DGRT NEEDED?

The number of emergency incidents involving dangerous goods has been steadily rising over the past ten years. In the City of Edmonton, for example, the DGRT responded to 50 emergency calls in 1985 and more than 1,000 in 1995. Three major factors have contributed to this dramatic rise in call volume: changing technology, environmental concerns, and litigation concerns.

The factor of 'changing technology' encompasses a broad spectrum of issues relating to increasing demands for dangerous goods response. The most obvious effect of changing technology is the increased usage and dependence upon human-made chemical products. The widespread use of vinyl, synthetics, and other chemical based products means that an increasing volume of substances that may be classified as Dangerous Goods are found in businesses, industries, and households. The proliferation of chemical products increases the number of locations where chemicals may be found, and also increases the incidents where these products are transported and stored.

One of the major reasons for changes to our available technology is the continued focus on research and development activity by many contemporary firms. Research and development leads to the creation of new and more effective products such as resilient furniture, highly durable urethane finishes, blended gasoline, and life saving pharmaceuticals. As new products are researched and developed there is an ever increasing need for emergency managers and emergency responders to become familiar with the properties of such products and behaviours which are likely to occur in the event of an uncontrolled release.

The development of highly durable urethanes and lacquers, household herbicides and pesticides, fertilizers, and household cleaning products means that every home, garage, and storage shed has the potential to be a storage facility for dangerous goods. Many home owners unknowingly store volatile combinations of chemicals together on the same shelf. For example, a household cupboard may contain ammonia based products and chlorine products side by side. These chemicals, when combined produce ammonium chloride, a dangerous and harmful gas. Similarly, a storage shed may contain Class 3 combustibles such as gasoline, Class 8 corrosives such as battery acid, and Class 6 poisons such as Killex, all on the same shelf.

Research and development also leads to new and different business practices which can have an effect on the likelihood of spills or uncontrolled releases. For example, research in the petroleum retail industry led to the creation of the self-serve gas station where the handling of fuel is literally in the hands of untrained customers. Statistics indicate that there is a much greater incidence of accidental fuel spills at self serve gas stations than at traditional 'full-service' stations.

Another concern arising from changing technology is amateur scientists attempting to produce or re-produce new products. This can lead to illegal or clandestine laboratories where commonly acceptable health and safety standards are ignored. During the past year in the City of Edmonton, the DGRT has responded to calls at an illegal laboratory as well as an illegal electronic component manufacturing lab. In each case the illegal activities were discovered when emergency crews were called to respond to fires which had resulted from unsafe activities.

Environmental Concerns

The second major reason for the dramatic increase in the number of reported Dangerous Goods incidents is the growing awareness of and concern for the environment. In days gone by it was common practice to flush minor spills of gasoline, oil, diesel fuel, and antifreeze (ethylene glycol) down the drain. Federal legislation such as the Environmental Protection Act, various provincial Acts, and municipal legislation such as sewer use bylaws now prevent such practices and dictate that dangerous goods spills, no matter how large or small, be cleaned up and disposed of properly.

Greater awareness and concern for the environment among the general public also means that suspicious substances and occurrences are more likely to be reported than in previous years. For example, ten years ago a bag of lime falling off the back of a masonry contractor's truck, or a pail of chlorine (sodium hypochlorite) falling off a pool servicing truck would likely not be reported. They would spread over the road by passing traffic and eventually be washed down the sewer by the rain. Today, accidents of this type are likely to be reported immediately and treated as serious dangerous goods incidents.

Concern for Litigation

The third major reason for the dramatic increase in reported Dangerous Goods incidents is the growing concern for litigation. Many corporations today are highly conscious of the potential for civil litigation and train their employees in the basics of due diligence. Many adopt the philosophy of 'when in doubt play it safe and cover your bases.' This often means calling in specialists who can provide an expert opinion as to the potential hazards associated with a particular product or situation. Reports of unknown substances and strange odours are ever increasing and are often initiated by persons who are 'playing it safe.' From an emergency manager's perspective, this type of behaviour is highly desirable as often these types of investigative calls result in the prevention of the occurrence of truly disastrous incidents. But this also means that emergency managers and fire officers must be willing and able to train and equip the personnel necessary to respond to such calls.

In terms of emergency response operations there are also issues which relate to legal liability as it pertains to due diligence in the care and control of an incident. It is a generally accepted legal principle that once an emergency response agency appears at a Dangerous Goods incident and takes steps to mitigate the incident, that agency is expected to take every reasonable measure necessary to ensure that the incident is properly handled and that environmental legislation is complied with. Emergency response agencies that do not have properly trained and equipped personnel run the risk of being deemed by the courts as not being reasonably prepared and/or failing to act in a duly diligent manner.

WHAT SHOULD A DGRT BE ABLE TO DO?

Dangerous Goods can be defined as any material or substance that presents an unusual hazard to life, the environment or property when burned, spilled, or otherwise released from its normal use, handling, storage, or transportation environment. In addition, any material or substance that must be classified under the Federal or Provincial Dangerous Goods Act is included in this definition. Typically, dangerous goods incidents cannot be managed or mitigated by use of conventional or traditional Fire Department protective clothing, extinguishing agents, tactics, tools, or appliances. In such cases a DGRT is necessary to provide support and assistance in the following areas:

1. Product Identification.
2. Research.
3. Leak and Spill Control.
4. Extinguishment.
5. Monitoring (gas, radiation, etc.).
6. Sampling (for product ID, evidence, investigation).
7. Hazard Control.
8. Neutralization of Manageable Quantities.
9. Site Safety.

A dangerous goods incident can be defined as an unplanned or uncontrolled release of a hazardous substance from its means of containment in such quantities that there is a real or perceived threat to life, property, or the environment. These incidents often occur during different modes of transport such as road, rail, air or marine. While many dangerous goods incidents occur as a result of accidents or equipment failure during transport, transportation is just one area where dangerous goods incidents can occur. They can also occur in storage facilities, manufacturing plants, processing operations, retail establishments, and recreation facilities. Medical facilities such as hospitals and clinics can also be involved in dangerous goods incidents as can construction sites, schools, shopping malls and private homes.

Dangerous goods incidents can range from a major spill resulting from a damaged or overturned rail or road tanker carrying flammable liquids, to a minor spill of formaldehyde in a neighbourhood pharmacy or high school chemistry lab. A particular product may be spilled or released in a number of different locations and circumstances, requiring a range of different mitigation strategies for the same product. For example, in Edmonton over the past several months there has been a rash of mercury spills at various locations including a hospital, a medical clinic, a drugstore, a construction site and a number of private homes. The containment and mitigation techniques utilized for a large spill on a smooth tile floor in the hospital were far different from the techniques used to remove the mercury from between the floor boards and joist space in a building which was being renovated.

In many types of dangerous goods incidents it is advisable to collaborate with other agencies and response teams. This is particularly the case for incidents involving explosives. When dealing with explosives of any type, very specialized training and equipment is required. Larger municipal police departments typically have a bomb disposal team, as do most provincial police forces and the RCMP These police teams typically have specialized equipment and facilities where they can transport and dispose of dangerous explosives.

Given the large number of different product types and possible locations for dangerous goods incidents to occur, there is no one right answer or magic formula for developing a DGRT. The training and equipment required depends very much on local conditions. There are, however, some basic guidelines and principles that should be followed. First, the requirements for a DGRT should be defined by a comprehensive hazard assessment and risk analysis process. This process should include an assessment of the fixed sites within the jurisdiction which manufacture, store, or otherwise possess dangerous goods. The analysis should also include an assessment of the volumes and types of dangerous goods which travel through the jurisdiction by road and rail. The process should also include an assessment of 'worst case scenarios.' This should be based on past experience in the municipality and in other municipalities with similar target hazards, and should also take into account unique combinations of hazards.

The 'Worst Case' Scenario

As an example, when the level of risk in the City of Edmonton was assessed, a worst case scenario was developed. It was based on an analysis of the historical pattern of incidents and consideration of their implications and possibilities. It highlighted the fact that over a five year period from 1977 to 1981, there were five aircraft crashes in and around downtown Edmonton. The crescendo to this string of events was in 1981 when a ten passenger aircraft which was attempting to land at the Edmonton Municipal Airport slammed into the roof of the Royal Alexandra Hospital. The fuselage of the plane was embedded in the penthouse of the building, and the fuel ran down the stairwell and spread throughout the hospital. While the incident itself was rather severe, it was mitigated extremely well with minimal property damage and human injuries. There were major disruptions caused by the incident. More than 100 patients were discharged or relocated. The emergency ward and operating rooms were closed down for several days. Overall, however, it was generally agreed that the incident was not nearly as severe at it could have been.

In the analysis that inevitably follows incidents of this nature many questions were asked: What if the plane would have been a large passenger jet rather that a twin engine MU-2? What if the accident would have occurred during business hours when the hospital would have had more people in it? What would have happened if a spark ignited the aviation fuel? What if the plane would have crashed into the shopping centre only blocks away rather than the hospital?

Based on this real incident, it is possible to imagine many other potential incidents. This is an important exercise to undertake in order to brainstorm all of the potential disasters that could occur in your jurisdiction. The next step is to then attach a probability to each potential event. In the case cited above, for example, one may want to consider the flight paths in and out of the airport, the frequency of flights, the type of aircrafts, and the safety records of the aircraft types and of the airline companies involved.

In addition to analyzing the potential risks and the probabilities of major incidents it is also necessary to examine the potential for smaller, more routine incidents such as small spills at gas stations, fires at dry cleaning stores, and other more mundane incidents involving dangerous goods. Historical call volumes are instructive in this regard, and provide an excellent starting point. In new areas, where historical data is not available, it is possible to examine provincial data and estimate potential calls based on the statistics of incidents per population basis. Having assessed the different types of potential incidents, and having assigned probabilities to those different types, the next step is to conduct a capability analysis.

Capability Analysis

Through a capability analysis a number of different factors should be considered. It is important to realistically analyze the number of emergency response staff available to respond; the anticipated response time; the level of training of responders; and the capacities and capabilities of the apparatus and equipment. Through this analysis it is then possible to compare the incident types and probability of their occurrence to the capability to respond to them. If this analysis shows that the response agency has the resources and capabilities to handle the most likely scenarios, then the next step is to plan.

The U.S. National Fire Academy teaches a three step approach to planning for Fire Department operations at dangerous goods and other emergency incidents:

1. Sevelop a plan.
2. Conduct training exercises in accordance with the plan.
3. When the incident occurs, follow the plan.

This is not to suggest that every plan must be infallible and written in stone. It must be recognized that plans must be flexible and subject to change. One of the best ways to test a plan and to update and revise it is through an actual exercise. The most important step, however, and likely the step which is least followed, is to follow the plan when an incident occurs. The whole purpose in anticipating, planning, and preparing for certain incidents is to provide emergency managers with a strategic advantage when attempting to mitigate incidents.

The reason for pre-planning generic positions such as staging areas, collection points, exposures, and other key strategic locations, is to free up fire officers and emergency managers to concentrate on the unique characteristics of the incident. Yet often at times in the heat of the moment, the emergency plan is ignored and emergency responders in essence reinvent the wheel by committing managerial attention to establishing locations for these functions which have already been pre-established. The most important reasons for planning and conducting exercises according to the plan is to aid responders when the real incident does occur.

Gap Analysis

The three step planning process described above applies to situations where the capabilities of the response agency are suitable for the probable incident types and magnitudes identified. If, on the other hand, the capability analysis reveals the response agency does not have the resources and capabilities to handle the most likely scenarios, then the next step is to conduct a gap analysis and assess what resources, training and equipment are required to bridge the gap between the resources and expertise which are currently available and those required to address the potential hazards in the response area.

There are a number of ways to address gaps. The first, and most obvious, is to survey the immediate region and ascertain what personnel, equipment, and expertise may be available from other agencies. For example, if a rail line passing through the municipality is identified as a major hazard, and the response agency does not have the expertise or resources to handle a major rail incident, the first agency to contact should be the railway company. What plans and provisions do they have in place? How long would it take for them to assemble and dispatch a response team? What are the capabilities of their response team?

Other resources that may be considered include but are not limited to: other municipal response teams; transportation industry teams; chemical producer industry teams; company specific teams; industrial associations (e.g., MIACC); branches of provincial and federal government departments; and other municipal departments (e.g., Public Health and Safety).

An analysis of the possible resources available should be pursued for each potential target hazard. Once this process has been completed, a manager should have a reasonable and comprehensive impression of the size of the gap that exists between the potential hazards and the capabilities of responders. This analysis may demonstrate a need for a DGRT, or for an enhanced level of training for an existing DGRT. The bottom line is that the resources, training, and expertise of the response agency should be capable of adequately addressing the scenarios identified through the hazard assessment and probability analyses processes. Alternatively, contingency plans should be in place, through mutual aid contacts, fee for service contracts, or automatic aid agreements, in order to acquire the resources and expertise necessary to effectively mitigate potential incidents in the response area.

Containment versus Clean-up and Disposal

In assessing the specific needs of a particular jurisdiction, there is also a need to consider the range of service that a DGRT or other response agency should provide. In the mitigation and recovery phases of DG incidents there are different approaches that may be utilized. For example, in the City of Edmonton a policy decision was made to have the DGRT trained to perform rescue and containment activities, but not clean-up or disposal. This decision was based on the fact that many industry teams and private contractors are available to conduct the clean-up and disposal functions, and it was deemed that municipal resources were best directed at rescue and containment activities. In other jurisdictions where industry resources and private clean-up contractors are not available, there may be a need to establish internal capabilities for the conduct of clean-up and disposal functions. In assessing the needs of the community and the availability of necessary resources, a policy decision should be made as to whether a DGRT will be established, and if so, the specific functions for which its members will be trained to perform.

HOW IS A DGRT ESTABLISHED, MAINTAINED AND TRAINED?

As previously mentioned, individual community needs must be assessed to determine the resources and level of service required. The level of service and the corresponding decision to provide that service will result in several distinct deployment strategies. Logically, resource allocation for equipment, training, start-up costs and funding requirement projections for budget impact require careful consideration. Several alternate issues also bear scrutiny: data collection of past incidents involving regulated products within the jurisdiction, expertise available from local industry and funding sources other than the tax base.

A full scale cost/benefit analysis should be undertaken to ensure the greatest potential gain from expenditures of time and money. The results should help identify the desired level of service to meet local requirements based on quantifiable data and eliminate speculation wherever possible. An initial decision to determine the level of training required for 'First Responder' capability versus 'Second Responder' would have direct impact on equipment requirements. The NFPA Hazardous Materials Response Handbook and its 471, 472 and 473 standards define the training criteria for responders. These standards detail the levels of training required by personnel responding to incidents that involve 'regulated' products. The main difference between the standards involves 'defensive' and 'offensive' intervention by Fire Department, Industry or EMS personnel.

First Responders

First responders play a defensive role at dangerous goods incidents and as such the standard for their training reflects that role. The major responsibilities of first responders include identification of the hazard and site security. Naturally, the standards set by NFPA for first responders focuses on the issues of identification, site safety, control and the consideration of resources available for assistance in aggressive intervention. Direct intervention is not envisioned due to lack of technical training requirements or specialized equipment. Many smaller departments or volunteer organizations lack the funding justification of a fully trained and equipped DGRT. Moreover, a low frequency of incidents or low likelihood of major dangerous goods incidents is likely to minimize or even preclude the financial commitment required to establish and maintain a second responder team.

NFPA 1500 "requires all personnel who may respond to a hazardous materials incident to at least meet the requirements of first responder awareness/operations level." The set of training objectives for the awareness level require the first responder to:

1. Analyze a dangerous goods incident and forecast potential outcomes.
2. Devise an action plan with due consideration of resources both technical expertise and equipment.
3. Utilizing the local emergency response plan, department policies, standard operating procedures and available resources, mitigate the incident to the optimum conclusion.
4. Systematically assess action plans and revise them to ensure that efficiency, effectiveness and safety objectives are being maximized.

Administrators should access the complete texts of NFPA 472 to reference training requirements for personnel and assess equipment requirements.

First responder 'Operations' standards detailed in NFPA 472 identify additional training for personnel from a defensive posture. The definition provided by NFPA states "First responders at the operations level are individuals who respond to releases or potential releases of hazardous substances as part of the initial response to the site for the purpose of protecting nearby persons, property or the environment from the effects of the release."

Additionally, 29 CFR 1910.120 (OSHA) and 40 CFR (EPA) are similar to the NFPA 472 standard which requires fire personnel to meet this requirement for the response to dangerous goods incidents. This level of competency requires training beyond the awareness level. However, the overall strategy remains defensive. Training and competency are required in the following areas:

(a) knowledge of the basic hazard and risk assessment techniques;
(b) know how to properly select and use proper personal protective equipment provided to the first responder operations level;
(c) an understanding of basic hazardous materials terms;
(d) know how to perform basic control, confinement and/or confinement operations within the capabilities of the resources and personal protective equipment available with their unit;
(e) know how to implement basic decontamination procedures;
(f) an understanding of the relevant standard operating procedures and termination procedures.

Obviously, each department must determine how to implement these standards to maximize the efficiency and effectiveness of their service to the community. A municipality which ignores the probability that its fire fighters may face situations involving dangerous goods and fails to provide them with the necessary skills to be effective, courts disaster!

Second Responders

A specialized and full-time DGRT which provides a service to a larger urban centre or region requires training and competency certification to NFPA 472, Second Responder Technician. This level of certification corresponds to a major shift in the response strategy: from defensive to offensive. Significant, systematic and critical cost/benefit analysis should be undertaken by any organization contemplating this level of service to its customers. Direct expenditures for equipment, training, skills maintenance, consumption and service delivery require careful consideration. Not all jurisdictions require this service. Only those that have significant quantities of regulated products on transportation routes or in fixed facilities should consider this level of training.

Many industrial teams exist to assist local Fire Departments to meet their DGRT needs. However, these teams generally respond in concert with industrial associations to mitigate incidents involving their own products. Activation and deployment of this resource may not meet the needs of the community but this option should be explored initially in the assessment stage.

A hazardous materials technician is a 'second responder' who has met the training criteria for both 'first responder' and additionally the training competencies/medical surveillance program detailed in NFPA 472. The training objective for this level of responder "...shall be to provide responders with the following competencies to respond safely to hazardous materials incidents:

(a) the ability to implement a safety plan;
(b) the ability to classify, identify and verify known and unknown materials by using basic monitoring equipment;
(c) the ability to function within an assigned role in the incident command system;
(d) the ability to select and use at least Level B protection in addition to any other specialized personal protective equipment provided to the hazardous materials technician by the authority having jurisdiction;
(e) the ability to make hazard and risk assessments;
(f) the ability to perform advanced hazardous materials control operations within the capabilities of the resources and personal protective equipment available;
(g) the ability to select and implement appropriate decontamination procedures
(h) the ability to complete record keeping procedures; and
(i) the ability to understand basic chemical, biological and radiological terms and their behaviour."

Note that the criteria for the NFPA 472 specialist are generally for site specific products, containers or systems. On the other hand, members of most DGRT are 'generalists.'

Individual training programs will meet these objectives but the degree of competency will vary depending on the course curriculum. For example, the Edmonton Emergency Response Department course for DG technician (specialist) level entails three months of training. The course is comprised of two months of theory and one month of practical training. Some certifications that meet minimum criteria, are obtainable within one week. You are advised to exercise caution when evaluating individual course curricula to ensure personnel are adequately skilled to function effectively and recognize their limitations in the areas of equipment or expertise. Emphasis must remain on the need to assess the individual service level required for each jurisdiction and on designing the appropriate training standard to meet the identified need(s).

Skills and Equipment Maintenance

Once personnel have received training commensurate with the desired service level, skills maintenance becomes an issue. Acquired knowledge, whether theory or practical, will decrease over time unless a systematic review process is in place. Opportunities for review may be enhanced through staged simulations, preferably with local industrial DG response teams or utilizing local facilities that store or transport dangerous goods. These exercises provide vital links with industry while exposing personnel to 'real world' logistical problems. Most fire fighters respond favourably to 'hands on' training and the learning curve increases when realism is increased. Skills maintenance for the DGRT is essential to ensure the effective performance of its personnel and reduce liability for their actions at an incident site.

Another issue of concern relates to equipment serviceability and inventory control. Responders' reliance upon specialized equipment is vital and a process should be developed to address this issue. Edmonton's Emergency Response Department has recently developed a system of assigned inventory using seven categories. This system ensures inventory control and helps demonstrate personnel competency on a semi-annual basis. Accordingly, each technician has a specialty and is responsible for either:

1. Protective clothing.
2. Test equipment.
3. Tools.
4. Containment.
5. Absorption.
6. Computer and library.
7. Communications.

Each technician is also tasked with maintaining records, operating the resource library and delivering in-house training. Team members are aware that unserviceable equipment, uncalibrated monitors or misplaced items will result in substandard performance and decreased level of service to the community. Safety is critical to offensive mitigation techniques. Therefore, maximum performance of personnel and equipment is essential to each successful intervention. Competency recertification is also a must and is an essential part of efficiency evaluations.

Deployment configurations for DGRT also requires careful analysis. Incident volumes may discourage single role responsibilities for most departments. One solution addresses this issue by utilizing fire/rescue personnel in a multi-discipline role. For example, Edmonton's DGRT consists of three officers and seven fire fighters manning a dedicated DG response unit, a pumper, an aerial and a decontamination unit. All personnel rotate with the pumper and aerial providing basic fire/rescue services while functioning in a backup role to the DG team. This configuration utilizes DGRT technicians as required while regular fire/rescue responsibilities are performed. Response units remain fully staffed while specialized units (the decontamination unit) are manned as required by the aerial crew. Additionally, each platoon has 21 technicians who rotate into and out of the dedicated DG station on a predetermined cycle. This system provides a high level of flexibility and cost effective service, while addressing skill maintenance, staffing and additional resource issues.

Additional issues for consideration are:

1. Public or industrial technical assistance (i.e., chemists COGNATIC or consultants).
2. Regulatory agencies (i.e., Environment Departments or the Transportation of Dangerous Goods regulatory bodies).

3. Certified disposal contractors for cleanup and disposal as per legislation.
4. Selection of suppliers of 'specialty' equipment and consumables.
5. Working relationship with various municipal, provincial and federal agencies for inter-agency responses.
6. Familiarity with appropriate 'disaster plans.'
7. Current contact list (i.e., name, telephone and fax numbers) of all possible resources.

Careful consideration should obviously be given to every possible organization, agency or contact that would enhance the DGRT's ability to successfully mitigate any probable incident.

Hazard identification and risk assessment within the response area will enable departments to strategize pre-incident responses, identify contingency plans, pre-stage resources, identify unacceptable risks, reduce risks at their source and form partnerships with industry/manufacturing companies. This process involves systematic gathering and storage of defined information for quick access, either manual or electronic. The resulting data can translate into quantifiable risk assessment. PPR (prevention, preparedness and response) is the mandate of the fire service and particularly the DGRT. This investment in time and money could pay tremendous dividends in terms of efficiency and effectiveness.

WHAT RESOURCES SHOULD A DGRT HAVE?

Specific, implied or recommended equipment requirements for urban or regional DGRT are available from NFPA, OSHA, CAFC, provincial fire training schools (where they exist), provincial Fire Chief Associations, the National Fire Academy, IFCA or a host of established teams including industry. Depending on the level of service desired, the peculiarities of the local jurisdiction, and with due consideration to budget constraints, a cost/benefit analysis is required prior to equipment acquisition. Advances in technology have resulted in greater selection, pricing, availability and serviceability of the required inventory. Consideration should be given to existing apparatus modification or construction to place equipment in the most 'user friendly' manner. Within existing budgetary constraints, personnel should be consulted in the acquisition and design process of equipment deployment models.

The Edmonton's Emergency Response Department employed this type of process when replacing two dedicated DG response units. A 'lead' captain volunteered to coordinate the direct input of all DGRT personnel with respect to structural design, power train, equipment placement and required inventory, within administrative budget constraints. The 'mechanical' component concerns were addressed via direct input from the Service Centre (i.e. mechanical) experts to ensure fleet compatability. This collaborative approach resulted in the creation of only one unit rather than two, an increase in its functionality and a streamlined inventory based on a needs analysis. Team personnel expressed innovative ideas, screened the recommendations, worked within budget and gained greater organizational perspective than was possible via traditional methods. The resulting apparatus proved functional, efficient and cost effective. Motivation and satisfaction were the results of this 'team building' process.

HOW DOES ONE MANAGE DGRT OPERATIONS?

There are many different approaches with which to manage DGRT operations. In the City of Edmonton the ever increasing number of incidents has lead to some recent changes in the approach taken by the Emergency Response Department. The DGRT was originally conceived as a highly specialized team which would respond anywhere in the city where dangerous goods of any type were involved. The team was composed of fire fighters who volunteered to take additional training in order to become qualified as DGRT members. As the number of incidents increased, a concern was raised as to the need for all fire fighting personnel to be able to provide assistance to the team by performing basic functions such as identifying products, ensuring site safety, assisting with decontamination and fulfilling other support functions. Thus, in 1990, the DGRT officers provided a DG First Responder Awareness course to all fire fighting personnel. This program was offered to all staff on an 'in-service' basis. In 1993, this program was expanded and all personnel received the DG First Responder Operations course. Once again, this course was facilitated by the DGRT Officers on an in-service basis.

In 1994, it was determined that the existing level of expertise among all personnel was at a level where response to minor dangerous goods incidents could be handled by a single fire company. Each pumper unit is now equipped with a DG Spill Kit (see Appendix F for definitions and SOP). The management rationale for this change was that the highly trained and highly specialized DGRT was travelling all over the city to respond to minor spills such as glycol spilled during a car accident, or gasoline spilled while fuelling a lawn mower. All DG incidents are logged by the DGRT officers, and responding pumper crews must file a report with the DGRT outlining the details of the incident and the actions taken by them.

For most fire service agencies, the first responder level of training is likely a good investment for all responders. In terms of the on-going management of the DG aspect of emergency response, it is important to have a tracking mechanism in order to ensure that DG incidents are properly logged and reported. Ongoing analysis of detailed response data allows for the identification of patterns and trends, and also helps to identify service, equipment, and training issues.

Electronic data bases are relatively inexpensive to establish and can provide great assistance in identifying problems and trends and allowing them to be addressed in a timely manner. Electronic data bases are obviously dependent upon reliable and accurate information. If data is entered into a data base on an ongoing basis the data remains current and readily accessible. A system for the collection, storage and retrieval of incident statistics is a necessary requirement for any DGRT.

Incident Management

In terms of managing a DGRT at an actual DG incident, it is recommended that the DGRT operate as a functional sector within the incident command structure. This applies to incidents which are primarily DG incidents as well as other emergencies which involve a DG component. At major DG incidents there is often a tendency for emergency managers to desire that DG trained personnel direct the entire operation. This is not, however, a particularly wise use of a specialized resource.

In the City of Edmonton, although DG officers are fully trained fire officers and incident commanders, there is a standing order that DG officers must not be required to assume command. The incident commander has many and varied concerns, and the DG officers can serve most effectively in an advisory role. Using DG officers as advisors to Command allows DG officers the ability to oversee and directly supervise DG operations without becoming involved in or distracted by other, perhaps larger issues or concerns of incident management.

Highly trained and equipped DG personnel have the ability to provide expert advice to Command on issues such as recommended evacuation zones, establishment of perimeters, and recommended treatment for exposed victims. Many of the functions and duties associated with executing these recommendations, however, can be carried out by non-DG trained personnel, leaving the DGRT personnel to concentrate on rescue operations as well as the containment and the control of the product(s) involved.

Cost Recovery

Most federal and provincial environmental legislation in Canada is premised on the notion of 'polluter pays.' Typically, legislation will allow a municipality the ability to recover response team costs from individuals who have caused an uncontrolled release which posed a threat to life, property, or the environment, through some form of negligence (i.e., act of commission or omission). The City of Edmonton has a municipal bylaw in place which enables the Emergency Response Department to recover clean-up costs. These are costs for services which are necessitated through negligent acts, criminal activities, violations of existing regulations, or unusual circumstances which should not be remedied using taxpayers' funds. Insurance companies will also honour claims for response costs, provided that they fall within the scope of the policy in place. Major dangerous goods transporters, manufacturers, handlers, and storage companies which are involved with regulated products generally have an insurance rider which covers accidental spill, equipment or vessel failure, and damage to the environment. Municipal response costs can often be recovered either directly from the company involved or from the insurance company.

The issue of cost recovery is an important matter to examine when considering establishing a DGRT or enhancing the abilities of an existing DGRT. For jurisdictions where private clean-up and disposal contactors do not exist or are not available, this area is also a potential revenue generating area of business. While it is sometimes controversial for public sector response agencies to go into direct competition with private sector companies, this is an area of business that may be pursued in regions where no other service provider is available.

SUMMARY AND CONCLUSION

The number of emergency incidents involving dangerous goods has risen dramatically over the past ten years, and is likely to continue to rise over the next ten years. Several reasons, including changing technology, environmental concerns, and concern for litigation were cited as contributing to the growing number of DG incidents. The establishment of a DGRT is a costly undertaking which involves highly specialized training and equipment and also requires on-going maintenance of skills and equipment. Prior to embarking on establishing a DGRT there are several steps that can be taken to analyze the needs of the community and its existing capabilities.

Community needs can be evaluated using a hazard assessment/risk analysis process. The process identifies key hazards and combinations of hazards that have the potential to create unique concerns for the community. The analysis of historical data and consideration of 'worst case scenarios' are useful steps in establishing the level of risk and probabilities associated with those risks. The risks and probabilities should then be compared to the response capability of local response agencies and of other agencies in the region. In many cases the 'gap' that exists between the potential risk and the existing capabilities will suggest the need for the establishment of a DGRT or the enhancement of an existing team.

There are essentially two different levels of DG responders. First responders are trained in basic hazard identification and containment and are able to implement a defensive strategy at DG incidents. Second responders have much more specialized skills and equipment and are able to pursue offensive strategies during DG incidents. Regardless of the level of training, DGRT members are best utilized as a resource to Incident Command. 'DG' should be established as a free standing sector which is not burdened with command responsibilities.

The Dangerous Goods Response Team is a highly specialized team. The training, equipment and maintenance costs of such a team are a major concern for many municipalities. Through the course of the latest rounds of belt tightening and budget slashing there has been a greater emphasis on regional initiatives and the sharing of resources. This appears to be a trend which will continue in the future, and one which makes sense both from an economic and operational perspective. Clearly not every municipality is going to face a major DG incident every month or even every year. But when that incident does occur, plans need to be in place and resources made available to deal with it. Regionalization and the sharing of resources appear to be the way of the future, and should be carefully considered by any jurisdiction which presently has a gap between the potential risk (and the probability of a major DG incident) and the capability of municipal resources to respond to it.

A Case in Point: Propane Truck Roll-over, Holden Alberta

At 07:00 hours on October 13, 1995, near Holden, Alberta, 65 kilometres east of Edmonton, a tractor trailer unit carrying 57,000 litres of Butane went off the road and sheared off a power pole. When the truck came to rest in the ditch, the bulkhead of the second trailer began to leak product through a four-centimetre tear which was sustained during the accident. The ambient temperature that morning was slightly below freezing which meant the leaking butane remained in liquid state. The product began to flow freely into the ditch and ran along the ditch towards a rail line which was less than 800 metres away.

The authority having jurisdiction over the response effort was the local volunteer fire department. Chief Ashley Emmerson of the Holden Fire Department quickly took command and contacted the county disaster officer as well as the Alberta provincial government's Emergency Response Centre's Coordination and Information Centre. Recognizing the incident was beyond the capabilities of local responders, local officials quickly requested that the Coordination and Information Centre obtain mutual aid from the City of Edmonton's Dangerous Goods Response Team.

The Edmonton DGRT, complete with their regional response unit and regional decontamination trailer, were on scene within one hour of receiving the call. The team reported to the local incident commander, Chief George Roddick of Viking, and then proceeded to conduct a size-up of the situation. Working in partnership with the local response agency, DGRT members employed a unique mitigation method by floating the product above the rupture in the tank, and then pumping off the product into containment vessels.

This incident is an excellent example of different response agencies, government environment officials, transportation officials, and industry representatives working together to mitigate a potentially disastrous incident. Full cost recovery for response services was achieved from the transport company. Although the local volunteer fire department did not have the in-house resources necessary to mitigate the incident, there were plans in place to obtain mutual aid and to draw on the expertise and training of a response agency in the region.

Picture 6.1

Dangerous Good cleanup.
(Photo Courtesy of Edmonton Emergency Response Department.)

Picture 6.2

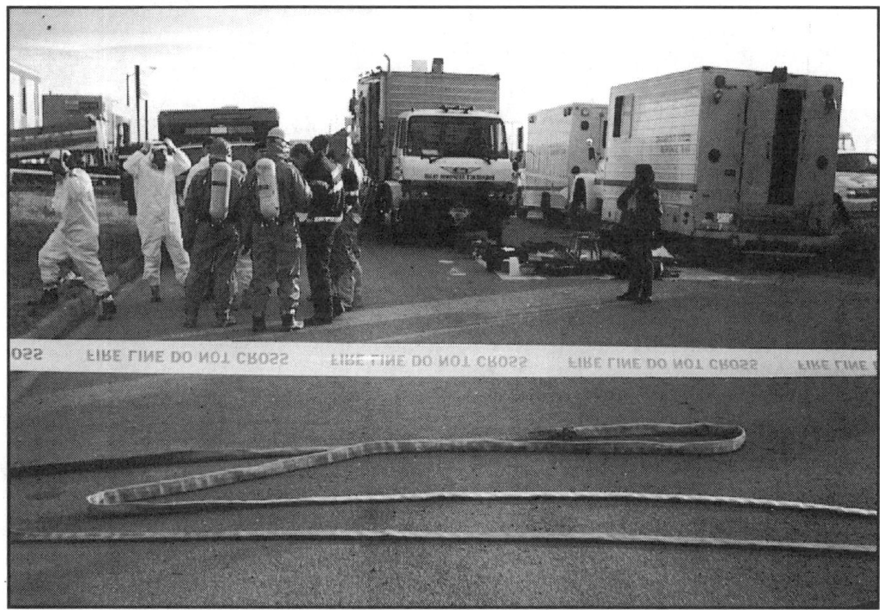

Multi-agency response to a Dangerous Goods incident.
(Photo Courtesy of Edmonton Emergency Response Department.)

Picture 6.3

Training the DGRT.
(Photo Courtesy of Edmonton Emergency Response Department.)

Picture 6.4

Decontamination procedures.
(Photo Courtesy of Edmonton Emergency Response Department.)

Exercise Design, Conduct And Evaluation

Ron Kuban, Ph.D.
President, Turning Point Consulting Corp.

Photo Courtesy of Fort Saskatchewan Fire Department.

Emergency exercises are an important component of effective emergency planning. No plan is complete without it first being tested and exercised. This chapter summarizes the design, conduct and evaluation of emergency exercises.

There is a well accepted maxim that emergency plans are not complete until they are tested and exercised. Emergency plans, like any newly designed and constructed mechanical contraption, need to be put through their paces. This process ensures that they perform as intended. It also provides their users with confidence in the ability of these plans to accomplish their intended objective.

The primary objective of emergency plans is to enhance the capability and effectiveness of the response effort so that lives can be saved, injuries minimized and property and other losses reduced. Effective emergency response demands effective preparedness and that requires the most effective plan possible. Emergency exercises are an important tool to enhance the quality of emergency plans.

This chapter addresses the topic of emergency exercises in four parts:

1. An overview an context.
2. The design process.
3. The conduct of these exercises.
4. Exercise evaluation.

AN OVERVIEW OF EMERGENCY EXERCISES

This part of the chapter answers the following questions:

1. What are emergency exercises?
2. Where do they fit in the Emergency Management continuum?
3. What are the myths and stereotypes relating to emergency exercises?
4. What are the benefits to be gained from exercising?

What are emergency exercises?

An emergency exercise is defined as a tool through which emergency duties can be performed, in response to a simulated event, to enhance the competence of emergency responders and their organization.

Emergency exercises should be distinguished from 'drills.' Drills are typically conducted by single agencies to develop the skills of their members. Drills are often related to the technical skills required by the responder (e.g., the laying of hoses or high–angle rescue). Often, the outcome of drills is individual specific, meaning that they aim to improve the performance of the individual and can result in some measurement (or rating) of that individual's new competence level.

Exercises, on the other hand, have a broader purpose. They are designed to test the disaster management process using portions of the plan as a framework. Exercises often involve teams of responders, from various organizations, in a test of the ... PLAN!

The key questions which emergency exercises are intended to answer are:

1. Does the emergency plan work as intended?
2. What obstacles, if any, exist in executing the plan as intended?
3. What revisions, if any, need to be made to roles, responsibilities, skills, resources and activity–scheduling to make the plan meet its intended disaster goals.

All exercises typically contain one or more objectives, a scenario plus inputs, a process for debriefing the exercise and an opportunity to revise the Plan (as necessary). However, they differ in their complexity. Moreover, they may be grouped into four categories, each with its own set of activities and outcome. These categories are:

1. The structured walk through.
2. Table–top, 'paper' or 'static' exercise.
3. Communications exercise.
4. The full–scale or 'field' exercise.

The structured walk through. This is the most basic and least complex approach to test the emergency plan. It involves a systematic analysis or 'walk through' of the plan.

The structured walk through is best conducted soon after the development of a draft of the emergency plan. The process should involve all of the key players who are made responsible in the plan for specific response actions and resources. These individuals should walk through the plan, step by step, and indicate whether the responsibility assigned to them is realistic, manageable and plausible given the realities of the time in the context of disaster situations.

The discussion may lead to the revision of the plan so that it reflects what can and may happen. When finalized, the plan is ready to be tested in a more specific disaster scenario.

Paper exercise. The paper exercise involves a test of the plan using a specific scenario. That scenario sets the context for the exercise and initiates simulated response action(s). The scenario is then followed by a number of inputs which are distributed to select participants throughout the exercise.

Each exercise input describes either the action supposedly taken by someone in the response team, or a change in the (simulated) disaster environment. The intent of the scenario and exercise inputs is to provide the participants with a context for their respective actions and to trigger them to take action.

This type of exercise is typically conducted on paper, hence the name. No resources are moved other than those simulated by paper tags, small toys or other such markers. Often, no communication tools (e.g., phones, radios) are used. And, the exercise is usually restricted to one geographical location.

Communications exercise. This exercise is more complex than the paper exercise. Like the paper exercise, it involves a scenario, inputs and key responders as exercise players. But, in addition this exercise involves a wide range of communication equipment. Hence its added complexity.

The various inputs and the communication among participants may be conducted in part or completely through communication tools. System overload, interference and delays may now be introduced to illustrate the limitations of all communication systems.

This type of exercise can and should be conducted with participants located in different locations. No response resources (i.e., rescue or Fire vehicles, ambulances) are used except those related to communications. It is ideal, therefore, to test the efficiency of the communication component of the emergency plan.

The field or full–scale exercise. No simulation is like the 'real thing' but the field exercise should come close to it. As the name implies, this exercise is conducted using the actual deployment of resources as part of the exercise. By necessity, therefore, it involves many responders and response organizations, varied locations and complex exercise administration.

This type of exercise can best provide responders with a simulation of what disaster response can be like. It is also the most extensive test of the emergency plan. Therefore, response organizations should strive to exercise their organization and its emergency plan using this category of exercise.

However, organizations should crawl before they walk, and walk before they run. So it is with emergency exercises. Fire Departments which have just drafted their first emergency plan should begin the exercise process using the structured walk through followed shortly after by a paper exercise. When confident of their capability they should explore a communications exercise. Then, and only when the organization is ready to handle it, a full blown field exercise should be attempted.

Remember, emergency exercises are designed to test the emergency plan, not its responders. So the intent of each exercise should be to test the plan without setting its responders for a fall. Exercise participants should not be caught in an unrealistic bind (i.e., have to use resources completely out of their reach) or respond to situations outside their mandate and responsibility.

Organizations which have an emergency plan should have one to two paper exercises a year, one communications exercise a year and one field exercise every two to three years. Since only small parts of the plan need to be tested at a time, these exercises can be relatively small and manageable.

Where do exercises fit in the Emergency Management continuum?

As noted in Chapter 3, emergency exercises are an important part of emergency management. In fact, emergency exercises are an integral element of emergency planning (or preparedness).

To be effective, the process of emergency preparedness should be a continuous cycle of activity beginning with hazard analysis, plan development, training, exercises and evaluation. The goal of this process is to enhance the community's ability to respond effectively to disasters. This goal is achieved through a number of activities. They include prompt operational response, protection of life and property, integrated leadership, the sharing of operational information and the appropriate use of resources.

The Fire Services, and many other response organizations (i.e., Police, Emergency Medical Services) are typically well versed in their day–to–day functions. Fire Services personnel receive on– going agency–based training to ensure their competence to deal with routine emergencies. Additionally, the training of some is augmented through the school of hard knocks, or the experience of responding to major calls.

However, the on–going in–house training often does little to address issues of inter–agency communication, decision making and coordination. In short, it fails to address one of the major issues which make disaster response more complex than routine operations!

As noted in Chapter 1, disasters operations represent a quantum leap of complexity from routine operations. Fire Officers, and their counterparts in other response agencies, must have the knowledge and operational tools to deal with the unique environment of disasters and crises.

Another key factor to consider is the nature of adult learners. Experience plays a big factor in their learning and their retention of information. Emergency exercises serve this need beautifully!

What are the myths and stereotypes relating to emergency exercises?

As in the case of emergency preparedness (see Chapter 1), the whole notion of emergency exercises is shrouded sometimes by a blanket of myths and misconceptions. These need to be clarified and corrected because they interfere with the effectiveness of these valuable emergency tools.

Exercises are expensive. To be sure, emergency exercises demand effort, attention and resources. They can be 'expensive,' but the cost of most exercises can be no more than the cost of some planning time and the time of their participants. Moreover, the costs of not conducting emergency exercises can be, and often are, monumental! Therefore, the maxim to remember is:

Effective preparation is not expensive.
Failure to prepare is.

Exercises always demand a major time commitment. Emergency exercises need not be large scale productions. Often, the greatest challenge for exercise designers and participants alike is to get full participation and cooperation. Some exercises (i.e., full–scale) can often involve a tremendous range of participants. However, most emergency exercises typically involve only those people who are needed to accomplish a particular objective.

To be fair, the biggest time expenditure in any emergency exercise can be attributed to the design of the exercise. If designed well, the exercise can provide a meaningful and valuable experience for its participants in a relatively limited period of time (i.e., two to three hours).

Exercises should always be a surprise. Surprise exercises are not the only way to measure the response capability of an organization. The preferred method should nearly always be to advise participants of the exercise location and timing but not its content and scenario.

Surprise exercises should be employed only when the organization is well experienced and 'ready' for more complex challenges. It should have its plan in place, the plan should have been exercises through walk through, paper, communications and full– scale exercises. And, the results should have been generally successful. Only then is the organization ready to take the next challenge.

The surprise conduct of an exercise may have significant ramifications for the organization. To start with the exercise may not remain secret for long leaving its supposed value of secrecy in question. Additionally, staff members could easily be overwhelmed by challenges and demands for resources beyond their capability or control. The results are bound to be irritation and frustration on the part of participants. Their negative experience with the exercise may well set the whole emergency preparedness program into a tail spin.

What are the benefits to be gained from emergency exercises?

Emergency exercises have many benefits; some are tangible others are subtle. Listed below are some of the key benefits of emergency exercises.

They provide a mechanism to test the plan. Exercises can be tailored to measure any portion of an emergency plan. They may have a limited objective or a range of goals. Regardless, they are ideal opportunities to flex organizational muscles and see what works and what does not.

Reality is that neither of the two alternatives to emergency exercises are viable. One is to do nothing, the other is to test the plan during actual disasters.

Exercises help meet training needs. Emergency exercises should not be designed or conducted as training courses. However, they do provide training opportunities if for no other reason than the experience they provide. As noted earlier, that experience is likely to be a more powerful teacher than classroom–style lessons.

Exercises are ways to familiarize people with new roles and procedures. Certain emergency responders may not be fully familiar with their emergency roles. That may be because, for these individuals, their emergency–related roles are secondary or tertiary. The exercise situation may be the first (and perhaps only) time for them to learn and experience their emergency functions.

Additionally, the exercise situation may provide an ideal opportunity to try out such unique roles as the Emergency Site Manager, Incident Commander and other critical coordination roles. In other words, the exercise environment allows for the practice of functions which are often neglected, unnecessary or beyond the range of day–to–day operations.

Exercises are simulations. Exercises involve simulated disasters. They are relatively safe environments where errors in judgement, procedure or activity do not result in fatalities, injuries or property damage. Therefore, they serve as ideal situations for the testing of new ideas, procedures and resources.

Emergency exercises are also public relation events. These exercises capture attention because:

1. They exist to test an emergency plan.
2. They are conducted within the community.

These exercise should be broadly publicized. After all, they are a positive event. The organization which conducts them is being proactive. It cares about its emergency capability. It accepts the fact that things may not work as they should but is willing to assess the results and improve the plan. Those are powerful messages for members of the public and individual responders alike.

The conduct of emergency exercises sends another, albeit subtle, message. It tells everyone involved that emergency preparedness is important; that the organization(s) conducting the exercise is (are) committed to the process.

Emergency exercises help build understanding and trust. As noted in Chapter 1, inter–agency cooperation requires an understanding of capabilities and limitations of all participants, as well as a strong sense of trust. Emergency exercises provide an opportunity for various agencies, which rarely associate with each other, to learn about each other and to work together.

The personal and organizational contacts made during exercise situations can help smooth over many obstacles during actual disaster response situations. Moreover, exercises provide one of the few opportunities for organizations (and systems) to try out the working arrangement which they would have to put into use during disasters.

Exercise help build confidence. Even when mistakes are made, as is inevitably the case, the focus should be on how to correct them. The important gain here is one of experience. If simulated properly, the exercise should give participants a real sense of disaster. After that experience, the real situation is likely to be less frightening. Participants may have a sense of "been there and done that."

EXERCISE DESIGN

Emergency exercises must be designed properly so as to provide as much realism as possible and, therefore, the best environment to meet the objective of the exercise (i.e., test the plan). It need not become a major Hollywood production. On the other hand, it needs to be well thought out and designed.

The important thing to remember is that exercise design is a process which includes:

1. Establishing the goal(s) of the exercise.
2. Involving key potential participants in the design.
3. Ensuring that the activities of the design process meet the goal(s) of the exercise.
4. Getting feedback.
5. Evaluating results.

The process requires the commitment of senior managers of ALL participating organizations. Without that commitment, the process is doomed to be plagued by unnecessary challenges and obstacles and its product (the exercise) may be of questionable value.

The design process must be treated as one would treat the development of an educational program. It must be logical, develop knowledge in a step–by–step fashion, build on what is already known, evolve from the general to the specific and, as much as possible, be ... enjoyable for the learner (or participant).

Designing Emergency Exercises

As noted above, the process of exercise design must be logical, methodical, all inclusive and consistent with current capabilities and knowledge of the response organization and its members. One of the secrets for the success of this process is that it must be a team effort.

The design process of emergency exercises generally includes a number of key steps. They are described below and include the following:

1. Determine current knowledge base and capability.
2. Determine intended gain in knowledge base and capability.
3. Identify the portion of the emergency plan which needs review or testing.
4. Set a general objective for the exercise.
5. Establish a design team.

6. Identify specific goals(s), context, parameters and participants for the exercise.
7. Develop the exercise through the following activities:

   a. Define the goal and objective of each major activity;
   b. Establish the general scenario;
   c. Develop a master event list;
   d. Develop detailed event list;
   e. Establish anticipated action(s); and
   f. Draft messages.

8. Establish safety systems.
9. Identify needed support requirements.
10. Develop the evaluation tool.
11. Establish exercise control mechanisms:

    a. Control staff; and
    b. Simulation staff.

12. Get approval.
13. Conduct the exercise.
14. Evaluate the exercise.

Let us look at each of these separately to gain a sense of the type of activities which these would entail.

Determine current knowledge base and capability. Keep in mind that effective exercises must build on what individuals know and what individuals and organizations are capable of responding to. Therefore, the first step must be to identify in general those skill levels and capabilities.

Those responsible for exercise design, called here 'exercise designers,' need to assess how much potential exercise participants know about emergency preparedness in general and about current plans and procedures in specific. Exercise designers can establish this by talking with key people and reviewing operational reports or reviews of recent incidents and exercises.

Exercise designers also need a clear appreciation of the hazards which affect the community and the resources currently available to support the response to these hazards. An invaluable source of this information is the local emergency plan. (See chapters 4 and 5 for more detail.)

Determine the intended gain in knowledge base and capability. The outcome of this step should be an understanding of the skills and knowledge that are still required to broaden the capability of the plan. While this is not the primary purpose of emergency exercises, it is a factor worth considering and may influence the choice made in the next step.

Identify the portion of the emergency plan which needs review or testing. This factor is particularly important for two reasons:

1. Few, if any, emergency exercises test the whole plan.
2. The decision as to which part of the plan is to be exercised has a direct bearing on all activities which follow, including exercise evaluation!

A number of factors should be considered when selecting a portion of the plan for exercise. These factors include previous exercises (their content and results), significant changes in the plan, operational emphasis and priorities as well as the needs stated by other response organizations or the public.

Set a general objective for the exercise. Exercises demand much effort and attention and their consequences are significant. They must be developed, conducted and evaluated to meet a pre–determined goal. That goal needs to be established at this point and become the focus of all exercise–related activity.

Exercise objectives can be specific or general. They must, however, be descriptive enough to clarify what the exercise is designed to achieve. Some examples may be:

1. To assess the response time of deploying (resource A) to meet the needs of (location B) in situations involving (item C).
2. To measure the response capability of the new Emergency Operations Centre.
3. To resolve coordination difficulties inherent to a multi–agency municipal response effort.
4. To test the reaction of the Dangerous Goods Response Team to a D.G. occurrence at the XYZ industrial park.

Establish a design team. Exercise design (and conduct) is a team affair! Not only does it demand many resources, but to be effective it must also include various perspectives. If many organizations are to be included in the exercise, each of their needs, perspectives and resources must be considered.

Members of the design team should be recruited to represent the various agencies or divisions (if only one organization is involved) which will participate in the exercise. Naturally, the bigger and more complex the exercise, the larger the team. Moreover, the establishment of this team also helps secure the commitment of participating organizations to the process.

Members of this team should have a solid understanding of their organization, its emergency preparedness plan and its emergency preparedness needs. They need not necessarily be familiar with the design process. However, the team's leader should be well familiar with the process. Because of the nature of the task, the team leader should also be someone who is adept at working with people and through problems.

The team leader should, as much as possible, be seen as a coördinator and not necessarily as representing his/her parent organization. The leader should guide the process so that everyone's key emergency needs are met.

Identify specific goals(s), context, parameters and participants for the exercise. Now that the team is established, it may wish to refine and agree on the goal for the exercise. Once they finalize and agreed upon the goal, team members should develop a series of objectives for the exercise. These are more specific and help provide more meaning to the intent of the exercise.

To provide clarity and preciseness, objectives must be specific, results oriented, realistic and measurable. They need to be specific because they will then lead to the design of exercise inputs and activities which will generate special response by the participants. These objectives must be realistic so as not to frustrate participants with tasks beyond their reach. And, they must be measurable so as to provide an opportunity for meaningful feedback and learning.

Also to be decided are such important issues as:

1. Which organizations should participate in the exercise?
2. How extensive (i.e., duration, geographical bounds, resource commitment) should the exercise be?
3. What type of exercise should this be?
4. What is the general scenario (or context) of the exercise?
5. What date(s) are best suited for the conduct of the exercise? (These dates should be set early in the process serve as a target.)

Develop the exercise. This is achieved through hard work, meticulous preparation and team effort. This effort has already began in previous steps, but is now refined into much needed specificity. The process is a mix between puzzle work, choreography and set design in a theatre. For all intents and purposes, the design team is putting a show together the success of which can only be assessed during opening night.

The first major task in this step is to clearly define the goal and objective of each major activity. Major activities may be:

1. The deployment of the Dangerous Goods Response Team.
2. The activation of the Emergency Operations Centre.
3. Requests for mutual aid.
4. The creation of operational links to local industrial sites.

The next sub–step requires the establishment of a general scenario. This scenario is a narrative which describes the general situation at the start of the exercise. It should provide participants with a broad view of the events leading to their involvement with this (simulated) disaster. It is a necessary context for their activities.

The scenario can not and need not be all inclusive. However, it should provide participants with enough knowledge to make meaningful decisions. Exercise scenarios could be as brief as two to four pages.

The design team must then develop a 'Master Event List.' This list identifies, in chronological order, all the major events intended to occur during the exercise. This list must be linked to the objectives of the exercise and is particularly important because it provides the backbone of all inputs during the exercise. As an example, the list may include the following:

1. Response agencies notified of the disaster.
2. Initiation of first response.
3. Initiation of a call–out.
4. Activation of the Emergency Operations Centre.
5. Deployment of the Dangerous Goods Response Team.
6. Notifcation of elected officials.
7. Notifcation of the public.

The design team should then flesh out the Master Event List by developing a Detailed Event List. This list takes each of the entries of the Master Event List and identifies what specific activities are necessary to result in the achievement of each of the items on the Master Event List.

For example, note that the first entry in the Master Event List above is "response agencies notified of the disaster." This entry may generate the following detailed events:

1. Phone call received from a member of the public by fire dispatch.
2. Information is confirmed (independently) by a police constable at the scene.
3. A news bulletin announces the event.

Each of the entries on the Detailed Event List must be linked to the reaction anticipated of exercise participants (i.e., disaster responders). This link is critical because otherwise the exercise may unfold without purpose or without meaningful response by its participants.

By this stage the design team should have a very clear 'picture' of the exercise. They now must translate that picture into meaningful exercise inputs. These are the messages which the participants will receive during the exercise. The intent of these messages, or 'inputs' is to instigate action by participants and to provide them with another piece of the situation as it is (supposedly) unfolding.

Establish safety systems.

Not all exercises require an element of safety and security. Paper exercises, for example, contain no hazards. However, communications exercises have some and major exercises contain a great deal of risk.

The communications exercise, for example, may result in a mix–up between exercise messages and those which relate to a real emergency. Communication channels used for the exercise may result in the curtailment of needed (and perhaps limited) communication capability of the response organization.

Major exercises, like disaster situations, contain a high degree of risk because emergency–response resources are moved about in response to a disaster simulation. If simulated accurately, the situation should be chaotic and demanding on those who respond to it.

Regardless of the degree of risk, the design team should consider the need to ensure safe exercise environment. Where necessary, particularly during major exercises, the team should establish:

1. A way to quickly revert from the simulated disaster to address the needs of real emergencies.
2. Ways to avoid injuries during the deployment of resources.
3. Ways to ensure swift response to injuries should they occur in the course of the exercise.

Large exercise may require the dedicated effort of one or more individuals to ensure that the exercise is conducted safely. The concern for safety should include all those who participate, act in (i.e., as simulated casualties) or observe the exercise.

Identify needed support requirements. All exercises require administrative support and a number of resources. The larger the exercise the more the demand on resources. This demand must also be considered and planned for by the design team. Consideration should be given to:

1. Facilities for the design team's meetings as well as for the conduct of the exercise and the debriefing.
2. Communication equipment.
3. Exercise materials (from paper inputs to fire apparatus).
4. Support staff.
5. Maps, emergency plans, copies of SOPs and much more.

Field or major exercises require many more resources. For example, they require simulated casualties, response vehicles and other pieces of equipment, closure of certain areas for the sake of the exercise and the deployment of staff in various exercise capacities (i.e., simulators, observers, safety staff).

Develop the evaluation tool. The key purpose of emergency exercises is to test the plan. By this step, much effort has already been made to establish goals and objectives for the exercise. All of that has been developed to ensure that something is learned from the exercise. One possible lesson may be that everything is working as it should. And that would be great! Another exercise may highlight glaring problems with the plan. In any case, both exercise results are valuable.

To learn as much as possible from the exercise the design team needs to establish an evaluation tool. The most common, and perhaps most effective evaluation tool is the appointment of one or more observers. Their primary role is to monitor the unfolding of the exercise and to report, at its conclusion, about their observations.

Observers must be directed to specific areas of interest to the design team. In other words, observers must be given a set of questions for which they must find answers. They may also be told to focus on specific elements of the response effort, specific organizational components or the reaction of response organizations or units to specific inputs.

Only in rare exceptions should they be given a free hand to observe and report at will. This open approach is workable only if the observers have extensive knowledge of the field and are experienced in their role as observers.

Establish exercise control mechanisms. Emergency exercises, regardless of their size and complexity, require a process to guide them and keep them on track. Failure to achieve this function successfully may result in the failure of these exercises to meet their intended objectives.

Each exercise must have an Exercise Director whose sole responsibility is to ensure that the exercise flows as intended regardless of obstacles along the way. Exercise Directors can achieve their function through two separate but connected cells—Exercise Staff and Simulation Staff. The members of these two cells, their roles and resources should be defined by the design group. Each cell may contain one or more people. (During the exercise, both cells should report to the Exercise Director.)

The primary role of exercise staff or 'controllers' is to help the Exercise Director guide the flow of the exercise. They need a separate space from which to monitor the exercise and issue inputs. Where possible they should also be given their own communication network (i.e., separate radio channel or phone number).

Members of the simulation cell, or 'simulators,' have an equally important role. Emergency exercises succeed only when a sense of realism is created and maintained among the participants so that they remain motivated to perform their respective response tasks in a realistic way. The role of the simulators is to create and maintain that realism.

Various tools are available to assist the simulators to create the illusion of a disaster. These include the insertion of inputs (i.e., both verbal and written), positioning of key resources, simulations (e.g., damaged area, injuries, fatalities), or role playing. Simulators may also serve to 'complete the picture' by pretending to be members of organizations not directly represented or involved in the exercise. For example, one simulator may represent the entire provincial government. In fact, simulators are only limited by their imagination.

In small to moderate size exercises, controllers and simulators are often the same people. Just the same, they require specific instructions for each of their important roles. These instructions should be provided by the design team.

Get approval! Approval should be sought in increments as the process unfolds. This could remove unpleasant surprises just before the exercise is to be conducted. However, when the exercise design team has completed its task, it must seek approval to proceed with the conduct of the exercise.

Each organization represented in the design effort should be approached throughout the process to ensure its continued commitment. This seemingly trivial and tiresome task will pay big dividends during the conduct of the exercise. On the other hand, failure to secure that commitment may result in the exercise never seeing the light of day.

All is now ready for the big show. And, if all activities in the design process have been conducted as they should, the conduct of the exercise will not only be relatively easy, but may actually be ... fun!?

CONDUCT OF THE EXERCISE

There is nothing mystical about the conduct of an emergency exercise. In fact, all the hard work has already been done during the design stage. The success of the exercise is now dependent on two factors:

1. The effectiveness of the design team (i.e., the realism of their goals, clarity of the scenario and usefulness of the inputs to initiate and maintain action).
2. The ability of the Exercise Director and the control team to manage the conduct of the exercise.

The Exercise Director should strike a balance between over and under–control. Over–control occurs when participants are allowed no leeway in their response actions. They are led down a narrow path and have few opportunities to make mistakes and learn from their actions. This typically occurs when participants can not make decisions without first checking with the exercise control team. As a consequence participants may feel frustrated, used and may fail to take the effort seriously.

Under–control occurs when participants have too much flexibility resulting in the elimination of the Exercise Director and the control team being left out of the simulated response picture. The consequences can lead to breaches of safety rules (and injuries), total chaos and failure to meet any of the exercise's objectives.

One of the key rules of this phase is that the Exercise Director is the exercise's sole director. He or she should have complete control over the conduct of the exercise and have the power to terminate it for issues such as safety or the needs of real emergencies.

All controllers, simulators and observers (as applicable) should be under the control of the Exercise Director. Each of these individuals must be well briefed about:

1. The overall intent of the exercise.
2. The overall scenario of the exercise.
3. The intended flow of action.
4. The roles of responsibilities of the various cells.
5. The key principles and rules relating to free–play, safety and the early termination of the exercise.
6. The use of the control/safety radio net.

The larger the exercise the more the need for a dedicated radio channel or phone line for the use of exercise staff. This can also double–up as a safety net.

Exercise controllers should keep track of the flow of the exercise. They may do so by following the inputs and the response to them. In communications and field exercises, they may also rely on the observers to advise them of any difficulties before they become major obstacles to the flow of the exercise.

When necessary a 'time out' may be called by the Exercise Director. This stops all action and allows the exercise control staff to sort things out. When order is restored the Exercise Director may again resume the exercise by sending a message through the various available channels.

Another control tool is the insertion, where necessary, of an exercise input that would initiate the desired action. Sometimes, exercise participants fail to take an action which they were expected to take and on which another response unit is dependent. After some delay, the intended action may be deemed to have been taken and an input maybe made appropriately.

Ultimately, the effective conduct of an exercise requires ... common sense, balance and adaptation to rapidly changing circumstances. In that regard, there is little difference between the management of an exercise and the management of a disaster scene.

EVALUATION OF THE EXERCISE

As noted earlier, the whole purpose of the exercise is to learn something about the plan and the intended process of managing disaster response. It is not to test the capability of individuals.

There are two extremes in the evaluation of emergency exercises; both are failures! The first is the failure to conduct the evaluation. It provides no information. The other occurs when the evaluation results in everyone patting themselves (or each other) on the back saying 'aren't we great' despite glaring evidence to the contrary. The ideal is a balance between the two.

Excessively positive talk after an exercise comes from people's natural dislike of giving or getting criticism. One must again recall that the sole focus of the exercise are emergency procedures and the plan. Therefore, observations and feedback should be directed to make them better.

The actual process of the evaluation should be determined during the design phase. In any case, it should aim to get answers to the famous five W's ... Who, What, Where, When and Why. The answers to these questions will answer the question, primary on everyone's mind during the debriefing process: "How did we do?"

As you probably realize by now, the evaluation process actually begins very early in the design stage. A carefully prepared exercise provides evaluators and participants with the tools they need to extract valuable and meaningful information on their emergency management system.

The exercise evaluation process should, therefore, relate to the objectives of the exercise. In fact, as you may recall, much effort is made during the design phase to develop meaningful and measurable exercise objectives. The time invested in the careful development of exercise objectives, Master Events Lists and Detailed Events now pay back in useful information.

The evaluation of an exercise can materialize in three ways— debriefing, questionnaires and evaluators (or observers). All three methods are very useful and complement each other well. Therefore, wherever possible, all three methods should be used.

Debriefing is the process whereby exercise participants meet with exercise staff (i.e., the 'controllers') to exchange information on what happened during the exercise. As much as possible, this should occur immediately following the exercise while memories are freshest. Participants should be encouraged to bring their exercise operational logs to the debriefing and be prepared to speak about their activities, challenges and observations.

The debriefing may be conducted by the chairperson of the design team or the Exercise Director. (In many cases they may be one and the same person.) Their role during the debriefing is to take notes and keep the discussion both moving and on track. The latter may prove to be a challenge. Just the same, the focus should be on operational and management problems encountered during the exercise.

The second evaluation tool is a questionnaire developed by the design team and distributed to participants. The questionnaire can solicit more thoughtful responses. Their topic areas could complement those explored verbally during the exercise debriefing. Questionnaire questions can also home–in on specific issues of concern for the design team.

The third evaluation tool is the evaluation team. Its members had the task to monitor the flow of the exercise and their observations now can be quite valuable as they may provide another interesting perspective.

Regardless of the evaluation technique(s) used, the last step has to be the integration of the lessons learned and recommended changes into the appropriate procedures and emergency plan. Only then can one truly say that the exercise has served its purpose.

SUMMARY

Emergency exercise are an important tool to ensure that the emergency plan, and its related procedures, work as they should. There is nothing mystical about the design, conduct and evaluation of emergency plans. They require organizational commitment, creativity and thoughtful preparation. Their success can lead to the enhancement of both the plan and the capability of the community (or organization) to respond to disasters.

Picture 7.1

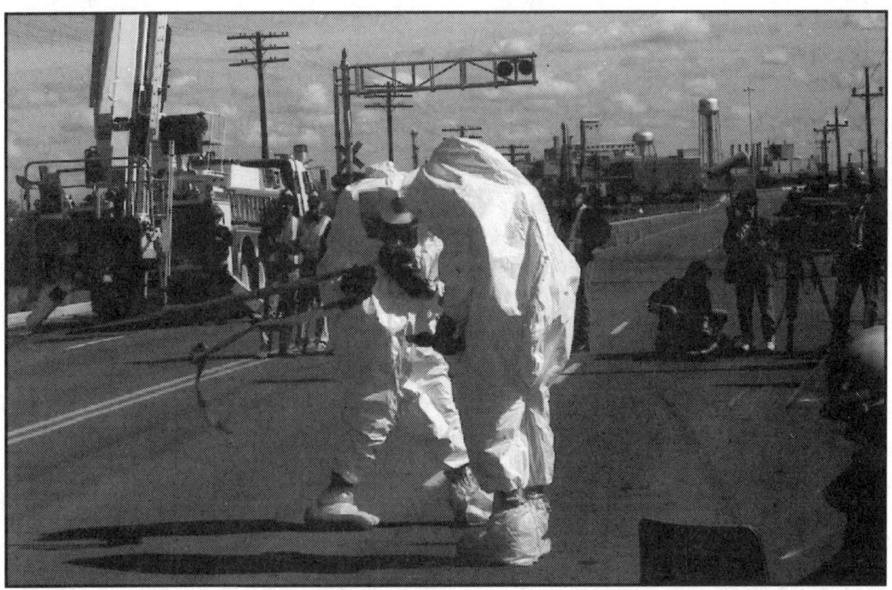

Exercise evaluation of a Dangerous Goods occurrence.
(Photo Courtesy of Gerry Emas, Edmonton Emergency Response Department.)

Picture 7.2

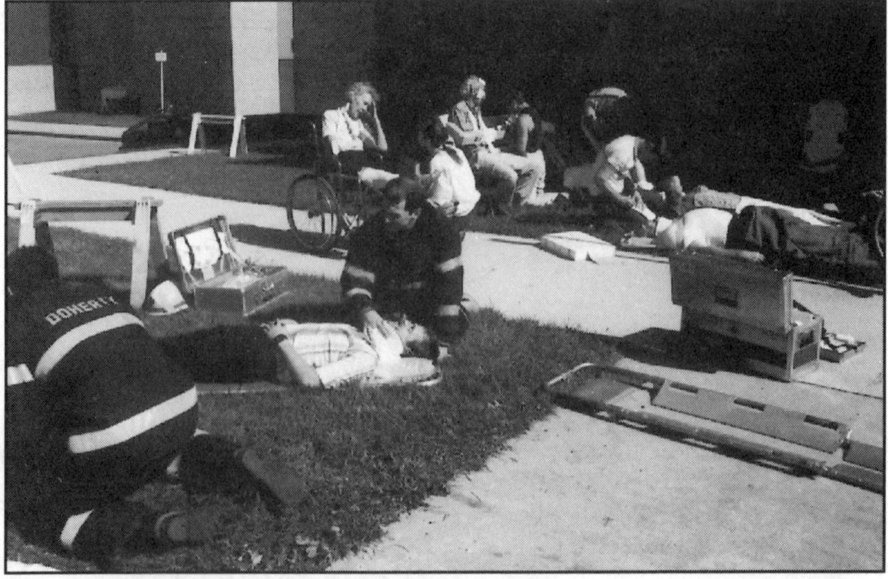

An exercise involving a health care facility.
(Photo Courtesy of Gerry Emas, Edmonton Emergency Response Department.)

Picture 7.3

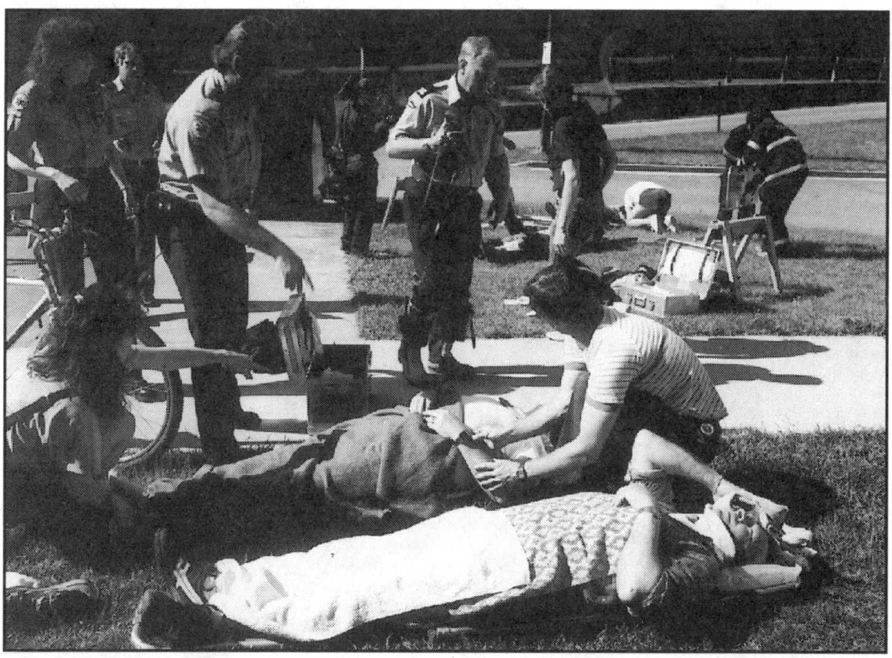

Conducting triage during an exercise at a health care facility.
(Photo Courtesy of Gerry Emas, Edmonton Emergency Response Department.)

Picture 7.4

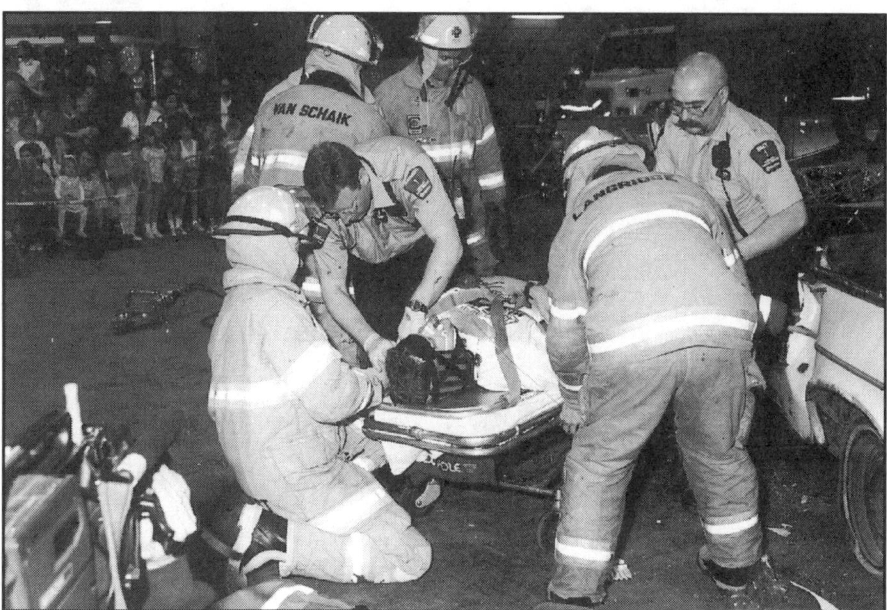

Some exercises, like this one, are open for public viewing.
(Photo Courtesy of Gerry Emas, Edmonton Emergency Response Department.)

Fire Command Systems:
From Fireground Command to the Unified Command System

Captain Gord Sweetnam,
Calgary Fire Deapartment

Photo Courtesy of Gerry Emas, Edmonton Emergency Response Department.

Major fires, dangerous goods incidents, natural disasters and technological accidents are commonplace. In fact, hardly a day passes without a major emergency occurring somewhere in Canada and demanding an appropriate response effort. This 'response' often involves the local Fire Services and a variety of other disaster-response agencies.

Disasters and other emergencies place tremendous and immediate demands on all response agencies. These agencies must quickly neutralize the hazard and help return life to normal. To do so successfully, response agencies must be organized or 'systemic' in their approach. To that end, many Canadian Fire Departments have adapted a variety of command systems designed to help manage personnel and resources at the emergency scene.

This chapter describes the various command systems which are currently employed by many Fire Departments across Canada. Also described are the key training requirements which must supplement these systems to make their implementation successful.

On the surface command systems may appear to be complex and even intimidating. They are based on Standard Operating Procedures (SOPs), General Operating Guidelines (GOGLs) and organizational flow charts (or order models) which are often different from system to system. However, at the basis of all these systems are similar goals. The first goal is to provide company officers with an operational framework. This 'framework' does not explain how to respond to an emergency incident. Rather, it describes the management of personnel and resources during a range of incidents, from small fires to large disasters.

Generally speaking, command systems guide operations. These systems are often accompanied by a set of guidelines and procedures which explain and supplement the general framework of the corresponding system. Moreover, to be fully effective, these systems should be well documented and appropriately distributed so that they can be taught to practitioners, reinforced, reviewed and revised as needed.

Current Fire Service command systems must, and often do, address the special requirements of fire operations. However, as discussed below, each system approaches the task in its own unique fashion. Moreover, while some Fire Departments have applied these systems in their original form others have adopted the systems with various modifications. Fire officers are, therefore, advised to understand these different approaches and apply them appropriately to their own needs.

FIREGROUND COMMAND

The most widely accepted command system within the Canadian Fire Service is the "Fireground Command." The system was developed in the early 1970s by Chief Alan V. Brunacini of the Phoenix Fire Department. The basis of the Fireground Command system is to clearly define specific objectives including the roles, responsibilities, functions and tactical priorities for any given incident.

The system has gained broad recognition and popularity. The main reason for its appeal is that it is a system specific to the fire services. It was written by a fire fighter for fire fighters.

The Fireground Command system centres around the 'fireground commander' who is typically the most senior Fire Officer at the scene of a disaster. The system attempts to simplify and guide the management of the scene. Among other things, the system separates the fire ground commander's function into identifiable segments called 'sectors' and outlines the major roles and responsibilities needed at each.

The Fireground Command system can be applied at any small fire or incident. It is typically activated by the arrival of the first fire unit at the scene of a fire or disaster. The initial step in the activation of the system is the confirmation by the responding

Company Officer that he is assuming command of the Fire Services' response effort. That confirmation, which WILL also identify the location of Command (or headquarters) may be delivered by phone, radio, facsimile or runner.

The confirmation is a very important step because it serves as a basis for the organization and coordination of the response effort as it grows in complexity. It also identifies, for all responding personnel at the scene, the person in charge of the Fire Services (the likely lead service) at the scene and his exact location.

The key responsibility of the Fireground commander, or "Command" for short, is to delegate assignments to personnel based on his initial size up. At the basic level (i.e., a very small fire) Command may have to perform a number of functions in addition to the operational role. Moreover, Command may have to view the whole incident scene as a single 'sector' (see Diagram 8-1). However, with the escalation of the incident, Command is likely to receive more manpower and apparatus. This will increase the complexity of the operation and the capability of Command to respond. On the other hand, the escalation of his resource base may also require the Fireground Commander to 'sectorize' (or segment) the scene into more manageable geographical or physical segments (see Diagram 8-2). Sectors are given a designation based on geographical location (i.e., north, south, east or west sector) or by task (i.e., rescue, ventilation or staging sector).

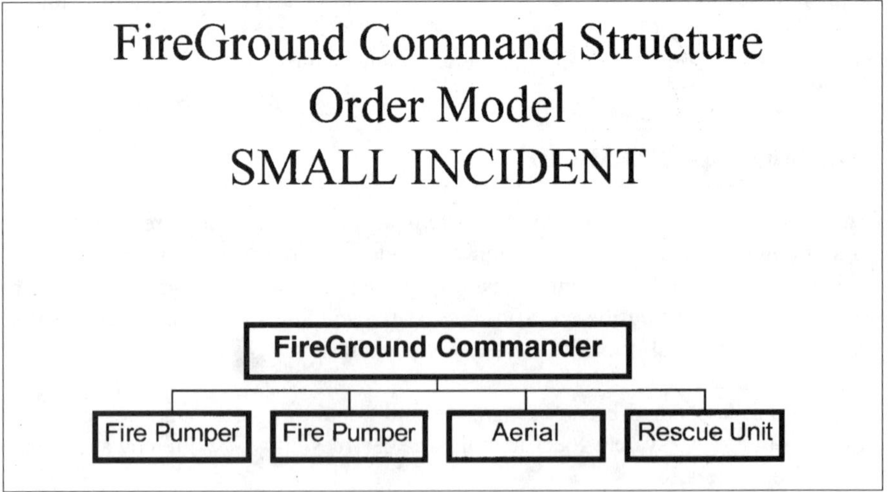

Diagram 8.1

The process of sectorizing entails appointing a number of fire officers to manage specific areas or tasks at the incident. Sectorizing creates another level of supervision in the fire response organization. It also breaks the role of Fireground Command into more manageable units reducing his span of control at the scene. In turn, Sector Officers operate at the tactical level and are each responsible with overseeing a designated area or function. This requires each Sector Officer to monitor, direct, coordinate and reallocate the personnel under his control. As a result, Command can then concentrate more fully on overall strategy and resource allocation.

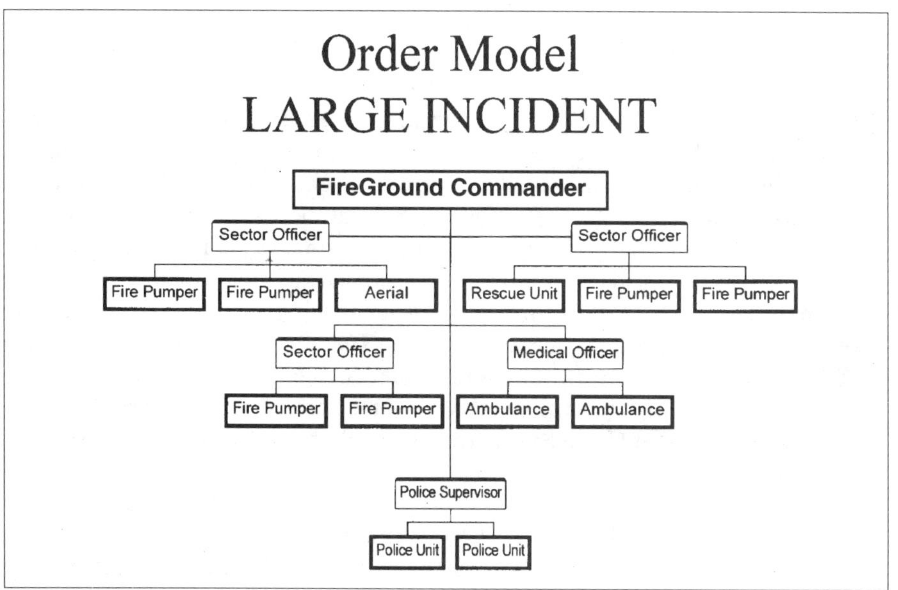

Diagram 8.2

Generally speaking, Fire Departments in Canada closely follow Brunacini's Fireground Command concepts while integrating their own policies and procedures. The outcome reflects their unique response mode, command options and other protocols set to meet their fire administration's wishes. Just the same, the overall concept of Command and its operations remains unchanged.

It is important to recognize that the Fireground Command system establishes Fire Departments as the lead agency at the incident. Consequently, the order model (or organizational chart) reflects Command as a fire officer. Furthermore, the system assumes that the use of Fireground procedures at all emergencies, including smaller ones, would afford company officers greater practice and competence with the system. The system and its procedures then become a conditioned reflex for officers during all incidents including major events like disasters.

The Fireground Command system is designed in such a way that the same procedure is applied in both small and large incidents. The difference between the two types of incidents is the number of sectors which are established. Naturally, the larger the incident the more sectors are likely to be established, manned and provided with resources. Moreover, when sectorized the order model can be easily modified to accommodate other response agencies at the scene (i.e., the Police and emergency medical personnel).

Brunacini's Fireground Command system has been adopted by some of Canada's fire training schools. They are using his text book and complementary workbooks. These help explain the Command system including valuable illustrations, self tests and practical exercises. And, although it was written in the United States, the Fireground Command model (or concept) is an excellent cornerstone for the Canadian Fire Service.

INCIDENT COMMAND

The term and concepts of 'Incident Command' are steadily gaining prominence within the Canadian Fire Service's operations. A key reason for the increasing application of the Incident Command system is the realization that Fire Departments are multi-faceted agencies with responsibilities beyond the traditional 'putting the wet stuff on the red stuff' (i.e., fire fighting). Fire Departments are likely to be involved in dangerous goods incidents, various technical incidents and natural disasters. The size and scope of these diversified emergencies requires the involvement of many agencies and resources at the emergency scene. Therefore, the Command officer can easily become overwhelmed with information, communications resources, planning requirements, the assignment of resources and the completion (or revision) of tactical work sheets. What Command Officers typically need is support, not just on the fire ground, but at the Command level.

The Incident Command System (ICS) operations are similar to those of the Fireground Command system. The general organizational structure, which exists to guide the operation, can be expanded or constricted based on the size and scope of the incident or disaster. The system supports the Command function by dividing the management function into four roles and assigning them to various officers. These roles include operations, planning, logistics, and finance/administrative (see Diagram 8-3). They are assigned to delegated officers who assist Command by reducing Command's span of control, areas of responsibility and work load. This matter alone has been a major factor in the evolution from the Fireground Command system to the Incident Command system.

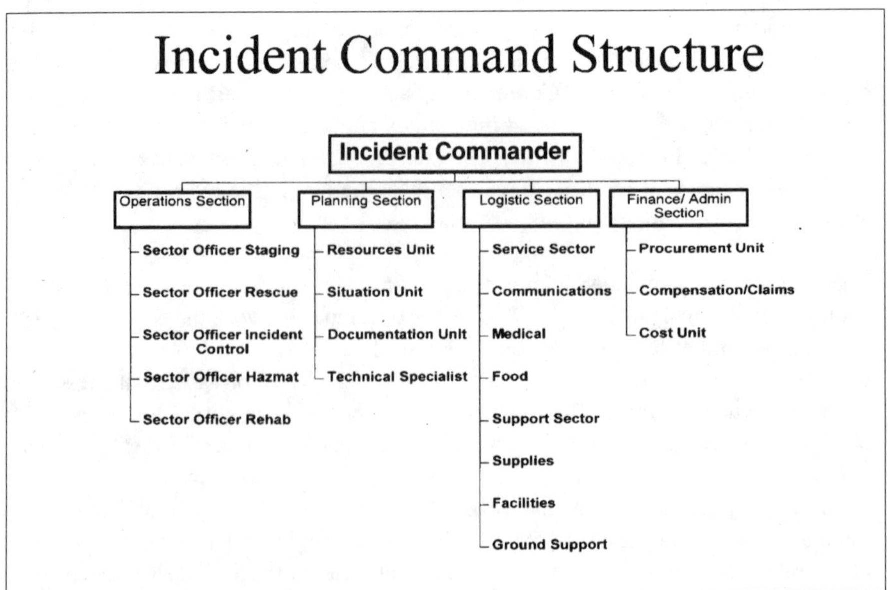

Diagram 8.3

Under the ICS approach, Command operates at the strategic level and is responsible for overall command and incident planning. Each of the separate 'Sections' has its own area of responsibility. These are discussed below.

The 'Operations Section' is responsible for the management of the incident's tactical priorities at the time. These priorities include rescue, fire or incident control, property conservation and the ongoing safety of personnel.

The 'Planning Section' has the task of gathering, analyzing and identifying important information needed for timely decision-making at major incidents. Command may have to deal with many sources of information such as the Police, Fire, mutual-aid, municipal agencies and Non-Government Organizations such as the Red Cross. Therefore, the Planning Section serves as a buffer for Command and prioritizes the information for him. This is intended to enhances Command's ability to make short and long term plans at the scene without being overwhelmed by useless information.

The role of the **'Logistics Section'** is to support the operation at the incident by providing it with all necessary resources. These may include fuel, food, rehabilitation shelter, medical and almost anything else that Command might require at the scene. The Logistics Section must also constantly forecast for future needs at the scene so that the operation does not stall while its personnel are waiting for needed but unavailable resources. Naturally, coordination between the Logistics and Planning sections is imperative throughout the operation.

The 'Finance/Administrative Section' is often overlooked at major incidents. However, it can not and should not be discarded. In cases where costs have to be factored into the operational equation (i.e., clean up of dangerous goods, the use of special equipment, compensation for special supplies) these expenses all have to be documented and accounted for.

As mentioned earlier, the Incident Command System's organizational flow chart illustrates the operation from the fire department's perspective. It permits expansion of the organizational structure, based on the incident and the agencies involved in the response to it. Yet, the integrity of the system remains. In other words, the involvement of more organizations in the response effort does not change the functional areas of Command or its various Sections. Nor does the organization change when it is wound down.

UNIFIED COMMAND

It is important to note that both the Fireground Command system and the Incident Command System provide for the inclusion of other responding agencies in the overall organizational chart or 'framework.' However, the flow charts of both systems are based on the existence of a single-command structure. That is to say, one commander is made responsible for the overall management of the incident regardless of which other jurisdiction, organization or agency is involved. This organizational structure ignores the existence of other emergency response jurisdictions and has the potential of creating needless friction between the fire services and the other disaster-response agencies. Moreover, it can easily lead to a situation where every response agency attends to its own operational priority with a consequent lack of coordination and communication among these groups. The way around this sensitive obstacle is through the use of the Unified Command system.

The Unified Command System (UCS) is designed primarily for major disasters. It recognizes the presence of many jurisdictions at a disaster site. It also recognizes the fact that each responding agency will continue to operate using its own lines of command, procedures and communication system(s). However, what the Unified Command System provides is a structure to coordinate the various response organizations (see Diagram 8-4). This is achieved by the creation of a 'unified' command centre with representatives from each of the Tri-services (i.e., Fire, Police and Medical Services).

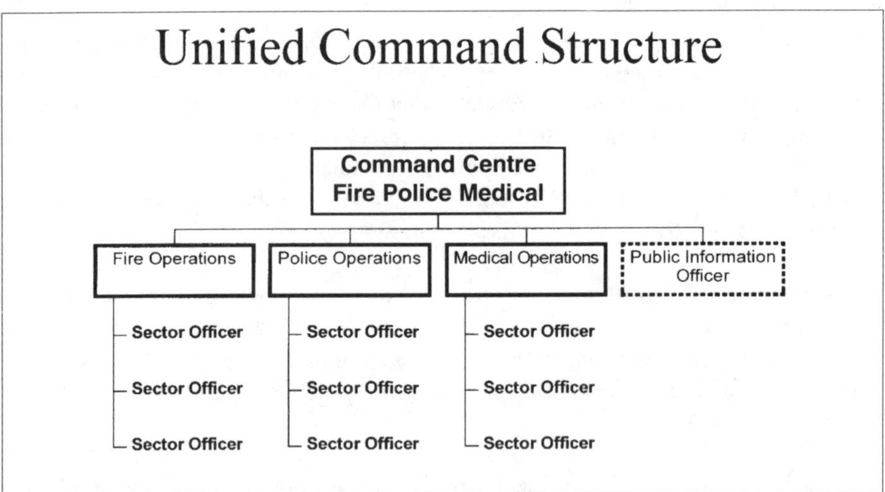

Diagram 8.4

The intent of this joint (i.e., 'unified') command centre should be obvious by now. It allows for the rapid coordination of activities and resources, as well as more effective communications among the key response organizations at a disaster site. In a rather subtle way, it also establishes the basis of a 'team' response and broadens the level of responsibility for the team's response effort.

From the Fire Service's perspective the Unified Command System operates generally the same as the Fireground Command system or the ICS. Often, the first arriving unit at the scene will set up Command. As the response effort to the incident increases in magnitude (i.e., resources, personnel, jurisdictions), Command will likely establish more Sectors and enlarge the Fire Service's operation. At the same time, other response agencies are likely to be going through the same process of deploying their resources, expanding their organization's presence at the scene and beginning to realize how their operations impact on the operations of other responders and ... vice versa!

At a certain point in the operation a decision will typically be made to establish a 'unified' command centre. (The sooner that decision is made the better.) Certain individuals, based on their jurisdiction or respective agency affiliation, will be appointed to the command centre. These designated officials will take charge of their own agency. At the same time they will also determine jointly the objectives, strategy and priorities of the operation.

The presence of all key players within the confines of one command post is significant and would facilitate both collective strategy formulation and timely decision making. Also, the working of these individuals in close proximity to one another, is bound to improve communication and response time. Relevant information can be disseminated and acted upon quickly. Plus the benefit of reduced radio traffic is a blessing at any emergency scene!

The Unified Command System, and its 'unified' command centre, helps deal with the thorny issue of "who is in charge?" This is because of the need for a unified (meaning 'coordinated') approach as well as the need to establish overall goals, objectives and priorities at the scene. While there may be instances when one agency or another has 'command' (or lead role), the system allows input and involvement by the other key response agencies or jurisdictions.

Ideally, all jurisdictional and operational disputes should be resolved well ahead of any incident or disaster-response effort. And, while the Unified Command System demands a coordinated response effort DURING the disaster, it begs for a coordinated emergency planning effort PRIOR to the disaster. Simply stated, what is needed before any incident response effort is a clear, concise document that outlines protocol in the event of a multi-agency response. This 'document' is part of the necessary emergency planning process (see Chapter 3 for more detail).

The Unified Command System has attracted many emergency departments. They have opted for this system because it allows for smoother joint operations, particularly at the command level, during multi-agency and multi-jurisdictional disaster response.

EMERGENCY OPERATIONS CENTRE

It is worthwhile, at this point, to briefly discuss the emergency operations centre (EOC). The EOC is a facility which is designed to facilitate the conduct and management of an operation. It is intended to become the focal point of the flow of communication, the making of strategic decisions and the coordination of key activities.

The EOC is particularly useful when incidents grow to disastrous proportions and involve various response organizations (and jurisdictions).

Each responding organization brings with it its own emergency/response plan, procedures, communication resources, protocols and personnel. Some of these may be compatible across agencies. Others may not and may, therefore, create added complications for the overall response effort. The intent of the EOC is to smooth out the wrinkles which may exist between the various response procedures, priorities and protocols.

Disaster response requires a multi-organizational response (see Chapter 1). Given this reality, the EOC structure facilitates the execution of any disaster response operation as a 'partnership.' Brunacini's advice is worth heeding: "When in trouble, take on a partner."

The Emergency Operations Centre is typically staffed by top level officials from the various organizations which participate in the response. The EOC personnel must have their roles clearly defined. This would help alleviate guess work, support the team, speed the response process and reduce the pressure on all who are involved. The role of the EOC staff is to make management decisions in support of the operations at the incident! They are also charged with obtaining additional sources of support, forecasting needs and prioritizing activities. To facilitate this, the EOC must contain all relevant communications equipment, work stations and space for meetings or 'conferences.'

The EOC staff should have at their disposal, and be familiar with, all relevant resource manuals, SOPs, mutual aid agreements and other related reference materials. The EOC should also contain appropriate contacts at government (municipal, provincial, federal), support agency and industry levels. Amateur radio and communications personnel are an integral part of the EOC's operations and should also be included as 'resources' within the EOC.

The EOC may be located anywhere and its layout depends on a variety of factors. These include the space available for the EOC, specific requirements for that space, the requirements of the agencies which may occupy it and much more. There is no right or wrong way to lay out the EOC as long as the layout facilitates the management of the disaster response.

Diagram 8.5 illustrates the organizational structure of the Unified Command System when the EOC is included. Please note that the existence of the EOC does NOT eliminate the need for a site commander but in fact promotes it! Moreover, from the Fire Service's perspective, the presence of the EOC does not in any way remove the need for a Fire-Service-specific 'system.' The Fireground Command system, Incident Command System or the Unified Command System are still required to guide Fire Service operations.

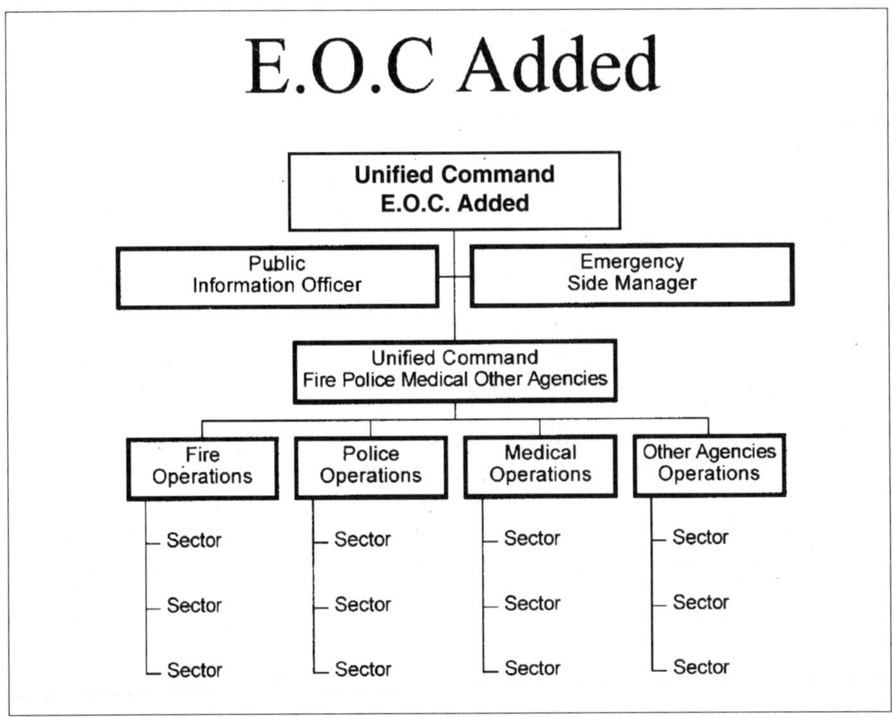

Diagram 8.5

EMERGENCY SITE MANAGEMENT

The Emergency Site Management system is by far the most complex disaster-management system because it looks at the whole structure of response within and external to the respective community where the disaster has occurred. The system is a derivative of both the Fireground Command system and the Incident Command System. It was developed during the early 1980s by Emergency Preparedness Canada and has been slowly evolving since. Chapter 9 describes the system in detail.

It would suffice here to note that the inclusion of an EOC in the response-management structure necessitated the appointment of an Emergency Site Manager (ESM). This individual is typically appointed by the EOC staff to manage and coordinate operations at the incident site. The ESM also serves as a liaison (or link) between the Emergency Operations Centre and other members of the command post at the site.

The position of the Emergency Site Manager (ESM) makes an excellent contribution to the response-team's chain of command by further reducing the span of control at the site. This may be achieved regardless of the command system used to respond to the disaster (i.e., single or unified). Some Fire Services personnel refer to the position of the Emergency Site Manager as "Operations" with an obvious reference to the structure of the Unified Command System. However, the two positions (and titles) are very different and using them interchangeably is misleading! The operations position is charged with the incident's fire-related tactical priorities. Fire 'Operations' reports to Command. On the other hand, the ESM's position is an important link between the on-scene agencies and the EOC.

The actual position of the Emergency Site Manager may be filled by a variety of people. Typically, the nature of the incident dictates the background required by the ESM. For example, in a major fire-related incident the senior officer-on-site will likely assume the role of an ESM. On the other hand, a Police related emergency (i.e., hostage taking) will typically require a Police official to assume the ESM position. Mass poisoning and other major medical incidents may require the services of a medical supervisor as an ESM.

The ESM may be appointed in a variety of ways. In some instances the ESM will be pre-designated by the Municipal emergency plan or its procedures. In other cases, the position may be staffed during the incident with someone appointed by the EOC. Regardless of how it is filled, the role of the ESM is critical in linking all components of the response effort both on and off the disaster site.

FORESTRY SERVICE'S INCIDENT COMMAND SYSTEM

Picture 8.1

A forest fire station at risk during a forest fire.
(Courtesy of Dale Huberdeau.)

Over the years, the Forestry Service in Canada has had to contend with many major wildland fires. The task of commanding an incident which is spread out over a vast area is particularly difficult and can be a very humbling experience. A further complication to the task are the specialized resources which are required for the job. These may include hundreds of additional fire fighters, aerial support, water supply problems, specialized equipment and other mutual-aid support. Obviously this type of incident can make the selection of Command staff critical. Interestingly there are a number of similarities between the operational response process of the Forestry service and that of the Fire Service.

When the Forest Service in Canada receives a report of a wildland fire a 'first strike team' is immediately dispatched to the scene. This 'team' consists of a small working group of Forestry fire fighters and one officer. If the strike team is unable to cope with the fire an escape fire analysis is done. This analysis consists of a forestry service officer who engages in an aerial size-up to set response priorities. Simultaneously, a fire overhead team is activated. This team is the foundation of the Forestry Service's Incident Command System.

The Forestry Service's flow chart (see Diagram 8-6) is similar in many ways to the US-developed Firescope Incident Command. A comparison of the two order models highlights many similarities between them. The difference between these two systems and the Fire Ground Command is primarily one of terminology. Naturally, the forestry command flow chart is specific to the tasks of the Forestry Service, but is capable of expansion to include other agencies—a similarity to the Unified Command System.

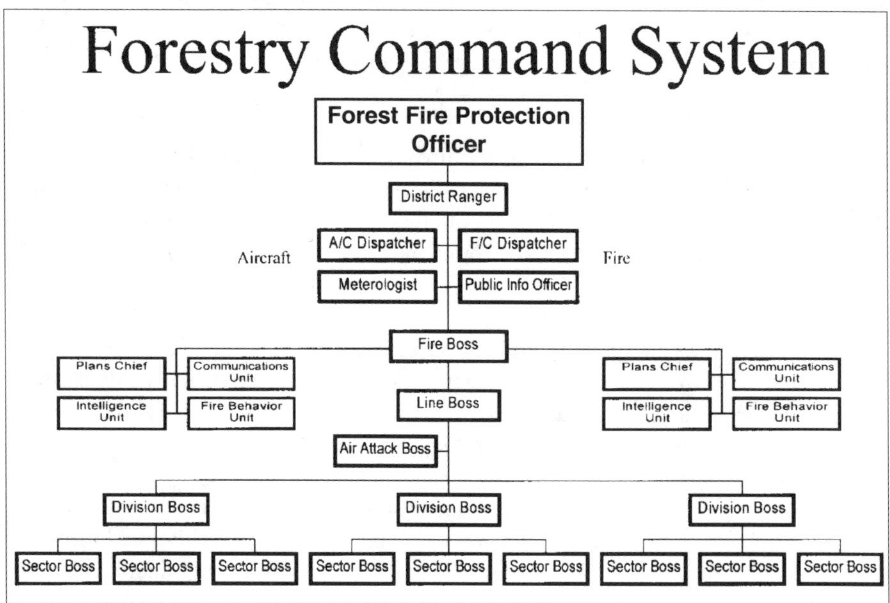

Diagram 8.6

THE SAME BUT ... DIFFERENT

The various command systems which were discussed above are similar in many ways. They all have a written description of their 'framework' (i.e., goals, roles and procedures). This framework also includes an order model which defines the parts of the system and how they are linked together. They all have a mechanism which allows their organizational structure to expand or constrict based on the needs of the situation.

The various systems are all aimed at making the management of the disaster site more manageable. They reduce Command's span of control allowing it to stay focused at the strategic level. They also attempt to facilitate communication, decision making and the coordination of resources and activities. To that end they are all successful. However, they are NOT suited for all occasions and require both careful analysis and appropriate application.

The Fireground Command system, for example, is ideal for the purposes of the Fire Services. It is a role for which the system was designed and is suited for it! The system concentrates on the jurisdiction, function and mandate of the Fire Services and overlooks the jurisdictional responsibilities of other response agencies. Its 'sectorizing' is done typically along geographical or tactical functions.

The Incident Command System, on the other hand, provides a somewhat different scope of operation by addressing the Command issue from a more 'functional' perspective. Recall the division of Command into Sections based on four management functions: Operations; Logistics; Planning; and Finance/administrative. This system too overlooks the jurisdictional powers of response agencies outside the Fire Services.

The Unified Command System, and its use of the Emergency Operations Centre, begins to involve other agencies (and jurisdictions) as partners in the response plan. This system recognizes the involvement of other agencies and acknowledges the need for inter-agency coordination (versus command) as well as a 'unified' decision making process.

The addition of the Emergency Operations Centre, as seen at the Unified Command System and the Emergency Site Management system, can be of tremendous assistance in the acquisition of needed resources from external agencies. The EOC concept can be easily integrated into any of the order models.

Finally, the Emergency Site Management system allows for the inclusion of the Emergency Site Manager. It is a relatively new position and role, divorced from any specific agency and responsible for the management of activities at the disaster site. As such, it moves away from direct responsibility for Fire operations into a more strategic view of the operation.

'I BE THE BOSS'

There are many obstacles to the implementation of a command system and they grow proportionally with the number of disaster-response agencies represented at the site. The Police, Fire and Emergency Medical Services may each have their own separate and distinct command system. Confronted with a major emergency all three agencies may also have their own separate response plans.

One of the key questions for all disaster or emergency responders is "who is in charge?" The question can be divided into two parts. One is "who is in charge of my organization?" The other is "who is in charge of the operation at the site?" The answer to the former question is simple. The chain of command within each organization typically is unchanged and remains within the original organization. The answer to the second question is slightly more complex. In essence it depends on the command system used to manage the response effort. In the case of the Fireground Command System and the Incident Command System the person in charge—or Command—is a Fire officer designated as having that role. He typically assumes direction of all other agencies.

On the other hand, when using the Unified Command System the function of Command is shared among representatives from a number of key organizations. There is a shift from Command to Coordination. In the case of the Emergency Site Management system, the shift if even more pronounced. It is from the role of Command to the role of an Emergency Site Manager with NO organizational affiliation other than to the whole response effort!

The ideal time to determine 'who is in charge' is BEFORE the response operation. As mentioned above, the mandate for this role should be established during the planning process and involve all key response organizations. Additionally, the planning process needs to also address where and how Command will be established and executed. Consider, for example, a situation with a person appointed as Command (or Emergency Site Manager) without sufficient communication links, resources or a command (i.e., operations) centre. This limitation would clearly cripple the management system and perhaps the whole operation.

THE SITE COMMAND CENTRE

Speaking of Command, one area that is often neglected is the on-site command post. In many cases the Fire Department, Police Department and Emergency Medical Services have their own Mobile Command Centres. Although individual command centre have their place depending on the emergency (i.e., hostage incident), any major emergency involving the tri-services (i.e., Police, Fire, Medical) should have one centralized command centre designated as the 'Site Command Centre.' The key here is to assemble all relevant personnel at the Site Command Centre. This offers them a place to make informed, collective decisions in an atmosphere that is quiet, with relevant equipment and materials. It should provide them the space and comfort to get the job done. Moreover, regardless of ownership, the Site Command Centre must be both user friendly and available for all key response agencies.

The command post should also be clearly visible in order to quickly attract the attention of responders from all agencies. It should have outside colours and markings that will readily identify it as the Site Command Centre. Such markings should not be restricted to one specific agency (i.e., the Fire Services) because this may alienate members of the other key response agencies. Instead, every effort should be made to make these markings generic or all inclusive. Moreover, the Site Command Centre vehicle must be large enough to contain all necessary equipment to manage the scene. This equipment must include such things as radios, cellular phones, a fax machine, police computer, television and other items which will facilitate the communication process.

The Site Command Centre should include both work stations for the immediate responding agencies as well as provisions for other support agencies. If possible, a small conference room/space should also be considered. Certain comforts have to be addressed for the personnel working in this stressful environment. Air conditioning, washroom facilities, and refreshments are all important to a well designed mobile command centre.

Like any retail business, the effectiveness of the Site Command Centre depends on its location. It should be situated in a conspicuous location giving Command a two dimensional view of the incident and, where possible, the surrounding area. Command should avoid the trap of being drawn into the scene by selecting a position too close to the incident. On the other hand fire apparatus and other emergency vehicles should be prevented from surrounding the Site Command Centre and restricting Command's view of the scene. (As an aside, vehicle movement to and from the scene should remain free of obstruction). Moreover, as noted above a visible command centre should eliminate the need for the standard question "Who is in charge and where is he?"

TRAINING IS A MUST

Regardless of how well a Fire Department develops its guidelines and designs its order model, one thing is apparent. Someone has to be in charge! The traditional (and accepted) Fire Department's practice is that the first arriving company officer will activate the command system. This will typically be either the Fireground Command system, the Incident Command System or a modification of the two. Should the incident remain small in size and manageable, the officer in charge may remain in command until the incident is terminated. However, in the event that the incident grows to require more personnel and resources from other agencies, a responding higher ranking officer may assume Command. (Naturally, the exact process will likely depend on departmental protocols for command transfer procedures.)

With this in mind, all responding fire fighters, company officers and chief officers must have a working knowledge of their respective command system. Fire fighters need an understanding of the command system, because they have to work within it. A senior fire fighter may be required to perform at the sector officer level until additional officers and personnel arrive to relieve him. Company officers must be well versed in the command system, as they are typically the first link in the confirmation and activation of the command structure at the scene. Organized properly by the company officer, the transfer of Command to a higher ranking officer could become smooth and orderly. Finally, chief officers are more likely to inherit an organized scene if all the right command procedures have been followed before their arrival.

If any command system is to run smoothly, Fire Services must consider ... training for their staff! This training should be conducted in as many varied forms as possible from classroom training to simulations and exercises. As much as possible, these training programs should involve responders from other jurisdictions. Moreover, training simulations and emergency exercises should often involve a review of the Command System and the process of its application. Without that review one may not detect problems which would otherwise surface during disasters.
Diagram 8-8 illustrates one version of a Fireground Command Check List. Many others exist and could serve a similar purpose. The key point is that the desired command system be exercised and evaluated using SOME system of evaluation.

CONCLUSION

In conclusion, it is important to note that incidents and disasters are events which can and must be managed. A number of systems currently exist to guide Fire Service's personnel through the management of their own service as well as the management of the scene. None of the systems described above are perfect. However, each offers an approach which is worth considering and implementing as appropriate.

Picture 8.2

Deployment of field Command Posts of the tri-services
(Photo Courtesy of Gordon Sweetnam, Calgary Fire Department.)

Picture 8.3

Mobile Command Centre.
(Photo Courtesy of Gordon Sweetnam, Calgary Fire Department.)

The Emergency Site Management (ESM) System

Ron Kuban, Ph.D.
President, Turning Point Consulting Corp.

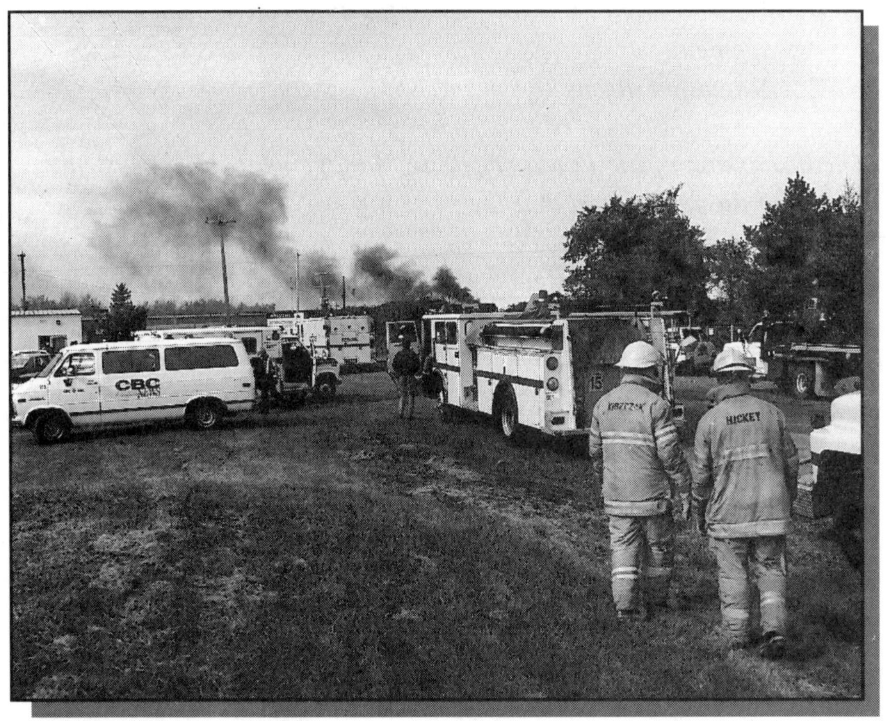

(Photo Courtesy of Gerry Emas, Edmonton Emergency Response Department.)

This chapter describes the Emergency Site Management (ESM) system for managing a disaster at a community (versus an organizational) level. The topic will be addressed in two parts:

1. *A discussion of the key principles of effective disaster management.*
2. *A detailed discussion of the ESM system.*

The discussion of the Emergency Site Management (ESM) system is based on the realization that the system:

1. *Is more closely aligned with the needs of Canadian municipalities than any other disaster management system.*
2. *Permits municipal elected officials and their representatives to maintain their authority over disaster operations.*
3. *Is more inclusive and maximizes the coexistence of varying jurisdictional authorities.*
4. *Permits the incorporation of a broad range of support from agencies external to the affected municipality.*
5. *Emphasizes coordination rather than simply the command of disaster operations.*
6. *Facilitates the flow of information despite a breakdown of one or more organizational linkages.*

Fire Services across North America have at their disposal a number of systems for the management of disaster scenes. Prominent among these systems are the Fireground Command, the Incident Command System and the Unified Command System. These systems are described at length in Chapter 8.

These disaster-scene management systems were developed in the United States to address the unique needs and culture of the Fire Services. While effective in meeting the needs of most, if not all Fire Departments, these systems may be insufficient for the unique needs of Canadian communities and of other key response agencies (e.g., Police, Emergency Medical Services, governments and industry). The scene management or Command systems of the Fire Services should, therefore, be complemented by a system which would take into account the needs of the whole community and consider the environment outside the disaster scene. The Emergency Site Management (ESM) system meets this requirement.

This chapter describes the ESM process through the following:

1. A discussion of the key principles of effective disaster response.
2. A detailed discussion of the ESM system.

THE KEY PRINCIPLES OF DISASTER RESPONSE

Any meaningful discussion relating to the management of disaster response must begin with an understanding of the unique context of 'disasters.' Only then can one put meaning to the applicability of the management system to one's organization. Only then can one better understand whether (and if so how) one management system is more practical than another. Chapter 1 provides that context. However, a few aspects are significant enough for the discussion in this chapter to merit a brief repetition.

By their definition, disasters are events of such large magnitude that the response to them is often beyond the realm of a single organization. Disaster response, therefore, often involves a multi-organizational multi-jurisdictional effort. The response to disasters at municipal level nearly always involves a broad range of response agencies. These include the Police, Emergency Medical Services, hospitals, transportation, Public Works, Social Services and many more. Also included are other orders of government, Industry and volunteer organizations.

Disaster response effort at a municipal level often involves all major organizations within that municipality. That is an important consideration for Fire Services personnel because few of the 'other' responders would have a 'Command' structure, organization structure or culture similar to that of the Fire Department.

Moreover, the multi-organizational and multi-jurisdictional nature of disaster response demands both cooperation among its response agencies as well as coordination of their activities at the scene. This is a 'truth' born out of much research and actual disaster response effort. Failure to achieve these two key requirements typically results in the breakdown of communications, failure to effectively allocate scarce resources, disjointed operational tasking and the inability by ANY single organization to effectively meet its disaster response requirements.

Effective disaster response demands effective communications. It demands that equipment such as radios, phones, telex or computers remain functional. It demands the timely transfer of information from one person or organization to another. And, it absolutely demands that all concerned clearly understand what they are told.

The requirement for effective communications exists within each organization, between (or among) organizations and between these organizations and the public. Without it any effort to coordinate resources and activities assumes the risk of failure. However, almost predictably, both the exchange of information and the hardware that facilitates it are prone to overload and failure. A major part of the problem is the nature of disasters. They are typified by the lack of what they must have most; accurate, timely and useful information.

The absence of meaningful communications presents a monumental obstacle to effective decision making. Disaster response demands that decisions be effective and made quickly. The consequences of faulty or unnecessarily delayed decisions are likely to be fatalities, injuries and significant property or environmental damage. The making of effective decisions during periods of disaster or crisis is made more difficult by the vacuum of meaningful information.

Disasters are also stressful events. They beg for a system which would assist individuals from different organizations to unite quickly in order to resolve complex and unique issues at a time of great uncertainty and significant concern for health and well being.

Routine or daily management systems are designed to achieve organizational goals through the effective and efficient use of available resources. Disaster management systems are devised for the same purpose but with one key difference—their organizational goals are affected by the disaster. For example, needed resources may be destroyed by the disaster. Key personnel may be isolated, hurt or preoccupied by higher priorities (e.g., saving lives in their immediate area). People with specific and highly desired skills may be needed in more than one location. Or, mutual aid partners may be preoccupied with a disaster of their own and may, therefore, be unavailable.

Community-based organizations may be confronted by other complications. The day-to-day operations of some organizations may be stopped suddenly and unexpectedly. A few organizations may suddenly lose their 'jurisdictional authority' and be made subordinate to the municipality. The organizational integrity of some organizations may be severely tested as they become segmented and sent off to do various tasks in relatively new geographical areas.

It should be abundantly clear by now that disaster situations demand something different than day-to-day management practices. Disaster management systems and practices, particularly those which are employed by municipalities, must satisfy four broad requirements which recognize:

1. The unique environment of disasters.
2. The nature of municipal response (e.g., multi-organizational and jurisdictional, supremacy of elected officials).
3. The presence and capabilities of the 'local state' (i.e., members of other government agencies within the municipality).
4. The unique crisis-management skills demanded of effective disaster response.

Effective community-disaster management systems must be designed to meet a number of key principles. These include:

1. Appropriate response to unique situations.
2. Flexibility and adaptability.
3. Cooperation across organizations and jurisdictions.
4. Traditional supremacy of elected officials maintained.
5. Provincial and federal governments acting 'in support.'
6. Coordination of planning and response efforts.
7. Enhancement of the flow and distribution of information.
8. A functional Emergency Operation Centre (E.O.C.) must be functional.
9. Disaster site management through team effort.

Appropriate response to unique situations

All disaster management systems must be designed to permit their application during a wide range of unique situations. In other words, these system should not be designed to address a single type of disaster agent (i.e., earthquake) or a single type of consequence (i.e., flooding). However, those who employ the 'system' should be able to apply it to meet the unique needs of each situation.

Disaster management systems must concentrate on "process" rather than on well defined specific outcomes. During day-to-day management activities, the outcome of one's actions is generally pre-designed and predictable (i.e., "If we take action A we will get result B".) However, during disasters, the outcomes of one's actions are often unknown, unpredictable or beyond one's control. Disaster response organizations must, therefore, facilitate and encourage the necessary actions in an environment where knowledge about what happened and what needs to happen is incomplete.

Flexibility and adaptability

The disaster environment is typically 'fluid' (or ever-changing), unpredictable and demanding of a response. Responders and disaster managers often lack experience with the disaster and are surprised by its onset and unfolding. While they are encouraged to be persistent in their efforts, they cannot remain rigid in their approach. Flexibility and adaptability are, therefore, critical to the successful management of the unique environment of disasters (Auf der Heide, 1989; Drabek, 1986; Drabek & Hoetmer, 1991; Dynes, 1970; Perrow, 1984; Quarantelli, 1978, 1985).

Effective disaster management systems must encourage operational and organizational flexibility. Such systems must be designed to allow for variations in resource availability, jurisdictions, operational requirements and organizational structures. The 'system' of response can not depend on specific individuals or resources. Moreover, the response system must allow ad-hoc organizations, which are prevalent in disaster operations, to be incorporated into the overall effort and to be well managed.

Cooperation across organizations and jurisdictions

Community disasters demand a response that involves many organizations from diverse jurisdictions. The efficient management of their individual activities demands 'coordination.' This element is discussed below. However, any discussion regarding coordination must be preceded by a word or two regarding 'cooperation.'

'Cooperation' is the willingness of one individual or organization to work with another. It can not be coerced or manipulated. Moreover, this 'willingness' is a critical component to the sharing of effort which is at the basis of disaster response. Its intent is not the loss of one organization's identity, structure or culture to another. Instead, it is the free association of two or more individuals or organizations with an accepted joint purpose.

Cooperation, in the context of community emergency response, should exist through the planning, response and recovery stages of emergency management. It requires that the various organizations understand (and accept) the presence of hazards and risks, the roles intended for them and the outcomes which are expected of them. This is significant because it is at this point that the Emergency Site Management System parts company from the Incident Command System and its derivatives.

The various Incident Command System(s) are based on the realistic assumptions that, generally speaking, they will involve other Fire Services organizations. These systems assume that non-Fire organizations would be few in number and would automatically accept the 'lingo' and structure of the Fire Services and its 'command' structure. Many of the systems also assume that the overall 'command' of the response organization will be in the hands of a Fire Officer.

Reality paints a somewhat different picture. Fire Departments which respond to large municipal disasters are often outnumbered by the other organizations and jurisdictions which also respond to these events. Moreover, in a few instances, the Fire Services may be given a secondary role to the 'lead agency' (i.e., Police). Regardless, full and effective cooperation can not be instantly secured through command. To work effectively, it must be negotiated, accepted and planned for.

The various fire-scene management or 'command' systems can depend on the effective mix of cooperation and 'command'. After all, these systems are designed for organizations with relatively similar terminology, culture, resources and goals. These 'command' systems should be retained to manage the response within Fire organizations.

However, the management of the community's overall response effort must encourage and be more supportive of inter-agency cooperation. It must also take into consideration the multi-jurisdictional and multi-cultural element of the community's response organizations.

Traditional supremacy of elected officials maintained

When disasters strike Canadian municipalities, disaster response is often the responsibility of municipal elected officials. Stated differently, elected officials at the municipal level are responsible by law to prepare for and respond to disasters which might affect their public (EPC, 1992). Nested within that broad jurisdiction are elements of various other jurisdictions: Police, Fire, Emergency Medical Services and other health officials, dangerous goods specialists, members of local industry and officials from provincial and federal government departments.

Disaster response in Canada is generally the responsibility of elected officials at the municipal level. The rare exceptions to the rule are disasters with broad geographical impact (i.e., those affecting a number of communities), or those which affect areas under the specific jurisdiction of the provinces/territories (e.g., parks) or the federal government (e.g., military bases, parks).

When the jurisdiction of municipal elected officials is maintained during disaster response, even when other jurisdictions (i.e., provincial/territorial and federal) are present, a strong and valuable message is sent. It emphasizes the responsibility of the municipality's elected officials to their constituents. It also places the responsibility for effective emergency preparedness and response with those who have the best knowledge of their community, its hazards, resources, and capabilities.

There is another element to this principle. It relates to the fact that only rarely does a whole community shut-down due to a disaster. More likely, many of the community's residents continue with their daily routines even while the response efforts are still underway. Elected officials and their representatives must balance the 'realities' of the disaster response effort as well as the needs of the rest of the community.

An effective disaster management system must, therefore, integrate the responsibilities of the municipality's elected officials. The system must factor-in the involvement of elected officials and must ultimately lay the responsibility for effective response on their shoulders.

That is not to say that elected officials must direct the tactical or even strategic response to the the disaster. They should direct neither! However, they can not be ignored and all responders should realize that the response effort is typically the jurisdiction of these officials and all responders must be accountable to them.

Provincial and Federal governments act 'in support'

Disaster response invariably involves resources owned and controlled by other orders of government (i.e., provincial, territorial and federal). These resources may include unique goods and the skills of members of the 'local state', or the other government agencies and departments which are located within the municipality.

Members of the 'local state' may perform a number of concurrent activities. These may include: health inspections, dangerous goods inspections, environmental tests, structural inspections, and a broad range of other services. Similarly, these agencies may provide resources such as bridging equipment, telecommunication centres, power generators, airplanes and much more!

When these services and resources are offered, they are typically provided in support of municipal efforts. In other words, generally speaking the involvement of provincial or federal resources does not automatically mean a shift of overall jurisdiction away from the municipality's elected officials (EPC, 1992).

Coordination of planning and response effort

As mentioned above, disasters demand a multi-organizational and multi-jurisdictional response. In other words, no single organization (i.e., a Fire Department) can respond unilaterally. Additionally, the response of one organization can often have significant influence on the outcome of the response of others. Case in point is a situation where a Police control point could limit or delay access to the site by other responders (e.g., rescue specialists, dog teams, or other volunteer organizations).

The need to coordinate activities and resources is much more critical during disasters than during the day-to-day operations of an organization or a community. Limited time and the risk to life and limb dictate that things be done right the first time. This requires that the various response efforts be coordinated so as to avoid dangerous operational gaps, or working at cross purposes.

Here too it is important to note that the element of 'coordination' should not be confused with the term 'command.' Many researchers (Auf der Heide, 1989; Drabek, 1981, 1987; Drabek and Hoetmer, 1991; Dynes, 1970; Quarantelli, 1985) have noted that the para-military structure, with its centralized command system, is not practical as the primary system with which to manage peacetime municipal disasters.

Effective coordinated disaster response is best achieved through coordinated planning involving all key players. A community's disaster management system must permit on-going planning effort and facilitate a collaborative approach among its response agencies.

Enhancement of the Flow and Distribution of Information

Accurate and timely information is the lifeline of any management system (Barton, 1993). It is particularly critical during the response to disasters (Drabek & Hoetmer, 1991). Accurate, meaningful and timely information is the basis of effective decision making and coordinated effort.

Disaster management systems must, therefore, facilitate the flow of information within response organizations, across organizational boundaries and between the response agencies and the public (Quarantelli, 1985). To do so effectively, disaster management systems must encourage the creation of numerous channels of communications, streamline information processing and ensure that no key response organization is excluded from the communication loop.

An Emergency Operations Centre (EOC) must be functional

Some responders perceive that disaster response operations can operate independently of municipal coordination. Or, that these operations can be effectively managed without calling to bear the other resources of the community. A prevalent attitude among response agencies is that they 'can handle it.'

In a way, that attitude has some validity. Fire Departments regularly suppress small and large fires independently of municipal officials. Similarly, Police officers can effectively resolve hostage taking situations, Emergency Medical Services staff members can successfully respond to multi-casualty incidents, and industry personnel can overcome on-site chemical spills with efficiency and skill.

However, large catastrophic events which impact the 'community' create an entirely new operational environment with new requirements for coordinated response. These situations typically involve the rapid activation of all response agencies and require the coordination of their resources and activities. These events heighten public concerns and increase media attention. They also create a unique need: to seek mutual aid and coordinate its response within the community. All of these demand a more comprehensive coordination effort, at municipal (not organizational) level. This requires a functioning 'nerve centre.'

Effective disaster management systems must include a 'nerve centre' or an Emergency Operations Centre (EOC) for the community. Such a centre need not be continually in operation. However, it must be established and available within the community. (The EOC will be discussed in more detail later in this chapter).

It is important to note here that the need for a community Emergency Operations Centre is not intended to prevent the establishment of other EOCs or to minimize their importance. The specific response agencies within the community (e.g., Fire, Police, Emergency Medical Services, Public Works), provincial/territorial and federal departments, as well as industrial site operators may each activate their own emergency operations centres. These separate EOCs should ideally be linked to the community's EOC to permit for the rapid exchange of information and resources.

The manner in which the EOC Group and the Site Team operate and interrelate is discussed below in another section. Suffice it to say, at this point, that the role of the EOC is to support those who operate at the 'sharp end' (i.e., the site).

Disaster Site Management Through Team Effort

Response efforts at the site—the impact area of the disaster—can and should be managed by those who are there. In short, these 'responders' are physically located at the disaster site. They have the best view of local conditions, are best able to notice and adapt to changing conditions at the site, and are best equipped to take immediate action as necessary. Their first priority centres on the saving of lives and the prevention of further loss of life or injury.

Disaster responders at the site are likely to represent a broad range of organizations and jurisdictions. The management system best suited to their needs is one which encourages and permits a 'team' approach to disaster response, under the leadership of a site manager whose specific role will be discussed below.

THE EMERGENCY SITE MANAGEMENT (ESM) SYSTEM

Credit must be given to the developers of the Fireground Command and ICS systems. These systems provided the conceptual basis for the development of the Emergency Site Management (ESM) system which took root in Canada during the early 1980's.

It is worthy of note that each province in Canada has mandated its municipal elected officials to effectively prepare for and respond to disasters. This mandate fosters the expectation that municipalities conduct planning which involves all key response organizations within their community and those external to it.

This on-going planning process is important from a number of perspectives. It provides a psychological and operational momentum to the emergency management process (i.e., planning, response, recovery). The on-going attention assists in keeping updated existing procedures, contact lists and resource allocations. But most importantly, it helps maintain direct contact among those who will be involved in the community's disaster response effort. In essence, these people and their organizations form a disaster response network. The true value of this 'network' is fully realized only during disaster response operations.

An overview of the ESM System

The system is based on a multi-tiered interaction among various organizations at two primary locations: the disaster site and the municipal EOC. Members of the Fire Services have an important role at both locations.

The implementation of the ESM system typically begins with the separate deployment of each emergency-response organization. Often, each organization begins its response to an incident long before the municipality becomes aware that it is confronting a disaster situation. Consequently, fire apparatus, police cruisers and ambulances are rapidly dispatched to the scene. And, if warranted, additional municipal resources (e.g., search teams, dangerous goods specialists, utility workers) may also be deployed to the site based on the requirements of those at the site and the availability of these resources within the municipality.

Once at the scene, representatives of the various agencies often try to work together even to the point of establishing an informal command system. As more and more resources arrive at the site, someone usually assumes the role of 'coordinator' or quasi Site Manager and begins the coordination of these resources and of response activities. That is a natural progression in the response effort and should not be discouraged. Then, in many cases, when it is realized that the situation is severe and demands more resources, a call is made to activate the municipal EOC Control Group (Figure 9.1).

Two conditions are likely to bring about the activation of the municipal EOC and with it the full implementation of the ESM system. One is the realization that there is an immediate need to better coordinate the activities on and off the site. The other condition occurs when it appears that community resources may be or actually are insufficient to respond to the disaster. The request to activate the municipal EOC may be made by a responder (i.e., the Fireground Commander) at the scene, a representative of a key response agency off-scene, or a member of the municipal EOC Control Group (i.e., the Fire or Police Chief). Moreover, the request may be made by one or more of the response agencies.

The primary role of the municipal EOC Control Group, which includes the Fire Chief, is to support the response efforts of the emergency site manager and the site team. A second key role of the EOC Control Group is to funnel necessary resources to the emergency site. These resources may be secured from resources owned and operated by the municipality. Needed resources may also be provided by municipal-based agencies and businesses, as well as organizations located outside the municipality (Figure 9.2).

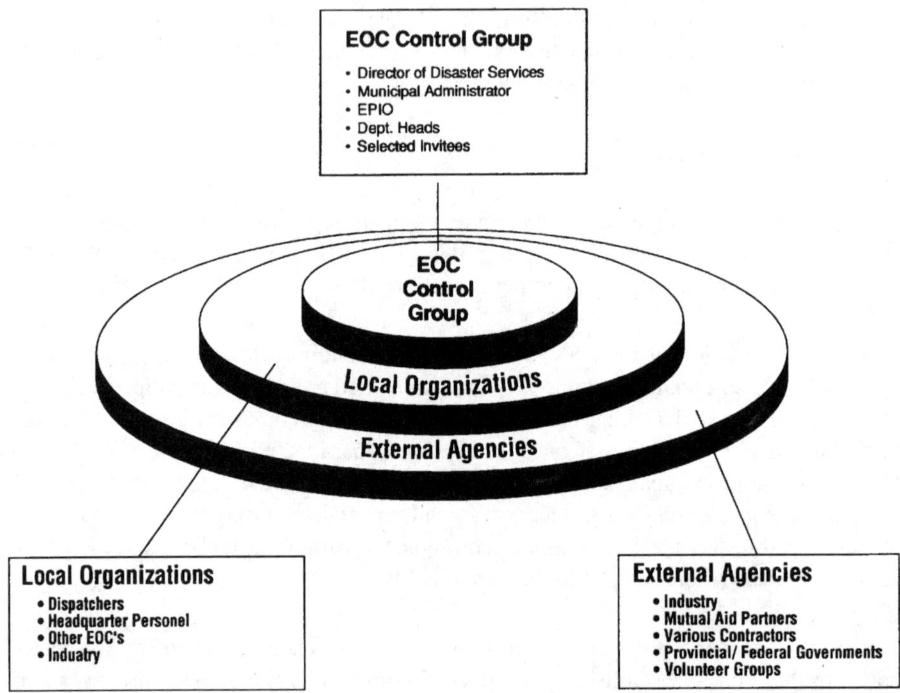

Figure 9.1 - EOC Control Group and its Extensions

Another key role for the EOC Control Group is the strategic (versus operational) management of the disaster response effort. This role involves a number of key activities. They include: contact with other orders of government, acquisition of necessary supplies and services, and the continued management of day-to-day life in that part of the municipality that was left unaffected by the disaster.

While the EOC is being activated, work at the site continues, often at an increasing pace. The primary role of those at the disaster site is to return life to 'normal' as soon as possible. This may involve fire fighting, rescue and health sustaining activities, evacuation of the affected area, and efforts to minimize damage to property and the environment.

During the early period of the response, the situation at the site predictably becomes more demanding. Additional resources and representatives of various jurisdictions rush to the disaster site and their presence often highlights the need for tighter coordination of the response effort. This is achieved through the efforts of a formally appointed Site Manager and the Site Team (Figure 9.3).

Once activated, one of the key tasks of the EOC Control Group is to formally appoint or 'recognize' a Site Manager and advise all responding agencies of the identity of that person. Some Municipal Emergency Plans have made the appointment of the Site Manager easy by designating the agency that will provide that person. (Site

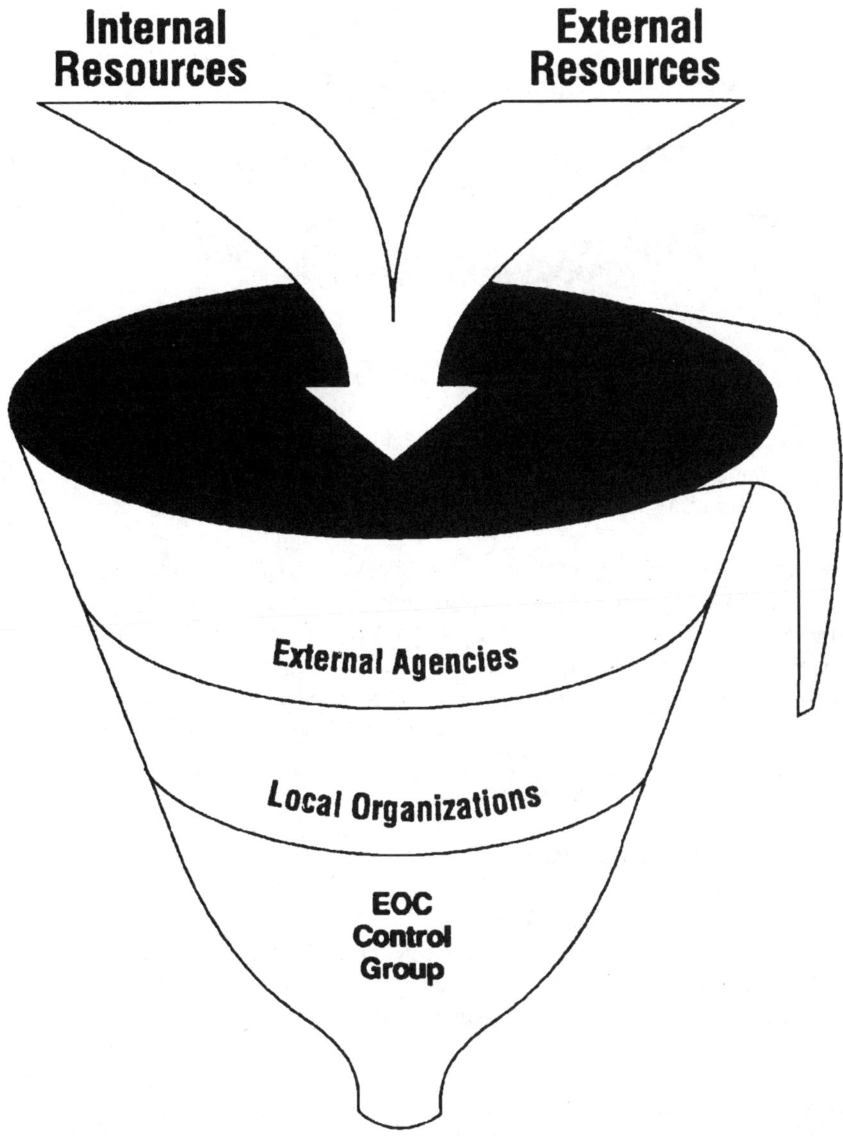

Figure 9.2 - Resource Funnelling Through EOC Control Group

Figure 9.3 - The Site Team

Managers are typically appointed from the ranks of the Fire or Police services.) In that case, the EOC Control Group needs to be notified of that person's identity by the respective Departmental Chief.

The notification of the appointment of the Site Manager is somewhat similar to the statement of the On-scene Commander (in the Fire-scene systems) that he or she is assuming command. The difference is that under the ESM system, the declaration is made from higher jurisdiction. Moreover, once that declaration is made, all key functions at the site should be coordinated through the Site Manager and the Site team. A key link is thus established between the EOC and the site.

Once appointed, the Site Manager should:

1. Establish the Site Command Post, from which he or she will coordinate the operation.
2. Gather and brief the Site Team.
3. Identify, with the help of the Team, Site-specific operational objectives.
4. Coordinate key activities at the Site and especially those which involve or affect a number of response organizations.
5. COMMUNICATE!!!

The motto of each member of the Site Team (and especially the Site Manager) should be: "When in doubt, communicate!" This requirement is particularly critical when the actions of one organization might have a significant effect on the overall operation, or impact on other agencies. Also, wherever possible decisions should be made through team consultation. These interactions can be facilitated by the collocation of the key members of the Site Team into or near the Site Command Post.

As noted above, the Site Manager and the members of the EOC Control Group must perform two important managerial functions. First and foremost they must enhance the communication flow between the various response agencies involved in the overall response. They must also coordinate the operational objectives and response strategies of these agencies. On the other hand, neither the members of the EOC Control Group nor the Site Manager are expected to replace existing command/organizational structures and communications of the various response agencies. That means that Fire Services personnel can and should continue to employ whatever 'Command' system they choose to employ in the management of their own resources. It also means that the function of the Site Manager is not intended to provide direction to the Fireground Commander on fire fighting, or guidance to Police officers on how to conduct an evacuation. Instead, the Site Manager functions as the coordinator of the general activities at the site.

Arrangements for Mutual Aid (i.e., call-out, deployment) should be left in the hands of the organization which called for it (i.e., Fireground commander). This call need NOT involve the Site Manager although he or she should be notified of its presence. Moreover, these Mutual Aid resources are best managed using a Fire Command system (as described in Chapter 8). In this manner, the two systems (Fire Command and the Emergency Site Management) are indeed complementary.

Who comprises the EOC Control Group?

Disaster situations are likely to result in the activation of a variety of emergency operations centres. These may include the command (or operations) centres of various local services (e.g., Fire, Police and Emergency Medical Services), departments (e.g., Public Works, Transportation, Social Services), organizations (e.g., Emergency Measures, Red Cross, rescue), Industry representatives and officials from other orders of government. Many of these EOCs are likely to be within the municipality while a few may be located elsewhere in Canada. Consider for example the accidental crash of a military aircraft near a major industrial site in a small community. Or, a major derailment of a train carrying dangerous goods within a national park. The response to these disasters will likely involve various EOCs at regional and national levels.

Regardless of how many EOC are activated, the affected municipality should be represented by only one EOC. This EOC should be the primary centre for the coordination of the response of the municipality (not its specific Departments or agencies). It should, therefore, be located at City/Town Hall or at another public facility which represents the municipality.

Figure 1 illustrates the general composition of the municipal EOC Control Group and the network of organizations which are linked to it. Please note that it contains three broad and distinct organizational 'circles.' The first and inner circle represents the members of the municipal EOC Control Group. They are the only ones actually located at the EOC. They could include:

1. The municipal director of disaster services
2. The City (or Town) clerk/administrator

3. The heads of key municipal departments (including Fire, Police and Emergency Medical Services)
4. The municipal Emergency Public Information Officer (where one exists)
5. Selected invited personnel (e.g., members of Industry or other orders of government) whose inclusion in the EOC Control Group may be temporary or permanent depending on community and disaster-response needs.

Wherever possible, the EOC Control Group should include the local Fire Chief. In this manner, the Chief can be directly involved in key decisions affecting the whole operation. Fire Chiefs who are unable to be present at the municipal EOC, should be represented there by a competent Deputy with the authority to act quickly and decisively for the Department. This will minimize the delays caused by 'checking things out' every time that a crucial decision needs to be made or vital action taken.

The municipality's elected officials are key players in disaster response operations but typically should not be a part of the EOC's inner circle. Often, elected officials have their own room outside but close to the EOC's location. There are two key reasons for this separation. One is the need to separate the 'Executive' function from the 'Operational' one. The other reason is the elected officials' unique public relation or 'political' role. It is best performed away from the municipal EOC so as not to distract its operation. These elected officials may visit the EOC and may request frequent briefings. However, they are also best advised to allow disaster response to be managed by those who are trained and equipped to do so.

The second circle represents municipal response agencies and other organizations within the municipality. They are the dispatchers (i.e., Fire or Police dispatch), key headquarters personnel, and crisis managers located with their respective Departments and agencies. All of them are away from the disaster site, but are available to support it as required.

The third circle represents a wide variety of non-municipal organizations, services and resources. These may include mutual aid partners, industrial operators, local contractors, provincial and federal government departments, volunteer groups, and the media.

Members of each of the three 'circles' typically operate independently of each other. However, the structure of the Emergency Site Management system offers the framework to coordinate the flow of information and resources between the beleaguered disaster site and the organizations which can support it. One of the functions of the EOC's Control Group is to influence and 'control' the quality, quantity and timing of needed resources to the site.

Who comprises the Site Team?

Because of its location at the disaster site, the Site Team typically has more diverse membership than that of the EOC Control Group. Just the same, the two organizations have a number of similarities. Both are multi-tiered, both include senior members of the response agencies, and both link organizations which are present on and off the 'site.'

The inner circle of the Site Team contains two key organizational components one of which is the Site Manager. As noted earlier, the Site Manager is the individual appointed by the EOC Control Group to manage the overall operations at the site. This person is typically a member of the municipal Fire or Police services, but may be a representative from the Emergency Medical Services, industry, or occasionally a representative from another order of government.

Site Managers appointed from either the Police or Fire services will typically be the senior person on site from that service. When Fire (or Police) officers become Site Managers they should 'change hats.' Their role is no longer that of Fire (or Police) officers within their respective Department. Instead, they must accept a larger role. It is the task of managing the Site and the overall response effort within it. They should try to avoid any preferential treatment of their parent organization to the detriment of others.

The inner circle of the Site Team should also include the most senior member of each agency that responded to the site. When the Site Manager is chosen from the Fire Department, the next senior Fire Officer on Site will become the Fireground Commander and will represent the Fire Department as a member of the Site Team.

Together, the members of the Site Team represent all the primary response organizations at the site and can quickly share information and coordinate their response efforts. The Site Manager should facilitate that interaction and move the process along. He or she should lead the group step-by-step towards the ultimate management of the disaster situation.

The second "tier" includes those who provide supplemental response resources at the site. These may include various volunteer organizations, non-government organizations (e.g., the Red Cross, Salvation Army), and local contractors. While potentially valuable to the overall response effort, these organizations are not the primary decision makers at the site. Moreover, these organizations should be coordinated by the site team through a number of liaison officers (LOs) whose function is to keep information flowing and activities coordinated.

The third organizational tier of site management includes all other applicable agencies which are available off site. These agencies might be placed on 'standby' or be called upon to respond to the site. They include the same agencies as those listed in the outer ring of Figure 9.1. When committed or deployed to a site, these agencies report to and are coordinated by the Site Manager. Should it be necessary, they may also join the inner circle of decision makers at the site, or serve in a more traditional supportive role.

The communication component

One can not overemphasize this truth: Communication is perhaps the most important principle of effective disaster response. It will either make or break the process. Effective communications should, therefore, be ever present throughout the web of interrelationships and networks which comprise the ESM system (Figure 9.4). To that end, the ESM system encourages a pattern of communications that is structured like a holograph. Through it, information can be relayed from one agency to another through various pathways. These are:

1. Within each organization regardless of its geographical location;
2. Between organizations at the municipal EOC;
3. Between organizations linked to the EOC and the EOC Control Group;
4. Between organizations at the site; and
5. Between the manager of the EOC and the Site Manager.

Using these networks everyone involved can be kept aware of the latest available information. Moreover, should a communication channel (or link) become inoperable or clogged, individuals could then use the other channels to maintain the necessary flow of information.

The following example should illustrate the point. The Fire Chief at the EOC may try to contact the Senior Fire Officer (i.e., Fireground Commander) at the site. Contact may be made by calling the Fireground Commander directly through Fire dispatch. Contact may also be made through the head of the EOC Control Group (i.e., Town clerk) to the Site Manager and then to the respective Fire Officer. Similarly, mutual aid partners may be called by representatives of the EOC Control Group or ESM team members. Regardless of how it goes through, the key concern should be that the appropriate message reaches its destination on time for appropriate action to be taken!

The ESM process should allow flexibility of operation at Departmental or agency level. The process should allow each organization to employ the operational system which best fits its needs, while still maintaining operational coordination at site and EOC levels. The secret of its success rests in on-going and timely communications.

Termination

When their respective services are no longer required, both the EOC Control Group and the Site Team should be disbanded. While the specific process varies from situation to situation, it typically signals the end of the disaster 'response' operation. However, as noted in Chapter 12, recovery operations may continue much beyond the end of the 'response' period.

In fact, operations at the Site (i.e., clean-up, restoration of services) may continue for some time past the return of most agencies (i.e., Fire, Police) to normal operations.

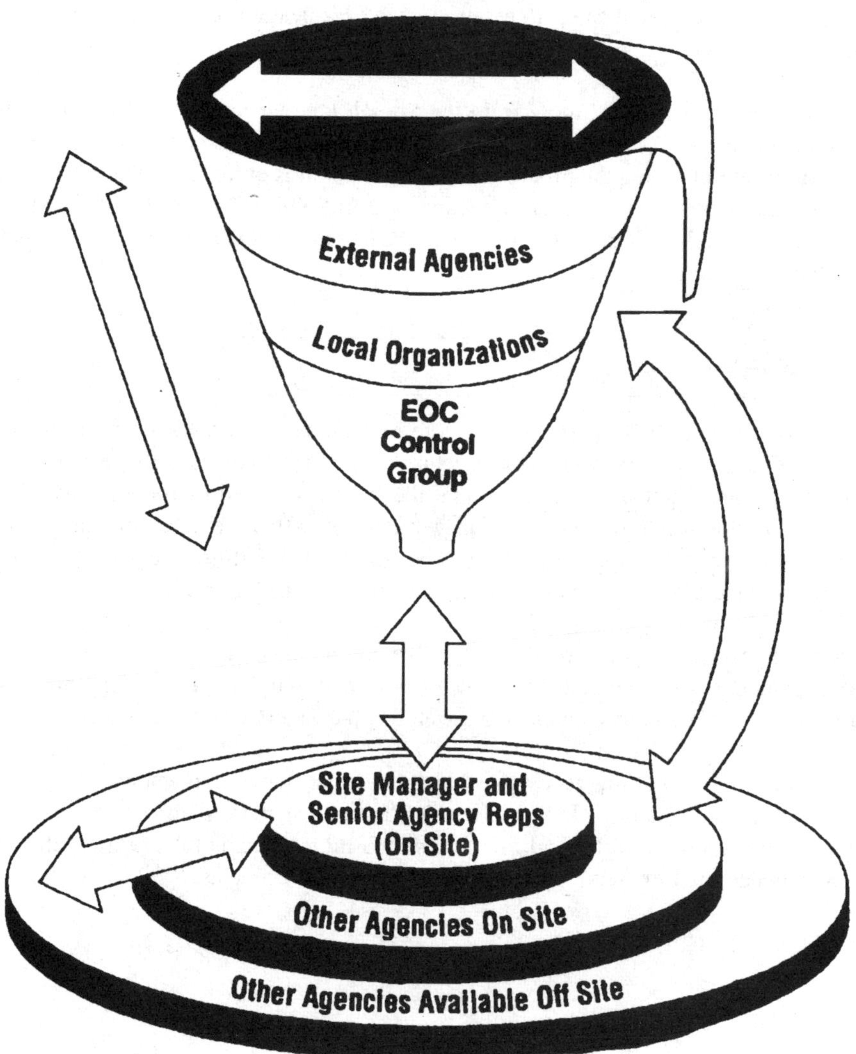

Figure 9.4 - Communication Flow

The ESM process requires, therefore, that all organizations remaining at the Site be advised that the Site Manager and the Emergency Site Management system are no longer employed at that Site. In essence, each organization reverts to its own separate procedures.

Before, completely disengaging from the Site all key participants of the Site Team should conduct a debriefing of their operation. This should be conducted informally and aimed at improving the process for ... next time. It is quite likely that most of the organizations involved in the current response effort will be involved in the next disaster scene and there is no better time than the end of one operation to start planning for the next.

SUMMARY

This chapter described the Emergency Site Management (ESM) system. It emphasized the need to provide a flexible structure with which to manage the response to a disaster at municipal level. It noted that the system is based on the effective management of the Site through a Site Manager and a Site Team representing the various key response organizations at the Site. The system also outlined the need for, structure of and roles of the municipal Emergency Operations Centre.

Effective disaster response requires effective communication. The Emergency Site Management system facilitates the flow of information by creating the organizational structure for it and by establishing a web for inter-agency communication.

As noted above, the Emergency Site Management system complements the various Fire Command systems. It links Fire Department operations to the more global municipal response effort. And, it establishes a more meaningful working relationship between the Fire Services and other key response agencies.

Medical Considerations In Disaster Situations

John R. R. Oakley, EMT-P
Emergency Management Instructor
Provincial Emergency Program Academy
Justice Institute of British Columbia

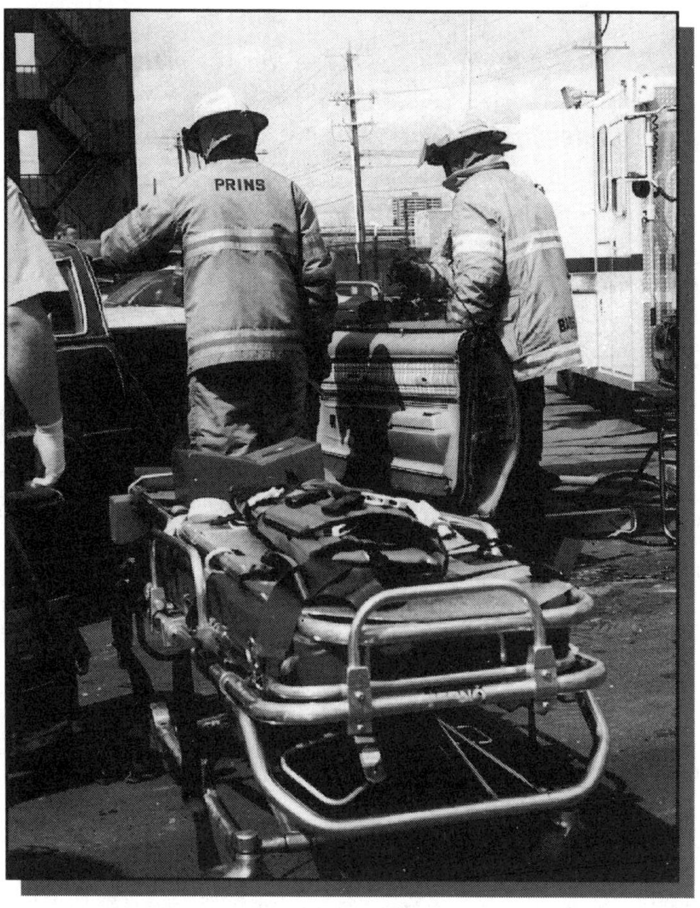

Photo Courtesy of Gerry Emas, Edmonton Emergency Response Department.

This chapter briefly highlights some of the key medical considerations and issues of relevance to Fire Officers. It accepts that many of the issues here may not be the jurisdiction of the Fire Services. However, by understanding these issues, Fire Officers can develop better plans and respond more effectively.

In the majority of emergencies and disasters, the emergency medical component of the response system plays a critical role in the success of the overall response effort. Naturally, the success of the Emergency Medical Service's (EMS) response effort is dependant upon various factors including the number of casualties it has to respond to, available resources and local conditions.

Although these factors will always be a consideration, their relevance may vary from disaster to disaster and from one community to another. For example, the number of injuries will differ from one multiple casualty incident (MCI) to another. This number may not be as significant on its own (i.e., five injuries) as its relationship to the resources available to deal with these injuries. Obviously, certain MCIs may be readily manageable as a 'normal incident' by large municipalities but would be a disaster–situation for smaller municipalities with fewer resources.

The disparity between municipalities in their medical–response capabilities is not limited to the local Emergency Medical Services. It also includes their capabilities (or lack of) regarding hospital facilities and trauma centres. Ultimately, these resources affect the survival rates of patients.

One key element is vital regardless of the size or resource base of the municipality. It is the need for a current, comprehensive and tested emergency plan. Without such a plan the medical response system will be inadequate and may fail during the time when it is operationally needed most.

As noted through many of the above chapters, disasters are events that overwhelm existing responders, facilities, equipment and the capability of response agencies to perform their much needed duty. Many resources are required during a disaster and their effective deployment requires inter–agency coordination and management.

The following are a number of key issues to guide Fire Officers in their emergency planning. Some of these may not be directly related but they are mentioned just the same to provide context.

GENERAL PLANNING ISSUES FOR EFFECTIVE MEDICAL RESPONSE

A number of issues are involved in this matter. Key among them are hazard analysis and community preparedness.

Hazard analysis

As noted in Chapters 3 and 4, emergency planning is an on-going process. Before one can develop emergency response plans it is important to consider the hazards, risks and vulnerabilities which exist in the community. Completion of a hazard, vulnerability and risk analysis is, therefore, one of the first steps in the emergency planning process. All relevant hazards to the community must be identified as potential disaster risks.

These should include, for example, the manufacturing, storage and transportation of dangerous goods; mass transit vehicles, airports, ports and railway systems; local fire threats and other potential natural hazards such as tornadoes, hurricanes, floods, snow storms, and earthquakes. They should also consider local sources of violent actions (e.g., gangs, drug laboratories). Obviously, each community regardless of its size and location will have its own disaster–risk profile. This profile will be unique in geography and time. In other words, one community's profile will differ from other communities and will differ over time as things change in and around the community.

The one key factor that must be considered when planning for the medical response of a community to a disaster, is the nature of that community's population. As noted above, disasters have the potential to cause severe harm to individuals' health and wellbeing. Those who are confronted by a disaster are affected by it, but often not in identical ways. Just like some areas are more vulnerable than others, so are certain segments of the population more vulnerable than others and require, therefore, special attention.

A number of factors or characteristics are of significance. They include the age of the survivors, the population density of the area or the community and the cultural diversity of the community.

The age of the survivors. There is a general agreement that the very young (i.e., children), the elderly, the disabled and the chronically ill are at a higher risk of death or injury in a disaster than those adults who are fully able to take response actions. Consider for example, those with limited mobility and their challenge to flee from collapsing (or collapsed) structures. Moreover, pre–disaster underlying physical weaknesses or ailments as well as mental conditions are all likely to be exacerbated by the stressors inherent to disaster situations. All, are plausible factors that make these segments of the population vulnerable.

Population density. As a general rule, the greater the population density the greater the number of people who are at risk. Events such as forest fires, floods, tornadoes or earthquakes which occur in uninhabited areas present less of a challenge than similar events which occur in heavily populated municipalities. It is worth noting that the majority of Canadians live in urban areas with high population density.

Cultural diversity of the community. In the past, Canadian emergency managers have paid very little attention to the effects of our multicultural society on disaster response. However, more and more, this is now becoming a factor in the planning process.

Findings from the United States emphasize that members of ethnic minorities are at an added risk during disasters. Disaster– related deaths among ethnic minorities are historically much higher than the main–stream segment of the population. A number of factors attribute to this. One is the possible diversity in their socio–economic status. Another may relate to the lack of language fluency generally inherent to minority groups. This becomes a major limitation during the warning, rescue and response phases because members of these ethnic minorities may not understand the directions given to them by the various responders or rescuers. This lack of understanding of the warning message and required response actions, can also result in a higher risk for responders who must undertake response actions which otherwise would not have been necessary.

This issue is well documented in the United States, but not in Canada. Just the same, there were over 300,000 people living in Canada in 1986 who did not speak either of our official languages. This issue is further complicated by the concentration of these people in specific areas. In other words, new Canadians often tend to reside in neighbourhoods where the population is comprised of persons with the same ethnic, cultural and linguistic background. Large Canadian cities have, therefore, large groupings of citizens who have difficulty relating to the language commonly spoken by the general population (and responders) in the area.

Community preparedness

Disaster situations require a response by the community at large. That is equally relevant to the emergency medical needs of the injured. Planning for such action prior to the event is critical in order to ensure the efficient and effective use of limited resources. The following areas should be considered during the planning process:

1. Provisions to accommodate patients with routine and minor medical conditions at locations other than hospitals (e.g., local clinics, health department facilities, physician's offices, evacuation shelters, dental offices), and by non– hospital staff (e.g., home–care and public health nurses).
2. A system to allow large numbers of medical volunteers who spontaneously respond to the disaster to set up temporary community clinics.
3. Provisions for integrating these external–to–hospital medical care efforts into the community's health care disaster response.
4. Provisions to send hospital-based medical teams to the disaster site(s).
5. Procedures for an organized effort to survey and assess community and public health care needs after the impact of the disaster.

EMERGENCY PLANNING FOR SPECIAL RESCUE SITUATIONS

Disasters may create a host of special rescue situations. 'Special rescue' situations are incidents where one or more persons are stranded or trapped and where their rescue involves skills and equipment which are not readily available. These special rescue situations may involve structural collapse, water rescue, confined space entry, trench collapse and incidents involving dangerous goods.

Industrial disasters

The increasing trend to industrialize has led to greater instances of production, processing, storage and transportation of large amounts of highly flammable, explosive and toxic chemicals. The increasing use and movement of these chemicals has been documented as the cause of growing risk to human health and the environment. Fires, explosions, leakages, or releases of hazardous substances can readily cause the death of, or injury to, a large number of people. The presence of such chemicals in the community should, therefore, result in some emergency health countermeasures.

If a hazardous substance is released during an industrial emergency, the toxicity of the substance and the routes and amounts of human exposure are important factors in determining the potential public health hazards. Planning, preparation and appropriate emergency response are the keys to minimizing human exposures to toxic chemicals.

On a personal level, it is worth noting that the health effects of a toxic chemical may differ depending on the route of exposure. Inhalation is often the most obvious exposure route, particularly during the acute phase of a release. However, with the passage of time, skin exposure from touching contaminated objects of from ingesting contaminated food and water may become more significant routes of exposure than inhalation.

Fire Services personnel should work closely with Emergency Medical Services personnel to identify ways to avoid contamination during disasters, or establish rapid decontamination as necessary.

Structural collapse

The most likely cause of structural collapse is thought to be earthquakes. A large earthquake may cause widespread damage and subsequent structural collapse conditions. However, buildings may collapse for other reasons. These include:

- Explosions	- Flooding	- Fire
- Poor construction	- Deterioration	- Rain
- Volcanic ash fall	- Land slides	- Overloading
- Accident	- Wind	- Snow (load)

Structural collapse situations may be the most hazardous of all special rescue situations. The collapse may be the result of flooding and may require water–rescue skills. Structural collapses may most likely also involve confined space rescue operations and dangerous goods specialists.

PROCEDURE CHECKLISTS FOR MEDICAL & PUBLIC HEALTH PERSONNEL

Fire Services personnel who mobilize medical resources as a response to disasters should consider a number of general procedures and public health issues. The key among them are listed below.

General considerations

1. Ensure that the emergency medical teams that responded to the disaster site establish a medical on-scene command post and that a single individual is placed in charge of all medical operations at the scene.
2. Coordinate the use of all public health services within the jurisdiction during emergency conditions.
3. Provide for the monitoring and evaluation of environmental health risks and hazards as required, and ensure that appropriate actions are taken to protect public safety.
4. Inspect for purity and usability of food, water, drugs and other consumable that were exposed to the hazard.
5. Coordinate with the Water, Public Works or Sanitation departments, as appropriate, to ensure the availability of potable water, sewage system, sanitary garbage disposal and the removal of dead animals.
6. Detect and inspect sources of contamination dangerous to the public's physical health.
7. Establish preventative health services, including the control of communicable diseases.
8. Inspect damaged buildings for health hazards.
9. Provide epidemiologic surveillance, case investigating, and follow-up as necessary.
10. Provide laboratory services required to support identification activities by emergency health and emergency medical services.
11. Monitor food handling and food sanitation service in all emergency facilities, including increased attention to sanitation in commercial food preparation and feeding facilities that cater to disaster survivors.
12. Advise the public on general sanitation matters. Whenever feasible, all information should be provided to both the public and the media through the Public Information Officer.
13. Ensure adequate sanitary facilities are provided in emergency shelters and at the site.
14. Implement action to prevent or control vectors such as flies, mosquitoes and rodents.
15. Work with animal care and control agencies to prevent the spread of disease through animals.
16. Coordinate with neighbouring areas and Provincial Public Health Officers on matters requiring assistance from other jurisdictions.
17. Coordinate health-related activities among other local public and private response agencies and groups.

18. Coordinate with the animal care and control agency to dispose of dead and contaminated animals (domestic and farm).
19. Coordinate operations for general or mass emergency immunizations or quarantine procedures as necessary.

Emergency Medical Services (EMS)

Some Fire Departments have amalgamated with their local EMS organization to form a coordinated response effort. Regardless of the arrangements which exist between the two services, the local EMS personnel should have the following roles and responsibilities:

1. Respond to the disaster scene with emergency medical units.
2. Implement a medical incident management system such as the Incident Command System within the overall framework of the local emergency management system.
3. Provide appropriate emergency first aid and medical supplies for disaster use.
4. Maintain a current resource inventory of emergency medical supplies and equipment.
5. Maintain a system to track injuries and patients.
6. Establish and maintain field communications and coordination with other emergency response teams (i.e., medical, Fire, Police, Public Works).
7. Maintain radio or telephone communication with hospitals, as appropriate.
8. Maintain liaison with volunteer service agencies (e.g., St. John Ambulance, Salvation Army, Red Cross).
9. Coordinate with business and industry emergency medical units for possible mutual aid.
10. Coordinate procurement, screening and allocation of critical public and private resources required to support disaster related health and medical care operations.
11. When authorized, provide information through the Public Information Officer to the news media on the number of injuries and fatalities.

Hospitals

The primary emergency roles and responsibilities of hospitals are listed below.

1. Implement their hospital disaster plan.
2. Provide medical guidance, as needed, to Emergency Medical Services units, field collection and/or treatment locations.
3. Distribute patients to and among hospitals based on capability to treat and bed capacity. This may include transfers out of the area and/or rerouting to alternative facilities.
4. Establish and maintain field and inter-hospital medical communications.
5. Coordinate transportation of casualties and medical resources to health care facilities or other areas as required.

6. Make available upon request qualified medical personnel, supplies and equipment located in the jurisdiction.
7. Coordinate with other area hospitals involved in caring for the injured.
8. Maintain liaison with the coordinators of other emergency services (e.g., Fire and rescue, Police, Public Works, emergency management agency).
9. Provide information as appropriate through the Public Information Officer to the news media on the number of injuries and fatalities.

Coroner or Medical Examiner

Those who occupy this position have a number of significant roles. Key among them include:

1. Coordinate local resources utilized for the collection, identification, and disposition of deceased persons and human tissue.
2. Select an adequate number of qualified personnel to establish temporary morgue sites.
3. Establish collection points to facilitate recovery operations.
4. Coordinate their activities with search and rescue teams.
5. Determine the cause of death of each fatality.
6. Designate an adequate number of persons to perform the duties of Deputy Coroners.
7. Protect the property and personal effects of the deceased.
8. Notify the next of kin of the deceased.
9. Establish and maintain a comprehensive system for the up–to– date accounting of fatalities including numbers, names etc.
10. Submit requests for mutual aid assistance, as required.
11. Provide information through the Public Information Officer to the news media on the number of deaths and morgue operations.
12. Coordinate the services of Funeral directors and morticians.
13. Secure and coordinate the services of dentists and X-ray technicians for purposes of body identification.

Mental Health agencies

These agencies are typically responsible for the following:

1. Ensure that professional psychological support is available for survivors during all phases of the disaster.
2. Care for residents of mental health facilities during disaster and emergency conditions.
3. Coordinate the evacuation of residents from damaged or threatened mental health facilities.
4. Prepare for and coordinate the reception of mental health patients evacuated from other such facilities.

SUMMARY

Fire Officers may or may not be directly responsible for emergency medical services during the disaster response period. Regardless, these Fire Services personnel need to be aware of the general roles and responsibilities of the Emergency Medical Services and related organizations. This knowledge should be incorporated into the Fire Department's and the community's emergency planning process. Moreover, this knowledge and the coordinated planning approach could greatly enhance the response capability of both the Fire Department and the community at large.

Picture 10.1

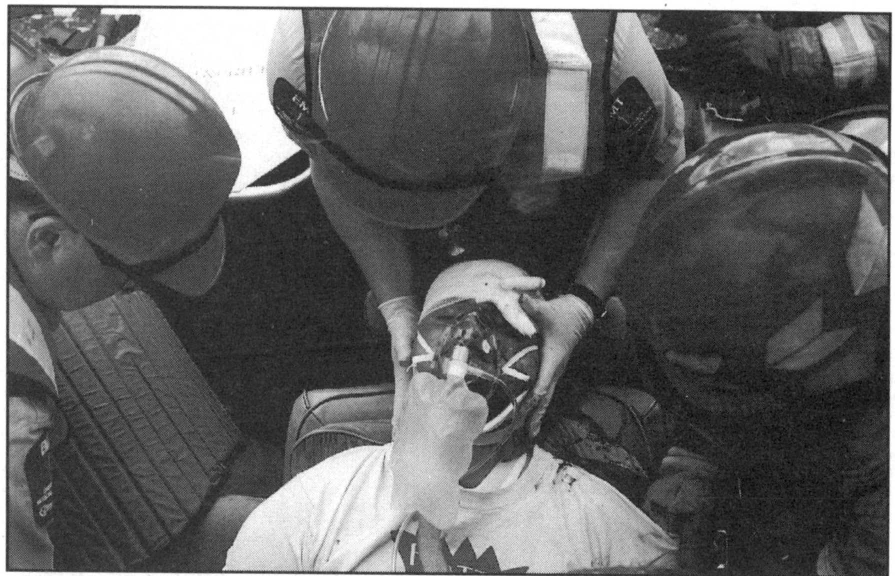

Stabilizing a casualty may require more than one person.
(Photo Courtesy of Gerry Emas, Edmonton Emergency Response Department.)

Picture 10.2

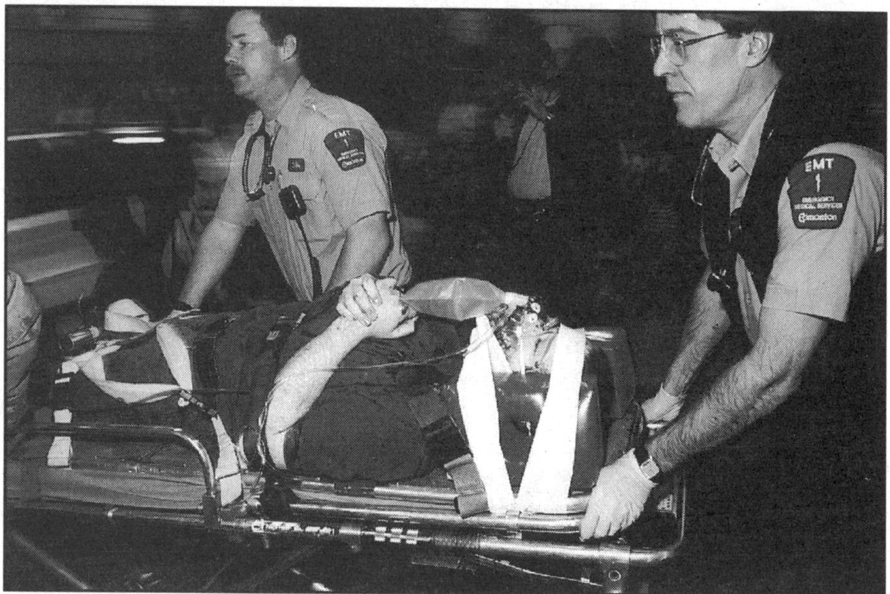

Speed of medical response has a critical bearing on the survival of casualties.
(Photo Courtesy of Gerry Emas, Edmonton Emergency Response Department.)

Small Community Fire Departments and Emergency Preparedness

Mike Lowing
Deputy Fire Chief, Yellowknife, NWT

Photo Courtesy of Gerry Emas, Edmonton Emergency Response Department.

This chapter focuses on the challenges for fire officers when they prepare their community for emergencies. The chapter views emergency preparedness and response from the perspective of Fire Departments in Northern communities. However, their unique environment and limitations present a valuable context for the emergency preparedness effort of Fire Departments elsewhere in Canada. The lessons are indeed transferable particularly for small and isolated communities.

Discussed in this chapter are the benefits of and pitfalls for Fire Departments in small and isolated communities. Also covered are some of the key issues of emergency preparedness as they relate to these communities.

The communities that stretch across the Yukon and Northwest Territories are unique within Canada. Their geography, environment, climate, history, residents and day to day life styles differ greatly from their neighbours along Canada's southern border. Accordingly, the Fire Departments that protect these northern communities have distinct needs for and limitations to their emergency planning and response efforts.

The factors that make northern communities unique for disaster planning are not strictly confined to the geographic boundaries of the Yukon and Northwest Territories. Whether north of the 60th parallel or south of it, small-size Canadian communities share many similarities. Not surprisingly, emergency planning in Spence Bay (NWT), Salmon Arm (BC), Pincher Creek (AB), Tilston (MB), Mattawa (ON) and Amherst (NS) have much in common.

Literally, the Fire Departments in thousands of communities across Canada share similar environment for emergency preparedness and response. One such similarity is their organizational make-up and operations. According to the National research Council (NRC, 1995), approximately 85% of communities across Canada are protected by Fire Departments staffed by volunteers who provide their community with some form of fire and life safety protection.

Why does a small community need to plan and prepare for a disaster? Joanne Duguay (1994) observed that Canada's relatively small population has not experienced the large number of devastating disasters that have afflicted other nations around the world. However, she also noted that Canadians have had their share of community based disasters and that "from 1982 to 1992 there were 67 major disasters in Canada causing 498 deaths, 1,417 injuries, 48,407 evacuations and 2.9 billion in damage" (p. 16).

Thomas Hawkins, Jr. and Hugh McClees (1988) noted that small communities are as vulnerable to crises as are the larger population centres. They calculated that a typical community in the United States encounters a disaster every 12 years regardless of its geographical size or population base. This estimate is based on the situation in the United States and may or may not be accurate in Canada. However, the warning delivered by Hawkins and McClees is particularly applicable in Canada. They stated that "no fire chief, even in small communities or in remote areas can afford to say, it won't happen here" (p. 321).

Unfortunately, residents of small and large communities alike typically share a high degree of apathy towards disaster preparedness. Auf der Heide (1989) noted that the apathetic response of citizens may be due to the competition for attention (and funding) between numerous community priorities including emergency planning which, in turn, is based on a low-probability event. The issues of employment, economic growth, government downsizing and the elimination of local government infrastructure funding are significant issues which currently confront many small communities. These issues detract from a community's motivation to expend energy and resources on matters relating to emergency preparedness. The situation may be more difficult in small-size communities because those who live there may be more focused upon the economic viability of their community than those living in larger centres.

Ironically, the emergency preparedness role of Fire Departments in small and isolated communities has perhaps a larger significance than a corresponding role in larger (i.e. urban) centres. Admittedly, all Fire Chiefs need to convince their community of the need for emergency preparedness. However, the challenge of overcoming the political and economic issues at the forefront of a small and isolated community can be a daunting task. Yet, that is a task which can not be neglected nor one which can be shuffled off to another agency.

The process of motivating a community to undertake an emergency preparedness activity may vary from one locality to another. However, for the most part the planning process undertaken by Fire Departments is essentially similar regardless of community size. One of the main differences, of course, is the type of hazards confronted by a community and their potential risks.

ENVIRONMENTAL CONSIDERATIONS

Small and/or isolated communities across Canada are confronted daily by a number of unique environmental considerations. One or more of these 'factors' affect their day-to-day operations and are, therefore, of significance to their emergency planning. They include weather, isolation, population base, resource availability, mutual aid, public utilities, transportation and community demographics.

Admittedly, the above factors may also be of importance in larger population centres. However, they are CRITICAL for consideration by those in small and isolated communities!

Weather

Each day of the year, regardless of season, weather plays a significant role in the lives of Canadians from coast to coast. One only needs to monitor the news to realize the impact of weather on any particular community or region of the country. Jim Bruce, Chairman of the Canadian Climate Program Board observed that community-wide disaster are as a result of weather (reported in Flynn, 1995a). He observed that:

> "Statistics suggest something has been happening in the past few decades to increase the frequency and severity of climate related disasters... The losses have been rising three times as rapidly for climate-related disasters as they have for earthquakes and other natural disasters" (p.4).

Bruce noted that the trend of disaster losses due to weather are likely to continue. A recent example illustrates the point. During June 1995 the northern half of Alberta was gripped by drought like conditions with a record number of large forest fires while the southern portion of the province was experiencing its worst flood in over 100 years.

A sidebar in the Emergency Preparedness Digest (1995) reported that "while it is the extreme disasters that get the headlines, in Canada much more common meteorological hazard events take a toll of human life and cause more damage. Extremes in cold and heat, lightning and flooding are examples of the hazards that kill an average of 150 Canadians annually" (p.11). This should send a chilling message to Fire Department personnel not to ignore weather in their overall emergency planning.

Isolation

For the most part, life in small communities is about living apart from larger urban centres. Many of Canada's communities, both small and large, are isolated to one degree or another from their neighbours. This is particularly true of the communities across the Territories and in the northern portion of Canada's provinces.

The issue of isolation is, therefore, a significant consideration particularly in the evaluation of mutual aid requirements and in the analysis of deployment times during disaster planning. And, since many communities are affected by geographical isolation, this factor must be also considered by their mutual aid partners including provincial and federal governments.

Population base

The term 'small communities' often means communities with small population base. The size of 'small' communities vary across regions and provinces. For example, Newfoundland has a population base of 585,100 located in 290 incorporated municipalities and three cities. It has a population density of two inhabitants per square kilometre (Flynn, 1995b). Saskatchewan's million inhabitants live in 834 communities with a population density of about 1.6 people per square kilometre. Ontario's more than nine million inhabitants live in 831 municipalities (Synder, 1993).

The diversity of sizes among small communities also has a corresponding effect on local emergency planning effort. This too must be considered during the emergency planning effort.

Resource availability

When confronted by disaster, Fire Departments (and other community-based agencies) may not always have the resources needed or desired to do the job. While this is the reality in both small and large communities the situation is more acute in small-size communities. These communities typically have extremely limited resources to deal with the same type and size of disasters that strike their larger neighbours.

Moreover, by virtue of their size and limited resources, small communities are also more dependent upon outside help to manage the crisis. According to Rubin (1991), small to medium-size communities that suffer a large amount of damage to their infrastructure are more likely to be dependent upon provincial and federal agencies for disaster resources. He emphasized that reliance upon external resources does not mean a loss of control to manage the disaster. He added that "by effectively asserting local leadership and organizing its administrative capabilities, a small community can maximize control over its recovery and its future" (p. 236).

Mutual aid

The matter of mutual aid for small and especially isolated communities is one of great necessity but limited immediate applicability. In many cases, mutual aid response can often be measured not in terms of hours but in days! Moreover, for the most part, small communities do not have the mutual aid capabilities that exist in metro Toronto or in British Columbia's lower mainland area.

However, not all is lost for a small community's mutual aid. Innovative ways have been developed for communities to network together and provide mutual aid to one another despite great distances between them. One example is provided by Janice Synder (1993). Writing about mutual aid in the province of Saskatchewan she noted:

> "The only way emergency planning could work in Saskatchewan was to group communities to share resources. The result has been the formation of Mutual Aid Areas, which do just what their name implies: Communities coming together for mutual aid in time of emergency. There are now 53 Mutual Aid Areas encompassing about 83% of the population" (p. 2).

Public utilities

The infrastructure for providing telephone, water, power and fuel sources for heating is a critical element to the survivability of any small community. However, utility providers in small communities typically do not have the same networks as they do in larger centres. Utility feed points typically enter a small community on a single line (or service medium). Generally speaking, utility systems in small communities do not have multiple feed points, grid systems or supply networks. As a result, just like the small communities that they serve, the public utilities distribution system can be disrupted or disabled by a disaster.

Utility maintenance crews are not immune to disaster. Much like Fire Department personnel and resources, they can be overwhelmed by a crisis and be unable to respond effectively. Gillespie (1991) noted that when disasters cause extensive damage to utility networks it is not likely that repair crews will be able to quickly bring services back on line. Fire Chiefs in small communities must, therefore, consider including representatives from each utility company and seeking their input when it comes to disaster planning. Gillespie emphasized the value of this involvement. He noted that "minimal cost is involved in developing inventories of equipment, identifying experienced personnel, establishing mutual aid agreements, and maintaining inter-organizational and inter-jurisdictional disaster planning" (p. 74).

Transportation

Transportation routes into and out of a community are that community's life line especially during disasters. These routes, their carriers and their cargo must, therefore, all be analyzed by Fire Departments during their emergency preparedness process. This analysis provides Fire Departments with two significant gains. The first is that they have a better understanding of their community's hazards due to the threat of transportation accidents.

Bahme and Kramer (1992) provided a broad outline for the hazard analysis of transportation routes in small communities. They observed that "transportation accidents can be divided into three classes: those in the air (landing and take-off of aircraft), those on the ground (highway and railroad disasters), and those on water (rivers, lakes, and seas)" (p. 340). The specific outcome of the hazard analysis will vary from jurisdiction to jurisdiction. However, its importance to Fire Departments remains the same.

The second area of significance pertains to the community's capability to respond including its evacuation plan and its accessibility to mutual aid. As in the case of other utilities, the vast majority of small or isolated communities are usually accessible by a single highway or road. Some are totally inaccessible by road. For example, two thirds of the communities in the Northwest Territories are only accessed by aircraft. In a similar way, many small communities in Newfoundland are accessible only by boat. Flynn (1995) noted that "many of the 156 towns and the 131 communities [in Newfoundland] are considered rural coastal and only accessible by water" (p. 9).

Not surprisingly, when disasters strike a community they will most likely have an impact on the transportation routes in and out of the affected area. This can greatly complicate the response effort especially when external resources are required or when the community must be evacuated.

Community demographics

The most unique element of any small community is its residents. For the most part, people in small communities will be long-term and established residents. These residents will most likely be of a more homogeneous make-up and know each other on a far more personal level than their urban counterparts. One of the direct outcomes, as noted by Brighan (1991) identifies, is that people in small communities, especially those that grew up in small towns, are more likely to help each other than those who grew up in cities.

Generally speaking, inhabitants of small communities will want a more active role in disaster response efforts than their urban counterparts. The emergency planning efforts of small communities must, therefore, reflect this desire.

Moreover, Fire Officers must realize that small community residents are neither likely to panic nor will they flea their homes. Auf der Heide (1989) noted that "not only is panic flight an uncommon response to disasters, but it is often difficult to get people to leave when disaster threatens" (p. 198). The residents of a small community can be far more reluctant to leave their homes than the often transient short-term population of larger urban centres.

Another important element in small communities is the ethnicity and race of its residents. Often, the homogeneous nature of many small communities can be traced to one or two ethnic groups. This creates strong bonds among residents and provides a degree of community cohesiveness which can be invaluable during periods of disaster response. Consequently, Fire Chiefs must become aware of and take into the account the ethnic make-up of their community. This is especially the case when any of these ethnic groups use their mother tongue as the primary means of verbal communication.

On a related note, different cultures relate differently to disaster warnings and respond differently to a disaster. Their response may surprise and aggravate Fire Department personnel, especially if the Fire Department staff members are of a different ethnic background.

Perry and Mushkatel (1984) noted that "membership in an ethnic minority group structures the individuals' world view, both in general and specifically in the way in which threats from natural disasters are conceived" (p. 34). Fire Chiefs must, therefore, make contact with the various groups in their community and through joint consultation establish a planning process that takes into account the various ethnic groups within the community. Failure to do so could result in members of an ethnic group taking their own course of action which may be separate from the community's intended emergency response.

For the most part, the largest single ethnic group in the North is Canada's First Nation people. According to Gerber et al. (1994) the First Nation people represent almost 6% of Canada's population and make up the largest population segment of communities throughout the Yukon, Northwest Territories and the central to northern portions of most provinces.

The presence of aboriginal groups in communities of all sizes is a growing trend due mainly to their shift from traditional ways of life to living in established communities. This trend is typified by the Inuit of Northern Canada. They have moved from the land to communities due to increased industrial development, reduction in the game supply and the need for employment and schooling (Gerber et al. 1994).

Fire Departments should, therefore, strive to involve band members and aboriginal councils in their community's emergency preparedness effort. This may not be an easy task. Perry and Mushkatel (1984) reported that for minorities, "the struggle for economic viability was immediate and continuing, and in comparison, warnings about threats from the environment seemed to pose less relative importance" (p. 33). They also noted that in some instances members of ethnic minorities may not accept danger warnings from a non-ethnic 'authority' as credible and discard the warning.

Regardless of the obstacles before it, the involvement of First Nation people in the planning process is important enough to merit the extra effort. Failure to make this effort risks the chance of meaningful contact and communication with aboriginal residents during a disaster.

THE IMPORTANCE OF SMALL COMMUNITY FIRE DEPARTMENTS TO THE EMERGENCY PLANNING PROCESS

Evolution in the Fire Service

The Fire Service has changed dramatically over the last two decades in Canada. All communities, both large and small, have seen significant changes in their population base, buildings, and infrastructure. Even from a fire protection perspective alone, the possibility of a community crisis developing from a large conflagration fire has become very real. Hawkins and McClees (1988) emphasized the need of a small community to plan, prepare and respond to a "fire" disaster. They wrote:

> "Increasingly, small and rural departments face the responsibility of protecting large developments and even high-rise structures. These incidents show why all departments should be prepared to move smoothly from a routine response mode to one requiring large-scale, multi-agency incident management" (p. 321).

This demands that Fire Chiefs in small communities look at emergency preparedness as a logical extension of basic fire defense planning.

Changing mission statements

The role of emergency planning for a Fire Chief is not confined strictly to fires. Gerard Hoetmer (1991) identified three types of disasters that can impact a community: natural, technological and civil. A Fire Department in a small community would have to respond to any or all of these types of disasters. This requires small community Fire Departments to take a lead role in their community's planning process.

In essence, the various mission statements of many Fire Departments provide a logical and natural link to the emergency planning process. Kramer (1990) wrote:

> "whether a fire is raging or a major disaster is in the making, human lives and property are endangered. Since the mission of the fire department is to save lives and property, this can include most events that pose similar threats, including all types of disasters" (p. 1-9).

This was reinforced by Bahme and Kramer (1992) when they wrote that:

> "It is obvious that the fire department has a role in both disaster and fire defense control...Although the fire department more commonly is perceived as a fire suppression and protection force, it is nonetheless the logical organization to respond to other disasters as well" (p. 9).

THE BENEFITS OF FIRE DEPARTMENT'S INVOLVEMENT IN EMERGENCY PLANNING

Resources and equipment

Every community in Canada typically has some form of fire service organization. Fire Departments in many of these communities are likely the only locally-based emergency response organization (aside from the Police). They typically have a functioning command and management hierarchy which provides them with structure and leadership. Their members are trained in emergency response and are usually the first responders at a disaster scene in their community. In many cases, these Fire Departments are probably their community's ONLY response agency with the ability to mobilize its entire organization through a call-out system and in a relatively short time frame. Additionally, they may also have the ONLY communication system (separate from the Police) upon which the community can rely during disaster periods.

Training and community knowledge

Kuban (1995b) noted that Fire Department personnel have a good knowledge of the community they protect. He argued that they are a trained resource that could and should be used for disaster planning. He wrote:

> "Fire Departments and their personnel typically have the basic skills and resources required for life saving in emergencies. These skills and resources, as well as their dispersion throughout the community, provide fire personnel high visibility and immediate recognition as 'rescuers' and disaster responders" (P. 29).

Because of the nature of their (small) community, Fire Department members are more than likely to know and have established relationships with other response organizations in the community. Hawkins and McClees (1988) noted that "in addition to their personnel, facilities, and equipment, volunteer department's often have access to critical resources in the community at large" (p. 331). The linkage between the Fire Service and other responders in the community is invaluable. And while it may occur more easily in a small community, the process should not be taken for granted or assumed to exist well.

Continuity in the planning process

Kuban (1995b) also identified that Fire Department staff members could provide an element of continuity in the emergency preparedness effort of their community. He wrote:

> "Another factor in favour of Fire Department personnel is that they are typically less transient than members of other response organizations (notably the Police and provincial/federal public servants). As such, they are better able to provide much needed continuity" (p. 29).

In many small communities the turnover of members on the community's emergency planning committee can be very high. As a result, the lack of continuity in the planning process can severely hinder the development of a comprehensive disaster plan. That continuity is enhanced by the involvement of those, such as Fire personnel, whose presence in the team will be long term.

THE LIMITATIONS OF SMALL COMMUNITY FIRE DEPARTMENTS

Time lines

One of the key limitations facing Fire Chiefs who undertake a leadership role in their community's emergency planning process is ... time! The demands of day-to-day Fire Department operations, the Fire Chief's personal life and his/her primary employment can be staggering. Many planning committees have started large planning projects only to falter and fail after becoming burdened by an excessive load. Realistic planning goals, functional time frames and delegation of tasks and responsibilities to other senior officers are the keys to managing and surviving the planning process.

Regardless of the workload, Fire Departments must participate in their community's emergency planning process and be an active player in its emergency plan. Hawkins and McClees (1991) noted that:

> "Any volunteer fire department should be represented on the disaster planning team. Volunteer departments often are the first to respond to an incident, the first to begin operations, and the first to establish an incident command system. How they react will in some situations determine the severity of the incident" (p. 331).

Based on this statement, the Fire Chief must recognize the limitation of available time and participate with the intent of completing components of the plan over (perhaps) a longer time frame. Failure to set realistic time lines will likely result in a long delay in the completion of the plan and possibly in the loss of the desire to conduct the planning process.

Equipment and resources

"Disasters" are defined differently from one community to another. Similarly, the resources available to manage disasters vary from one Fire Department to another. Therefore, Fire Departments in similar size communities may not be able to respond to similar disasters in the same manner. Cohen (1989) remarked on the role that resources and equipment have in defining the extent of a community's crisis:

> "It is important to remember that the operational definition of a disaster is not the type of incident, but rather, whether or not it overwhelms existing personnel, facilities, equipment and capabilities of a responding agency or institution. What may be a major incident for one service, may be routine for another. This holds particularly true when one compares a small rural area to a large urban one" (pp. 38-39).

The equipment roster and resources of the Fire Department can be a large limitation in planning for and responding to a disaster. As a general rule, equipment needs are often the last item to be assessed by Fire Departments. Dernocouer and Mackie (1980) noted that "of all the components essential to good disaster planning and response, that of equipment preparedness consistently takes the back seat to communications, scene control, and interagency duties" (p. 56). To make matters worse, the resources of Fire Departments in small communities are often more finite than those available in larger communities.

Fire Chiefs must, therefore, assess the community's resource and equipment needs. Moreover, this assessment should be based on the hazard analysis. And, within financial limitations, needed equipment and supplies should be purchased. In small communities, the reality is that many items will be well beyond the Fire Department's budget. To alleviate this problem, FEMA (1981) advised Fire Departments to conduct an assessment of the resources available to other agencies in the community.

Fire Chiefs should also review external agencies (i.e., mutual aid partners, provincial/territorial government agencies) to complete the needs assessment for needed resources. The main objective should be to acknowledge the finite amount of resources available to the Fire Department. Naturally, Fire Departments must also reciprocate by making their resources available to other response agencies, as necessary. What is important in this exchange is not how much resources a Fire Department has, but rather how efficient these resources are used during a disaster.

PITFALLS FOR FIRE CHIEFS DURING EMERGENCY PLANNING

The road travelled by a small community's Fire Chief in pursuit of emergency planning is often littered with roadblocks and land mines. Each can easily derail the planning process. Many of the obstacles can be accidental, created through ignorance of the hazards faced by the community or other political considerations. The obstacles to emergency planning may be equally generated by participants in the political arena and by members of the planning process.

There are two messages the Fire Chief must remember when undertaking the development of a disaster plan in a small community. The first is: Don't take the pitfalls personally. As much as possible, focus on the long term goal(s) of the plan and attempt to avoid the short term 'political' agenda. Secondly, perseverance in disaster planning always pays off for the community and for the Fire Department. Your planning efforts will always be vindicated because it is only a matter of time before the community's plan (and your work) is tested by a crisis. Hawkins and McClees observed that "the situation is clear: Every day that passes brings the community one day closer to the next disaster" (p. 345).

Public apathy

The first major pitfall to a community's emergency planning is apathy. This can be especially significant if a small community has no history of disasters. Fire Chiefs who undertake disaster planning should expect to encounter two separate types of apathy.

The first type may be associated with the residents of the community. Auf der Heide (1989) identified public apathy as being attributed to a lack of awareness around disasters and an underestimation of the risk presented to the community. He noted that "public awareness of disasters is generally poor. Even in communities where disasters have occurred relatively frequently, the public has often failed to demand the most rudimentary protection" (p. 14). The demands of life in small communities will often overpower any concerns regarding emergency planning.

The public's apathy should not, however, be seen as a stumbling block. Rather, it should provide an incentive to start the planning process. Drabek (1991) remarked that "it is true that many programs compete for a community's attention and funds, and emergency management may not seem to rate high on the public agenda. Research indicates, however, that the public assumes that preparedness efforts are being undertaken" (p. 22).

The second type of apathy that Fire Chiefs will likely encounter centres around the other members of the planning process. Local government officials will often cite the lack of concern by the public and fiscal limitations as reasons for the lack of political support to the emergency planning process (Auf der Heide, 1989). Perry and Mushkatel made this observation:

> "In practice, most community governments assign a low priority to comprehensive hazard management...In a recent survey of state and local [officials], Wright and Rossi (1981) found that problems associated with five natural hazards (flooding, fire, hurricanes, tornados, and earthquakes) were ranked near the bottom of a list

of eighteen problems facing local and state governments, which suggests that in general natural hazards were not defined as serious or pressing problems compared to other issues" (p. 10).

One of the most effective ways to counteract this (governmental) apathy, is to involve representatives from the provincial and territorial Emergency Measures (or Preparedness) Organizations in the community's emergency planning process. Their insight and experience in working with various government agencies (including reluctant government bodies) can be invaluable.

In some situations a telephone call or a letter from Provincial or Territorial emergency planners may open a number of doors and avenues for coordinated effort. Generally speaking, provincial representatives are very willing to help Fire Chiefs overcome the hurdles in the local emergency planning process.

Where feasible and appropriate, Fire Chiefs could also capitalize on a recent disaster in another community or region of the country. Auf der Heide suggested that "if there is a preparedness program lacking support, one should be ready to take advantage of a disaster to reintroduce it - even if the disaster has occurred elsewhere" (p. 29). Should the opportunity present itself, Fire Chiefs should obtain the details related to the disaster and present them to their community's council or senior administrative officer. A prepared action plan in the eventuality of a similar disaster in the community will also help advance the overall planning process.

Auf der Heide (1989) recommended that emergency planners be prepared to show how their emergency preparedness efforts can be adapted for use in regular emergency response. Moreover, the linking of the management of disasters to the day-to-day management of routine emergencies makes emergency preparedness more attractive to senior officials.

Role overload

Fire Departments are often the only emergency response organization within their community. They are recognized as such. As a result, many organizations in the community try to pass their own emergency preparedness roles on to the local Fire Department. The common assumption is that the Fire Department has the necessary personnel and the training to do the job ... alone. To make matters worse, some Fire Departments already have multiple roles. This role overload is likely to cause serious complications for Fire Department staff.

One of the most significant complications is that Fire Departments could end up with far too many roles and may not be able to perform any of them well. Another is represented by Fire Departments which are tasked with too many emergency response roles. The personnel of these Departments may be forced by some disaster situations to perform all their assigned roles at once. Either way, these conditions reduce the Fire Department's response capability.

Organizations which relegate their emergency roles to the Fire Department typically begin to lose their vested interest in their own and in the community's emergency preparedness. Without their participation the disaster plan may become unrealistic and ultimately fail to meet the needs of the community. It would also lead to the failure of the primary role of the planning process, which is to have all relevant organizations take ownership of the plan and their own emergency roles.

This is not to say that Fire Departments cannot assist or perform certain roles for other organizations. However, Fire Chiefs must ensure that the primary responsibilities of their Department have been performed before any personnel (or needed resources) are assigned to other functions or roles within the community.

One of the key methods of preventing role overload is the review of every agency's mandate and responsibility within the community's emergency plan. FEMA (1981) suggested that "when planning assigned tasks, care must be taken to ensure that the assignments are in accord with legally-mandated responsibilities and that there are no contradictions or unnecessary overlapping of duties" (p. 27).

FEMA (1981) also noted that "when sorting out emergency roles in different agencies, logic is the key word. The various necessary emergency response and support functions should be assigned to agencies most logically capable of dealing with them" (p. 27). Fire Chiefs have a natural role to play in this process.

Personality clashes and turf wars

As with day-to-day operations in a small community, personality clashes and turf wars will sneak their way into the emergency planning process. Fire Chiefs are encouraged to avoid these clashes and focus their efforts on identifying what is at their root. Gillespie (1991) noted that "proposals to redirect scarce resources impede coordination by threatening both organizational autonomy and organizational identity" (p. 60). He also explained that the planning process itself can be threatening to some managers who are not familiar with it.

Fire Chiefs should not get drawn into the fray of these interpersonal and inter-agency conflicts. Instead they should anticipate these types of conflicts and attempt to prevent their interference with the community's emergency planning process. Gillespie (1991) observed that awareness is the key to overcoming these obstacles to a well coordinated planning effort. He described the actions to take to prevent a loss of organizational autonomy and identity as follows:

> "The principal technique emergency managers use to overcome them is [through] clearly written proposals that benefit the community as a whole. Proposals should take into account the potential threats to each organization's autonomy (perhaps by developing guidelines of fair exchange), the mixing and matching of various professional groups, the range of technologies and resources that need to be strategically linked, and political compromises to achieve coordination" (p. 60).

Proposals should recognize the unique characteristics of each organization involved in a small community planning effort, emphasize community needs and respect the organizational identity of each participant. In writing such proposals, Fire Chiefs can quarterback the planning process past the destructive pitfalls of personality clashes and turf wars.

Dominating the planning process

There can be a tendency by some Fire Chiefs to dominate the planning process, especially when they organize participation and coordinate the process. The domination of the planning process by any one person may derail the whole process and may result in long lasting bitterness and inter-organizational mistrust.

FEMA (1981) observed that planning groups require a group coordinator and a committee chairperson. Both are very important. However, Fire Chiefs should typically perform the role of committee chairperson. It is a role which is essentially quarterbacking, not controlling, the process. Moreover, the addition of a 'group coordinator' into the team and the planning process will help reduce a Fire Chief's potential tendency to dominate the process.

The role of the group coordinator should be performed by a qualified planner who is familiar with the community, its needs, and the organizations involved in the planning process. Small communities often do not have this resource readily available. However, as noted by FEMA (1981) the Fire Chief may fill the position with another Fire Department member. The Fire Chief can then focus on the immediate job of being the planning group's chairperson and not its taskmaster.

Only Fire Department focus

A frequent flaw in community disaster planning is the dominance of the process by Fire Departments. They dominate the planning process, limit its focus to Fire Department issues and restrict membership to it by selecting its participants. These, and other similar limitations, can severely reduce the overall worth of the planning process and its outcome.

The recommended approach is for Fire Chiefs to consider their role as leaders in the process of developing a comprehensive emergency management plan for their community. By necessity, they need the direct participation of other organizations. Kuban (1995b) added a qualifier to the Fire Department's leadership role in the process. He noted that "this role of leadership need not, and should not, exclude other agencies currently involved in emergency preparedness within the community. In other words, the fire department should avoid even the perception that they are usurping power" (p. 28).

One-Time planning process

One of the pitfalls of emergency planning is the assumption by many of its participants that the process is a one-time effort. Failure to correct this misperception may result in subsequent neglect of whatever 'plan' is created through the original planning effort. Fire Department personnel must work to ensure that the planning process is seen as an ongoing effort. One way to achieve this is to conduct ongoing evaluation and revision of the plan, and to include new community-related hazards as appropriate. As Kreps (1991) noted, having an out dated plan can be worse than having no plan at all.

By keeping the process alive, Fire Chiefs can again play an important role for their community. They must continue to champion the planning process and ensure that the disaster plan does not become a stale and static document.

GENERAL PLANNING IN SMALL COMMUNITIES

Small community Fire Chiefs need not re-invent the planning process. The material presented in the previous chapters should help in the development of a disaster plan. Naturally, the recommended process, resource requirement/application and roles/responsibilities should be considered in the context of one's community.

However, two important criteria are critical when developing a disaster plan in a small community. They are cooperation and coordination. Kuban (1993) observed that "the multi-organizational and multi-jurisdictional nature of disaster response demands cooperation among response agencies. It also requires the coordination of their activities at the scene" (p. 6).

As Fire Chiefs work their way through the planning process, they must ensure that the planning process and the various components to the 'plan' address the criteria of 'cooperation and coordination.' If they are not addressed the disaster plan will not adequately meet the needs of the community during the crisis. Kuban (1993) warned that "failure to achieve these two key requirements - coordination and cooperation - typically results in breakdown of communications, failure to effectively allocate scarce resources, disjointed operational tasking, and the inability of these agencies to effectively meet their respective response objectives" (p. 6).

The following points should be considered when developing a small community's disaster plan.

Fire Department disaster plan

Before leading the community's disaster planning effort, Fire Chiefs must ensure that they have completed their Fire Department's disaster plan. This document provides the structure to a department's disaster response activities. In describing the scope of this plan, FEMA (1981) noted that "a fire department disaster plan exists to provide coordinated guidelines for emergency response actions taken by the fire department before, during and after a disaster" (p. 21).

FEMA (1981) observed that "the absence of a Fire Department emergency plan for coping with atypical emergencies quite often results in poor performance on behalf of the fire department. Lack of communications, poor command and control, and numerous other problems often are by-products of poor fire department plans" (p. 21). However, well prepared departmental plans can also serve as valuable role models for other community agencies.

Reflect a moderate-sized disaster

Unchecked, the time demands upon Fire Chiefs during the emergency planning process may be significant. Therefore, it is important that Fire Departments concentrate their time and energy on planning for the most probable events (i.e., moderate-sized disasters). Auf der Heide (1989) observed that community "preparedness for moderately sized disasters may be more realistic and achieve greater acceptance by those who must pay for and carry out the preparations" than the few more devastating catastrophic events (p. 24).

Traditionally moderate-sized disasters are the most common to afflict small communities in Canada. Planning for this size of crisis will be time efficient. It also provides spin-off benefits to the planning process and serves as a preparation tool in itself for larger (more complex) disasters. Auf Der Heide (1989) observed that:

> "The advantage of a focus on moderate disasters is that the procedures involved are more likely to be used and, therefore, learned. They are also more likely to get funded. Furthermore, the skills, training, procedures, and supplies developed for moderate disasters are a logical step toward preparedness for larger events" (p. 25).

Develop modest plans

The desired final product of the planning process should be modest. Keep it simple. There often exists a mentality that disaster plans should be comprehensive and detailed. Again, the Fire Chief's time and effort is valuable and therefore should be spent on a plan that will be used and not ignored due its large size and complexity. Kreps (1991) reinforces the necessity for modest plans, "particularly at the local level, a modest degree of preparedness is all that can reasonably be expected unless emergencies occur frequently" (p. 36). Modest plans are more apt to be completed and benefit the residents of a small community. Details in a disaster plan are important, however disaster planning should be streamlined (Kreps, 1991).

THE PLAN SHOULD REFLECT THE COMMUNITY'S RESPONSE TO A DISASTER

Auf Der Heide (1989) observed that"disaster plans are often written in the belief that people ought to behave according to the plan. The plans state what people 'should do.' A more successful approach is to design the plan according to what people are 'likely to do.' Plans are much easier to change than human behaviour" (p. 37).

As noted earlier, residents of small communities are more apt to be involved in disaster response than are residents of larger communities (i.e., cities). They will also have a stronger desire to help others. A small community emergency plan should, therefore, accurately reflect the nature of response of its population. It should avoid the kind of myths which are expressed in Chapter 1.

Identifying positions in the Plan

Some small communities can be plagued by high turnover in local government and Industry positions. This can result in key people being unavailable at critical times. Small communities typically do not have abundant resources to establish elaborate backups. However, such backups are needed to ensure continuity of operations when key people are away or unavailable.

Auf der Heide (1989) recommended the solution to the problem. He wrote:

> "It is important that participants in the disaster response know how to carry out the plan even in the absence of certain key individuals. Therefore, plans should be written in terms of positions (for example, the on-call administrative supervisor, or the acting chief), rather than in terms of particular persons" (p. 43).

Knowledge of the community's plan

One can not be expected to perform well according to a plan when that plan has not been clearly communicated and understood. Unfortunately, this simple truth is missed time and again. The examples speak for themselves. Some Fire Department's emergency plans are not circulated to, discussed with and exercises regularly with all members. In many communities, one response agency is unaware of the plan of other response agencies. In many communities, emergency plans are developed in isolation and are rarely tested jointly.

Emergency plans are useless unless they become known by those who are expected to carry them out. As Daines (1991) noted, "experience shows that if responders do not fully understand procedures or responsibilities, serious problems will arise during efforts to respond to an incident" (p. 184).

Taking care of Fire Department personnel

Disasters that impact a community will also affect disaster responders, their homes, business, and most importantly their families. This is particularly the case in small communities. This is a reality that can not be ignored. Consequently, Fire Departments must develop a "mini-plan" to look after its members and their families following disaster events.

Hawkins and McClees (1991) recommended the following steps:

> "Department members should be encouraged to work out a plan of action for their family members in the event of disaster. The department should also establish procedures to determine the well-being of dependents and assign specific personnel to coordinate this activity" (p. 337).

They also suggested that the plan could include an evacuation centre for fire fighters' families. All of this, however, is not to suggest that fire fighters' dependents have a higher priority than other residents of the community. It does suggest that disaster responders need to focus on their disaster roles and responsibilities. Fire fighters who know that their family members are safe and are being cared for, are more likely to undertake the response action without hesitation.

Command philosophies

The use of a command system is essential to a community's planning and response efforts. A number of Fire-based management systems are currently available. (For more information refer to Chapter 8.)

This discussion is not about which system is better, but about simply using a command system all the time. Because of a low emergency call volume, many small community Fire Departments may not use any form of 'command' system. Some communities which have a command system may not use it consistently.

Small community Fire Chiefs, and their Departments, must use a command system. The system they use must be practiced as intended and must be used consistently for all emergency response in the community. The command system must be able to take into account mutual aid response and management of the "crisis environment" in a disaster. Fire Chiefs should ensure that the command system is known to and understood by all participants of the community's emergency planning committee. The command system should also be incorporated into the community's Plan.

Offensive/defensive strategies

The establishment of offensive and defensive strategies should be conducted after the completion of a hazard analysis. The Fire Chief should review the actions that the fire department will take to control a disaster as identified by the hazard analysis. For the most part the Fire Department's actions will be offensive, that is the full commitment of resources to control an incident. However the resource limitations of a small community must also be considered when deciding a strategy format.

The Fire Chief should also consider identifying defensive strategies for each hazard. A predetermined defensive strategy may avoid the over commitment of resources to a situation that is not manageable (e.g., a large structural fire). If the fire was beyond the control of an offensive strategy, a pre-determined defensive strategy could be put into place to avoid the tying up of all Fire Department resources.

This approach is not intended to in any way demean fire suppression. Instead, it is intended to point out that other roles (i.e., evacuation, removal of trapped people) identified by the Fire Department's disaster plan may be more important. Sometimes, the needs of the community as a whole may be more pressing than the specific needs of the Fire Department. A predetermined offensive/defensive strategy format can ensure the most effective and efficient use of a small community's Fire Department resources.

Pre-fire planning

Many Fire Services across Canada are advocating the use of pre-fire planning to produce tactical plans for buildings, industrial sites and other community hazards. These tactical plans could be the Fire Chief's road map for managing an emergency involving pre-planned buildings or sites. Jenaway discussed the scope of the tactical plan:

> "The ultimate use of the pre-planning effort is the determination of a tactical plan to address the potential incident. The key to the tactical planning is the knowledge of what lies in the enemy. By knowing what lies in the enemy, we can conduct an appropriate size-up before the incident" (p. 131).

Pre-fire planning in small communities is relatively easier than it is in larger habitation centres. The number of buildings and sites that needs to be pre-planned is often realistic and more manageable. Once conducted, the hazard analysis can be used to determine the priority of completion of the tactical plan. Pre-plans can then be conducted on structures (e.g., hospital, schools, evacuation centres) that are important to the community's disaster plan. The pre-fire planning program provides structure and benefit to both routine emergencies as well as disasters, and essentially satisfies two requirements at the same time. In his discussion of pre-fire planning, Jenaway (1992) noted that:

> "There is no difference with disaster planning than there is with pre-planning. It does take work (they both do) and they must be integrated. Just like pre-planning, disaster planning helps determine in advance if you are in an area/situation where there is a possibility for a specific type of disaster, and helps identify the potential problem which might develop. It also assists in preparing procedures for responding to disasters before, during, and after the crisis" (p. 116).

Evacuation planning

Any sizeable evacuation of a community is likely to involve the Police and the local Fire Department. Police presence, especially in small communities, may be small. Fire Department presence, on the other hand is larger. That and the fact that fire personnel are trained in evacuation of structures requires the involvement of Fire

Department personnel in ALL major community evacuations. This is reinforced by Kramer and Bahme (1992). They wrote that "while police and occasionally military personnel are involved in a primary manner with evacuations, it is the fire department that usually provides expertise and direction" (p. 498).

Evacuations are often made more difficult because members of the public often fail to see the danger which they confront (Auf der Heide, 1989). Members of the public will accept warnings of danger and will undertake the suggested course of action ONLY when they consider the sources of this information to be credible (Perry & Mushkatel, 1984). Fire Departments are well advised to build their credibility within their community.

On a related note, to be a part of an effective evacuation process the Fire Department personnel must also be a part of the pre-evacuation planning process. Kramer and Bahme (1992) identified key questions on evacuation to which all fire department personnel must have answers. They are: why evacuate, who is evacuated, who orders the evacuation, how is the evacuation to be done, how long is the evacuation, how is re-entry conducted and when, where are the evacuees to go, and what of the costs of the evacuation.

Fire Chiefs must pay specific attention to the presence of ethnic groups within the community. They should bring the unique needs and interests of these groups before the planning committee and, where appropriate, incorporate them into the plan. Issues of ethnicity, culture and language become critical during an evacuation of a small community and can not be ignored. Scanlon (1991) observed the outcome when an ethnic group is not considered during the evacuation planning process. He reported that:

> "Problems are especially likely to arise when a threatened population is evacuated to a community with a different cultural and ethnic mix...In such situations, billets may be difficult to find, and misunderstandings may result from different cultural expectations" (p. 93).

Contact and dialogue with the various ethnic groups in the community are the Fire Chief's key tools for ensuring an evacuation process that looks after the whole community.

The evacuation of a small community is typically handled differently than a similar evacuation of a larger community. A large urban centre (i.e., a city) can often absorb more of the disaster's impact through its much larger infrastructure. Residents may move more easily to other parts of the city.

A small community, on the other hand, will most likely have less resources with which to manage the evacuation. As well it will have less flexibility and space to relocate those who are evacuated. The local Fire Chief must, therefore, ensure that the planning process for an evacuation is realistic and supported by the local (provincial, territorial, federal) government. Saint-Pierre (1992) observed that "smaller municipalities must depend on volunteers to organize their emergency services. This approach can be effective provided that the person named to head the services has credibility and is known and recognized by the municipal administration" (p. 19).

Fire Chiefs and their Departments can play a valuable role in developing the evacuation plan for their community. However, a number of key points must be considered. First, the role of the Fire Chief in evacuation planning should be one of leadership and support. This role requires Fire Chiefs to support those organizations, which are responsible for the housing and the feeding of evacuees, to develop their own plans. The Fire Department's involvement should not compromise its primary roles and responsibilities as identified in the Department's disaster plan. Fire fighters should be used for the physical evacuation and movement of residents but not with the reception, housing and feeding of the evacuees.

Planning for the secondary impact of disaster

The International Fire Service Training Association (IFSTA) (1984) observed that:

> "Some disasters trigger a multitude of secondary incidents that create a more intense disaster management problem than the primary event ... Planners must consider these secondary disasters, which could be of major consequence. The plan should provide ways to manage these secondary incidents, which might have to be handled simultaneously with the effects of the primary incident" (p. 20).

Because of the size of their infrastructure, small communities are more likely to suffer the brunt of both the initial disaster and its secondary consequences (i.e., aftershocks). Fire Chiefs must, therefore, plan for these eventualities. As in other types of planning, the first step is the conduct of a hazard analysis. Godschalk (1991) observed that the risk of secondary events must be identified and correlated to the primary disaster. Planning committees must then prepare for both the primary and likely secondary disasters.

Failure to plan for secondary disasters, the aftershocks of the initial disaster, is akin to failure to plan. Period. Small communities particularly are advised to consider all ramifications of being overwhelmed by the initial disaster and (once again) by its 'aftershock.'

Industrial planning

The presence of industry in small communities is quite common. Often an industry provides some of the attraction for individuals to move to or stay in the community. Invariably, industrial sites and operations bring a certain element of risk to the community. By necessity, representatives of industry must be involved in the community's emergency planning process.

Robert Kelly (1989) observed that:

> "It is vitally important that community officials be involved in the company's emergency planning process and that the company be involved in the local planning ... Community involvement during the planning stage will also enable local officials to assess their own capabilities to respond to an emergency at the local facility" (p. 72).

During disasters, most industries can also be a contact for resources which are not readily available to the community. As noted below, industry members may also serve as a community's first source of mutual aid.

Mutual aid

It is easy to brush off 'mutual aid' when one lives in a small and isolated community. That need not be the case! Mutual aid is a requirement ESPECIALLY for small and isolated communities. However, in order to overcome the barriers of geographical isolation Fire Chiefs must be creative. They need to look within their community and external to it for 'partners' to their emergency planning requirements.

Fire Chiefs should be able to look to communities located hours away and establish contact with people there who could provide necessary mutual aid response. They should assess their respective capabilities and needs. The must look beyond the immediate response and look at the response and recovery effort in much broader terms. The City of Yellowknife's Fire Department, for example, has a mutual aid agreement relating to fire fighting personnel and resources with the Town of Hay River's Fire Department. The distance between the two centres is 30 minutes by air and six hours by road. However, one can still provide the other the necessary back-up and relief.

Mutual aid need not be restricted to other communities. It may include various resources which may be provided by other orders of government: provincial/territorial and federal. Often, a small community could access pre-established mutual aid 'districts'. As an example, Snyder (1993) reported that the province of Saskatchewan has twelve districts which contain three to four mutual aid areas for the purpose of planning mutual aid and networking scarce disaster resources.

An assessment of externally-available resources should be conducted by a small community to complement its hazard analysis. Both tasks could, and should, be led by the Fire Department.

The resource-availability assessment could include a review of the type and quantity of resources, their location and availability, the way in which they can be accessed, time delays and so on. When applied in actual disaster response, this assessment must bend to the reality of conditions at the time. For example, a much needed resource (e.g., a fire apparatus) may not be available due to the closure of the only road access to the community.

Moreover, one must not disregard the resources of provincial/territorial emergency measures organizations. They have access to many locally-unavailable resources and are part of a wide network of organizations and experts.

Having noted the above, Fire Chiefs must still be prepared to manage their community's disaster for at least 24 hours before they receive help from outside their community. That is not to say that the mutual-aid concept and practices are of little value to small communities. While the application of mutual aid is more difficult in small and isolated communities, its presence is critical for the success of long-term disaster response and for recovery. Therefore, Fire Departments need to pay close attention to establishing viable mutual aid programs and treating both the process and their partners with respect.

Intra-community resources

When needed for disaster response, many resources may be found within the affected community. Chapter 6 provides more specific detail on these resources. The point which I would like to make is that the 'finding' of these resources may require some creativity on behalf of Fire Department personnel. It also requires determined effort, knowledge of the community and pre-planning. It is true that some resources (e.g., volunteers and some resources) may 'suddenly appear' following a disaster. However, these unsolicited resources may typically be lacking in organization, skill or specific resources.

Gargan (1991) observed that "we in the emergency services somehow have been overlooking a community resource that is second to none in equipment and manpower" (p.49). That resource is the community's organization responsible for Public Works. Such an organization exists in every community and, invariably, it has valuable resources and trained personnel. They may all invaluable in disaster response.

It is essential, therefore, to cross-train the community's Public Works personnel on their emergency preparedness roles. Fire Chiefs can act as recruiters and catalysts in the process of dovetailing the functions of their Fire Department and those of the community's Public Works organization.

In the event of disaster, one is likely to find Public Works personnel among the first responders. According to Gargan (1991), the challenge to Fire Departments is to organize the coordinated the response efforts of these two organizations. This coordination is best began during the planning process and not during the call-out to a disaster scene.

Other valuable resources are all the private sector and Industry-based companies which provide maintenance services. They too may be brought in, as appropriate, to support the community's emergency plan.

Small community's should pay particular notice to existing service and volunteer organizations. Because of the nature of 'small communities' these organizations can blanket the community and provide necessary organization and credibility to perform much needed tasks (e.g., conducting call-outs, distributing resources and organizing searches).

One of the hidden benefits of including other community organizations in the planning process (and the response Plan) is the development of a 'buy-in' by these organizations and their members. In a small community, these members represent the public.

Communications

Communication facilities and resources are often limited in small and isolated communities. This situation makes communication systems particularly important during disasters.

Small community Fire Chiefs need to review the communication capabilities of their Department as well as their community's. This review should assess the current capabilities of the community's response organizations to communicate with their members, with other community response agencies, and with response organizations (e.g., mutual aid partners) outside the community. Each of these links is critical for the overall success of the response effort.

One of the often neglected assets in small and isolated communities are the ham radio operators which reside in the community. Their skills, resources, rapid availability and their ability to communicate across the world make these ham operators invaluable. (Brad Mann (1994) makes a reference to British Columbia's experience which can apply just as easily elsewhere in Canada.)

CONCLUSION

Canada's small and isolated communities are located throughout our country. These communities face various geographical limitations and reflect various population sizes and composition.

The challenges confronted by small and isolated communities during disasters are typically more daunting than those encountered by their larger counterparts. Similarly, and perhaps consequently, the challenges confronted by these small community Fire Chiefs are also more complex. The problem is, however, manageable!

Small and isolated community Fire Chiefs and their Departments need to provide leadership in their community's emergency preparedness process. They need to hone their understanding of the needs of their community and the resources which are (and are not) available to meet these needs. Fire Department personnel need to become educators in getting the 'emergency preparedness message' to their colleagues and to the public: "It can happen here." Finally, Fire Chiefs need to clearly define their Department's (manageable) role in disaster response and team-up with partners within the community and external to it.

When all is said and done, Fire Departments in small and isolated communities have a responsibility to guide their community's emergency preparedness. More often than not, they are seen as the experts in the field and are expected to perform all functions of emergency preparedness and response. This is doomed for failure because Fire Departments, especially volunteer-based Departments, do not have the resources to respond to large scale disasters. The only way that small communities could EFFECTIVELY respond to disasters is if their Fire Department takes leadership of the process and ... if this Department is able to develop the necessary mutual-aid partnerships. Small and isolated communities can not and should not be 'small' or 'isolated' in their emergency planning and disaster response.

Picture 11.1

Canada's winters can create monumental obstacles to fire fighting and emergency response operations.
(Photo Courtesy of Gerry Emas, Edmonton Emergency Response Department.)

Short And Long Term Recovery

Jack V. McAllister, Fire Chief (Ret'd), City of Barrie
Doug G. Skelding, Former Chairman, Emergency Services, The Canadian Red Cross Society
Ron Kuban, Ph.D., President, Turning Point Consulting Corp.

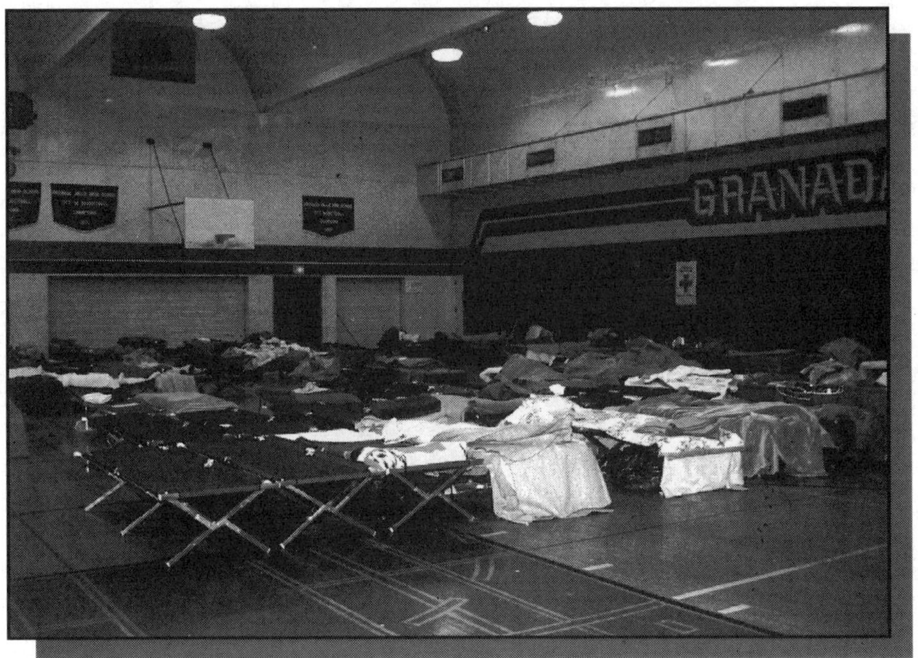

Photo Courtesy of Terry Chicoine, Canadian Red Cross Society, Western Division.

This chapter covers the recovery process of a community following a disaster. It highlights issues critical to the recovery process. The topic is presented in two parts: Short and long–term recovery. The former is addressed by Chief McAllister and Mr. Skelding, while the latter is covered by Dr. Kuban.

The previous four chapters of this book discussed issues relating to the response phase of emergency management. That phase involves activities critical to the saving of lives, minimizing property losses and ensuring that the crisis is resolved.

The end of the disaster response phase is typified by the following achievements:

1. The disaster area has been made secure.
2. The area has been searched for people who may be trapped, injured or dead.
3. The trapped have been found and rescued.
4. The injured have been treated at the site or moved to a health care facility.
5. The dead have been removed to a morgue.
6. Response agencies have returned to normal operations.
7. Access to the area has been opened and those who were evacuated began returning to their homes.

The response phase is the initial reaction to the disaster. Its completion does not mean that the disaster is over. far from it. There is still a need to return to the normal routine(s) of living. There is a need to 'recover.'

The process of recovery should begin even before the completion of the response phase. The process is complex and, depending on the extent of the disaster's damage, may have phases of its own and may unfold over a period of years.

Early recovery activities may include the provision of necessities (i.e., shelter, clothing and food) for the homeless, health care for the injured and counselling for those who were traumatized. These initial activities are referred to as the short–term recovery process. There are also long–term recovery activities.

Admittedly, the direct involvement of Fire Officers in their community's long–term recovery process is likely to be limited. However, Fire Officers must be cognizant of the key issues and activities which must be performed before the community can truly put the disaster behind it and consider the recovery process complete.

The discussion below is divided into two parts. The first addresses short–term recovery using two examples from disasters in Ontario. The second part addresses the issues of long–term recovery.

SHORT–TERM RECOVERY

It is difficult, at times, to determine exactly when disaster–related activities shift from reaction (or response) to the recovery phase. The transition is often subtle in nature. Just the same, the recovery phase is often an entity on to itself in that it involves unique problems requiring unique solutions.

The recovery phase is extremely important for the full recovery of individuals, organizations and the community as a whole. This phase is intended to re–establish normality as quickly as possible. For that reason, the process must begin as soon as possible even while the response phase is unfolding. Naturally, such response activities as search, rescue, containment and possible evacuation must take precedence over any recovery activities. However, the two sets of activities can be performed in parallel, provided that plans to do so have been made in advance.

There are many requirements to the process of short–term recovery. These include:

1. The temporary resettlement of those who were made homeless by the disaster.
2. The provision of psychological debriefing/counselling as required.
3. Feeding survivors (e.g., evacuees) and responders beyond the immediate response period.
4. Making arrangements for the feeding of livestock.
5. Testing and securing safe water supplies.
6. Reopening transportation routes.
7. Conducting site inspections for insurance and financial relief purposes.

The need for recovery efforts to be directed at the survivors of the disaster is obvious. Those who were directly affected by the disaster are clearly in need of help. Even such activity as the burial of the dead is as much to halt the spread of disease and reduce the trauma of the living, as it is to respect those who perished due to the disaster. However, it should be equally understood that the survivors of the disaster are not the only victims. Responders can also become survivors. They too need support and understanding, possibly as early as during the response period.

The effective management and control of the short–term recovery process requires two significant components. One is a plan which defines what will be done. The other is an organization (e.g., a Municipal Recovery Control Group) that will coordinate the process and execute the plan. This organization may need the help of a volunteer group (i.e., a non–government organization) to do what must be done. A number of such groups exist.

The recovery phase, like its predecessor the response phase, must be well planned and coordinated. It can not be conducted effectively as a knee–jerk reaction to the disaster. Therefore, each municipality must develop appropriate policies and procedures to address its recovery needs within its means and capability. Moreover, these policies and the recovery effort should not be conducted in isolation. They should be linked to other orders of government, local industries, local businesses and key community organizations.

The Municipal Recovery Control Group should be created at community level and involve senior representatives of municipal agencies and departments. Especially for long–term recovery purposes, this group should also include key people from the community who would represent the various interest groups within the community.

The Municipal Recovery Control group should be given responsibility for strategic coordination and financial management of the recovery effort. The group should manage the appropriate recovery funds, respond to requests for assistance and authorize the appropriate support as necessary.

As a minimum, the Municipal Recovery Control group should be in direct contact with Provincial officials. This contact may enhance both the response and the recovery effort. Depending on the severity of the disaster, recovery funds may well be available at both provincial/territorial and federal levels. Any request for financial assistance must be well organized, clearly justified and within established guidelines for such requests.

Municipal Recovery Control Groups will realize very quickly into their mandate, that the implementation of their recovery plans requires resources beyond those which are readily available to them. That is a major reason why volunteer groups are needed.

It is important to encourage non–municipal agencies to become part of the overall municipal recovery plan. These agencies could be asked to assume responsibility for recruiting volunteers to be active in a number of areas as designated by municipal officials. Moreover, if the recovery plan requires a large and complex volunteer effort, one of these agencies should be designated as the 'lead agency' or the coordinator of the effort by all other volunteer agencies.

This approach works well in practice and simplifies the recovery process by providing the Municipal Control Group with one telephone number to call and activate the remainder of the recovery process. The lead–agency's coordinator should link with whomever the Municipal Control Group designate as the contact for the municipality, and provide the agreed–to services and resources in accordance with the plan.

Two examples come to mind to illustrate the above comments during disaster recovery periods. Both are situations that we have encountered in recent times. However, each required a different short–term recovery process. The two disasters are the 1982 Medonte Township train derailment and the 1985 Barrie Tornado.

The 1982 Medonte Township train derailment

The story of this disaster begins in 1979. At that time, various municipal officials (i.e., the Fire Chief, the Police Chief and representatives from other city departments) were given the task of organizing and compiling an emergency response manual for the City of Barrie. It was intended to encompass every conceivable type of emergency. It was noted that coordination of non–municipal resources was a vital part of this plan since the Municipality had only a limited number of employees. It was agreed that the municipality would depend on one well–organized external agency to assist as required. This agency was tasked with the coordination of other agencies in the municipality so that the Fire Chief, Police Chief or the Municipal Emergency Control Group had to call only one telephone number to initiate the recovery process.

The plan was completed and provided a detailed tactical guide. As agreed it included one non–municipal group, tasked to coordinate support for those who might be displaced by an emergency. Also included was support for emergency workers through the provision of food and refreshments. The plan was finalized and left until needed in an emergency.

In February of 1982 a freight train loaded with chemicals derailed and ignited about three to five miles north of Barrie, Ontario. The derailment occurred in an almost inaccessible location. Additionally, the possible spread of poisonous chemical fumes by air became a very real and serious concern.

The response was quick and extensive. The Simcoe County Mutual Fire Aid Plan was activated. The Medical Officer of Health and the Ontario Provincial Police ordered an evacuation of all residents within a three mile radius of the wreck. But the question remained: Where were they to go?

The Canadian Red Cross, a well known volunteer agency, immediately opened a large shelter in the local College. Its intent was to provide a safe and secure shelter to evacuees. This was an important activity, especially because the evacuation order lasted for two days.

All evacuees were registered so that friends and relatives calling for information would know whether the evacuees were safe. Equally important, callers could find out the whereabouts of the evacuees. Arrangements were then made for the gathering and transport of evacuees to a more familiar environment like the homes of their friends and families. Refreshments and food were also available. Children were given games to play and books to read, things that they would have normally done at home.

Since we were dealing with a primarily rural community, arrangements were also made to allow farmers back on to their farms so that they could feed their livestock and perform other chores. The two–day evacuation order was hard on both farmers and livestock.

Another major concern during this emergency was the care of the emergency workers engrossed in containing the fire. The temperature in the region at the time was well below zero–degree Fahrenheit and emergency workers had to be supplied frequently with hot food and drinks while they worked. Consequently, food and hot drinks had to be organized and were provided around the clock for ten days!

One of the fortunate things about this disaster is that the evacuees generally did not suffer any particular trauma other than being away from home.

The 1985 Barrie Tornado

The response to the 1985 Barrie tornado provides another perspective of the recovery process. In an instant, a great many residents lost their dwellings, their personal effects and in some cases the lives of family members or neighbours. Hundreds of properties were involved in this disaster. The event produced serious psychological consequences some of which still exist today!

Once again it is difficult to ascertain the precise moment when recovery operations overtook rescue. This disaster was of such magnitude that it immediately forced the activation of the municipal disaster plan. Naturally, the process initiated the response of municipal organizations, and also activated local volunteer agencies. These non–government agencies immediately fielded a lot of calls to assure people that help was on its way. This action greatly assisted the municipal response agencies.

The next task for these volunteer agencies was the registration of disaster survivors and response to inquiries about them. Computers were brought to the local headquarters and a team was assigned to register those whose homes had been destroyed or damaged. Registration involved recording the names of all family members as well as their home address prior to the tornado. Also recorded were their new or temporary address (i.e., friend or family's house) where they took temporary shelter. A directory of all evacuees and their 'current' location was created.

Registering the evacuees was quite beneficial, if for no other reason than being able to respond to queries about them. Literally thousands of calls were received at the volunteer agency's headquarters from all over the world to determine if the caller's family members or acquaintances were affected by the disaster and whether they were safe. In most cases, agency workers were able to provide the caller with the new or alternate address and telephone number of the survivor in question. This one service alone provided a certain calming effect on the survivors and those who called with concerns about them. They all realized that someone knew the whereabouts of the survivors and could contact them if necessary.

Towards the end of the response phase, the Fire Department Command Centre, which had been used as a central control for search and rescue operations, changed its role to support the recovery process. Therefore, a number of additional people were made available to assist those in need. For example, municipal officials, insurance adjusters, building inspectors and members of the Engineering Department were all on hand. Inspections were conducted and building permits were issued to speed the process. Insurance adjustments were made and many claims were settled right on the spot.

In a number of cases immediate financial assistance was provided to meet the most pressing needs of individuals and families. In other words most of the bureaucratic red tape was eliminated or bypassed in order to render immediate assistance to those in need.

General security of the affected area was also established through the joint effort of the Police Department and personnel from Canadian Forces Base Borden. Together they successfully cordoned off the whole area and effectively reduced the possibility of looting. Their actions further enhanced the sense of security and safety of the survivors and their sense of confidence in their municipality's ability to response to and recover from the disaster.

Cleanup was perhaps the most visible of all recovery operations. The Mennonite disaster response team arrived from Kitchener, Ontario, assessed the situation and offered its assistance. The offer was immediately accepted. As a result, hundreds of Mennonite volunteers arrived early every morning, were assigned areas of work and immediately began to pick up and remove debris from streets and properties. The Mennonite volunteers also assisted survivors in salvaging appliances, furniture and other personal effects from the damaged homes.

The recovered items were placed in huge wooden storage boxes that were obtained and located by the city at each of the destroyed dwellings. When filled, these boxes were secured in a local moving and storage warehouse until the respective owner(s) decided what to do with these belongings. This approach proved to be another valuable confidence builder for those with property losses since their precious belongings were not only salvaged but safe in storage.

Each day, for two weeks, the Mennonite disaster crews arrived from their farms in the Kitchener area, worked from dawn until dusk and then returned home to perform their own required farm chores. These workers had to be fed and refreshed. The volunteer agency was supported by the local College which donated its kitchen facility and its untiring chef. Together they organized what was to become a massive meals on wheels exercise. Vans were obtained, directed, dispatched and controlled at the various work sites by amateur radio people. Everyone was fed three hot meals a day and refreshments in between. Food was supplied to hundreds of workers for the whole salvage period. The criteria for feeding was that anyone working on the relief effort—Mennonite disaster crews, property owners, or other volunteers—was to be fed. This feeding program was a highly visible and much needed service. It showed that the community was supportive of those assisting in the recovery operation.

The lessons for us

From the two examples above, it should be clear that emergency situations may be minor in their beginning but can quickly escalate into major proportions. Many situations or problems could evolve that require immediate attention. They often require the involvement of many people. Major highway closures caused by vehicle accidents or winter storms, major power failures in winter, floods in the spring and summer can all result in a great number of people being displaced in a rather short time period. Recovery from these types of situations could be long term and require shelter, feeding and medical attention.

The population of every community consists of a variety of people with diverse capabilities with which to respond to disaster. Some, like the very old, the very young or the disabled may need special assistance during disaster response and recovery.

Others may have the training, resources and capability to care for themselves and others. The key point here is that the recovery process should be planed and executed in a way that does not further aggravate the situation.

In the case of feeding, representatives of the Medical Officer of Health are likely to be involved and inspect food preparation and distribution methods. Recovery activity in these instances could involve not only medical people but also the Department of Health, particularly in the case of rural flooding involving septic tanks. Environmental experts could also be involved and be asked to assess air quality.

In cases of evacuation, shelter sites that have been pre–arranged must be opened and adequate parking must be arranged for a larger–than–normal capacity. The communications capability of recovery–related centres must be assured against the possibility of power failure or telephone switching centre overload. As in the case of the response phase, amateur radio clubs may be used to supplement the existing network.

Transport of evacuees must be considered not only for the immediate evacuation. Those who lost their vehicles or those unable to drive them due to road damage should, where possible, be provided alternate means of travel. Municipal bus systems could then become another element of the recovery team. The municipal Welfare Agency should play a key role in that regard, by identifying the needs of individuals and families.

Damage assessment in cases of extensive property destruction is also an important aspect of recovery. Building inspectors and engineers may have to be recruited from outside the affected municipality to deal quickly with the sheer quantity of damage. Police measures must be implemented to secure the affected area and keep out anxious property owners until each street is declared, by search and rescue officials, as safe to enter. For example, emergency crews should shut off any residential gas metres and electric power breakers to prevent accidental damage by fire should the power be re–activated.

Public Works, Utility and Parks departments should quickly become involved in clearing utility poles, wires and other large items of debris from streets. (Trees should be cleared using large wood chippers thus reducing the volume of debris and saving landfill space.)

As noted earlier, large wooden storage boxes should be obtained from moving and storage companies and placed in front of demolished residences. Residents returning to their home location may then recover what they can from the wreckage and place items inside a secure locked box. When filled these boxes can be moved to a main storage location until such times as the owner has determined what to do with the contents. In cases of wide ranging property and utility destruction it may also be necessary to place portable toilets at strategic locations within the damaged area.

A word of caution about equipment. There will likely be people who will visit the disaster site and drop off equipment (e.g., chain saws) to be used at the site. Emergency workers may not need these items, may not be aware that they were dropped off or may be unskilled in using them. Moreover, the people who dropped off the tools usually assume that these tools will be cared for by the emergency workers. That may not always be the case! The result, often discovered after the clean up has been completed, are complaints and ill feelings. Therefore, to avoid any claim against the community or its emergency department, it is vital to ensure that any request for tools be accompanied by an official purchase (or acquisition) order. This will also remove the likelihood of false claims for equipment that was never delivered or in poor order to start with.

Property owners should be allowed into the area only when streets are declared safe and open. Returning residents and property owners should be able to identify themselves to the Police who have secured the area. Facilities should also be provided for insurance company officials to meet the needs of those with, as well as those without, insurance.

The volunteer coordinating agency should be prepared to be accountable for the inevitable influx of donations of money, clothing, food and the multitude of items that are sent by external donors. A central location should be made available to receive, sort, distribute and store these items.

Unattended swimming pools can be a hazard worth mentioning. In the case of a tornado it is likely that protective fencing will have been destroyed. It is most important for protection of life that these pools be pumped dry to avoid the accidental drowning of children and adults. If pumping is not practical then snow fencing should be erected around the pool.

Day care facilities should be considered for children of disaster survivors. This will greatly assist their parents who will, in all likelihood, be engaged in salvaging personal property or arranging for replacement, repair, and much more. However, care should be taken NOT to isolate the children from their significant support system, especially during this traumatic period.

Since many personal property items are likely to be scattered throughout the disaster area, it is important that a lost and found facility and process be established. Its location and hours of operation should be broadly advertised. The presence of this facility will likely have an important positive psychological effect on people who have lost family photographs or other cherished personal possessions.

Experience shows that people are generally honest. When given the location of a lost and found site people make the effort to return the items they have found scattered about. Honesty also prevails when people come to view and identify their own recovered articles. They will likely retrieve only that which is theirs.

In cases involving fatalities, temporary morgues can usually be set up in arenas. These should be under strict control and well secured. Their location should be made known. Moreover, arrangements should be made for clergymen to be continuously available on site, or on call, for consolation and support.

The amount of debris arising out of a disaster will of course be determined by the extent and character of the damage. Debris should be separated into combustible and non–combustible material. To avoid overburdening landfill sites, combustible material should be taken to a safe location and burned under supervision. Where possible, non–combustible material should be transported to re–cycling plants.

The psychological needs of people vary with each person and situation. The 1985 Barrie tornado caused, in seconds, much property destruction and death. The shock of this event only became known days afterwards and was especially prevalent in young people and school age children. Professional teams were assembled by medical experts to visit schools to talk to the children in groups or, if necessary, on a one–to–one basis. These were similar to Critical Incident Stress Debriefing teams which now exist within most Fire Departments. Counselling naturally depended on circumstances and the trauma experienced. Even now, eleven years after that tornado, there are adults and children who are extremely fearful of normal thunderstorms.

The recovery period is also a time to reassess and learn from the experience. In that regard, it is very important that a meeting of all key response groups be held, as soon as possible after the event, to assess the overall response. The discussion should focus on what happened, how it was handled and where response can be improved should it be required again.

NEIGHBOURHOOD INITIATIVES

A new initiative is rooting itself in communities large and small. It is based on the realization that municipal agencies responding to major (i.e., catastrophic) disasters are likely to be taxed to the limit. This may leave some residents of these communities to fend for themselves until responders can get to them. Since delays in response are expected to last anywhere from a few hours to a few days the question is "how could the general population be better protected."

The answer to the question involves the creation of community–based self–help organizations which would initiate and sustain both response and early–recovery efforts. These organizations are usually structured along neighbourhood boundaries. However, they can not operate in isolation because they depend on general guidance from municipal authorities, and must be part of the municipality's recovery plan.

A number of varied approaches have been taken to organize neighbourhoods to deal with the issues of early recovery. These issues remain the same regardless of the approach taken. They include:

1. Light urbane search and rescue.
2. Care for the injured.

3. Food and accommodation for the survivors.
4. Security of the neighbourhood.
5. Communication links within the neighbourhood and with the media.
6. Liaison with municipal responders and other officials.

Each of these activities requires a team consisting of a team leader and a number of qualified workers. Each team must be trained and be prepared to perform its assigned responsibility. Additionally, the neighbourhood must have a person who would be in over–all charge of that neighbourhood's recovery plan.

It goes without saying that the neighbourhood recovery plan must have the support of both the community AND the neighbourhood. It must also be maintained and practised.

In summary, municipalities should have disaster–recovery plans that will complement their disaster–response plans. Moreover, the Fire Officer who is usually involved in the first response to a disaster must be aware of these plans, how they work and who to contact for assistance. The details of the recovery process would likely fill a book. However, here are some key items that should be included in a short–term recovery plan. Please note that many of these issues are equally important during the response phase.

1. Provision or arrangements for:

   - pre–arranged shelter locations, immediate and long–term
   - mass transportation (e.g., bus system)
   - sanitation facilities
   - security and protection of property
   - medical and hospital facilities
   - care for people with special needs (e.g., elderly, young)
   - communication network(s)
   - registration system for evacuees
   - morgue facilities
   - feeding (immediate and long term)
   - lost and found facility
   - means of conducting damage assessment
   - municipal welfare provisions
   - landfill policy
   - counselling for trauma victims
   - psychological de–briefing and counselling
   - media liaison.

2. The composition, roles and responsibilities of the Municipal Emergency Control Group.

3. The working arrangements with a dependable volunteer agency.

4. The working arrangements with the Provincial/Territorial government.

5. The process whereby the volunteer agency will:

   – provide and manage shelter facilities
   – register evacuees
   – field inquiries regarding their whereabouts
   – supply food
   – oversee feeding arrangements
   – search for personal belongings
   – Operate the lost and found facility.

These are but a few of the important major items related to disaster recovery. There are many more issues to be considered. However, each municipality must tailor its plan in accordance with its own environment and requirement. Naturally, these short–term recovery issues must be considered with other, long– term recovery, concerns and activities.

LONG–TERM RECOVERY

There is an old adage which states that "the job ain't done until the paperwork is finished." In the case of crises and disasters the process is not over until everything is back to normal. However, that is not to say that returning things to 'normal' means returning everything to pre–disaster condition. Truth is that such a task is bordering on the impossible, because things can never be 'the same' again. That is not altogether bad. As noted in Chapter 1, crises and disasters are turning points. They are opportunities for change, growth and development.

Unlike the well formulated concepts and practices of emergency planning and response, disaster 'recovery' is still in its infancy. As noted earlier in this chapter, there is a common misconception that because the hazards have been contained, the injured were treated, evacuees (if any) were returned to their homes or placed in shelters, and major transportation routes have been reopened the disaster is officially over. Alas, the job is far from complete. In fact, one may well note that the most difficult task, that of long–term recovery, has just began.

The underlying aim of long–term recovery efforts is to restore the capability of individuals, organizations, businesses and the community as a whole to resume their 'normal' day–to–day functions. That is no small feat considering the devastation which disasters and crises often wreck on human lives as well as on community resources and infrastructure.

Long–term recovery involves a variety of issues and activities. These, in turn, may reflect the concerns of individuals, organizations, businesses and various political entities. In short, the process demands extensive cooperation, agreement and coordination among a myriad of stakeholders.

Long–term activities

No comprehensive list exists to define all the activities of long–term recovery. However, listed below are some activities typically related to long–term recovery. In reality these activities are often interrelated and are difficult to completely separate one from the other. However, in this discussion they are grouped into general categories. This is done only for ease of presentation. This grouping is also intended to focus attention to the specific concerns, questions and issues which must be addressed as part of long–term recovery planning.

Health and welfare. In situations where people have been exposed to harmful chemicals or smoke, it makes sense that they should be checked and where needed also treated for the harmful effects. However, consider the following questions and related issues. What type of treatment are they entitled to? How long should they be monitored before they can return home, or go to work? Who pays for the health–monitoring activity and for the down time of those who are employed?

Should the general public be told about possible short and long–term health risks as a result of the disaster? If the answer is 'yes', who makes the announcement, what information is released and what is the public expected to do about it?

When is it safe for people to return to their homes? Is there a need to test the structural safety of buildings, cleanliness of drinking–water or the stability of banks, dykes, roadways, bridges and so on? Who performs these tests and in what priority? Which area of the municipality is tested (and re–opened) first, second, third ... ? How many times should these tests be conducted to ensure no long–term contamination?

Mental health counselling. This goes beyond the post traumatic stress debriefings which may occur during either the response or short–term recovery stages. This counselling is long–term and requires one–on–one treatment versus the group work which typifies the earlier stage of recovery.

This type of counselling may be required by emergency responders as well as the survivors of the crisis. Employers of those who need time off to deal with their grief and pain must come to grips with a number of questions. For example, how long will they allow employees to be paid while away from their duties due to trauma? Who pays for the counselling? Should (and could) the employee be reassigned to less stressful duties, and if so for how long? What of the employee's family members who were also traumatized?

Reconstruction and restoration. Damage, due to the disaster, may occur to both private and public structures within the municipality. Inevitably, each of these structures may be seen as a priority for reconstruction. But before ANY reconstruction is conducted there are a number of exceptionally contentious issues which must be resolved.

Should the community allow rebuilding of any kind on the area (i.e., flood plain, earthquake fault or slide area) which was damaged by the disaster? Which structure should be restored to its original shape in its original location? Which structure should be levelled and rebuilt anew? Where should buildings be reconstructed? In what order should buildings be demolished? In what order should they be rebuilt or restored?

What about rebuilding the community's infrastructure (e.g., roads, bridges, dykes, culverts, dams)? The questions which must be answered are the same as those for buildings and structures. Similarly, hard choices must be made through general agreement and be defended publicly. Additionally, the costs of rebuilding the infrastructure are often high and are often financed through higher orders of government. So, what arrangements are in place?

Should individuals be allowed to rebuild their damaged homes and business facilities? Or, should they wait for municipal review of the situation, analysis of available options and ultimate decision on a general approach? The former option allows individuals to proceed, but significantly reduces the opportunity for the municipality to undertake mitigative actions (i.e., perhaps relocate some structures from hazardous areas). The latter option takes time, dialogue, cooperation and agreement. By necessity it delays individuals from resuming normal life until the community has established its master plan. The second option is also likely to delay the re–opening of affected businesses and by doing so will significantly reduce their ability to stay in business.

Business resumption. One of the key elements of a community's long–term recovery is the recovery of its economy which is often represented by its business sector. Business resumption, also referred to as Business Continuity or Business Recovery is a specialized process which merits its own study.

The intent of the business recovery process is the same regardless of its title. It is to return business operations to full production as quickly as possible. The reason is obvious – survival of the economy and the tax base. However, 'as quickly as possible' means that the start of the process coincides with the start of the other recovery activities.

As noted above, a delay in the resumption of business operations can result in business failure. Statistics from the United States indicate that 43 percent of businesses which were affected by disasters never opened their doors following the disaster. Of the remaining businesses, nearly 30 percent did not survived the next two years! And, the devastation of business losses of this magnitude tend to ripple throughout the affected community.

The recovery requirements of business owners and operators may becomes obvious even during the response phase. They may press responders and politicians alike for access to their business facility. They will want to retrieve stock, important documents and data, or simply check on their property. These business owners and operators may not be satisfied with a cursory and brief visit. Instead, they may want to resume their operation while the community around them may be required to evacuate.

How much leeway should business operators get so that they could recover their 'business'? Who pays for their lost revenue caused through an extended and perhaps unnecessary evacuation? Should they be compensated for lost revenue due to their isolation from their customers, due to the closure of local roads for dangerous goods spill clean–up? And, if so, by whom?

Moreover, given the increasing trends toward home–based businesses, how can these businesses be accommodated in a way that does not discriminate against them due to their residential location? Should they be allowed back to their 'offices' while their neighbours are not allowed to go home? What are the biases in favour and against these businesses, and can they be remedied?

It is important to note that business recovery issues apply equally to public as to private organizations. As such, municipal agencies and departments must have the process and resources with which to recover, resume or continue their operations. Clearly, all organizations—large and small, public and private—should have a Business Continuity Plan specifically directed to this phase of emergency management.

Continued care for livestock. The section on short–term recovery addressed some of the needs of farmers and their livestock. These needs are immediate and may become obvious even before the impact of a disaster (e.g., floods). The longer the response stage the more complex these needs become.

The most obvious needs are those related to the care and feeding of livestock. Other concerns exist and may complicate the recovery process of the community as a whole. The needs of farmers during seeding and harvesting are often time specific and urgent. Failure to do either activity properly and at the appropriate time carries severe financial and emotional ramifications for the farmer and perhaps the community.

Farmers may likely press for early, if not immediate return to their land and livestock. When should they be allowed to do so? By whom and for how long? Should they be allowed to return before their urban neighbours?

On a different note, who monitors the farms and animals for possible contamination? What action should be taken if contamination is found? For example, should the public be told? What are the general priorities (i.e., farm land, water source, residential, business, parks, tourist sites) of 'clean–up' of contaminants?

Resumption of life. Disasters and crises are events which disrupt the normal pattern of life—home, work, social and recreational. The whole notion of recovery is to return life to some form of pre–disaster routine. This will require, for example, the resumption of schooling despite damaged schools.

The social, cultural, religious and sport–related needs of the populace must not be ignored. Sport events, concerts, theatre, services and other gatherings must all be considered and facilitated. Much can be done by using creativity and relying on donations. For example, concerts in the park, exhibition matches, performances by celebrity entertainers and other forms of entertainment can help provide a sense of continuity and perhaps even a welcome distraction from the recovery tasks at hand. Equally powerful are inter–faith events commemorating the event and the various stages of recovery from it.

The obstacles to long–term recovery

A number of significant hurdles stand in the way of successful long–term recovery. They include the following:

1. There is little information about the process and how it has been conducted elsewhere in the world.
2. Relatively few people realize the magnitude of the task and those who do understand it are often overwhelmed by it and their respective role.
3. The process needs a significant period of time to complete. The longer it takes the more obscure its final product and the reason(s) to perform it.
4. The goodwill, cooperation and latitude for action which are often found during the disaster response period are often missing during the long–term recovery phase. In other words the 'honeymoon' is over.
5. The process demands significant financial resources which, in turn, demand cooperation among various levels of government and industry. Bickering, political tug–of–war and turf issues can derail the whole process.
6. The process must balance the needs of individuals, businesses and the community as a whole.
7. Demands for quick action on behalf of individuals must be balanced with the time needed to conduct thorough planning for community–wide recovery.
8. The struggle between restoration and redevelopment will bog down any immediate action.

The process of and tips for long–term recovery

As noted earlier, disasters are opportunities for change, growth and development. Nowhere else is this fact more visible and meaningful than during the long–term recovery period.

Successful long–term recovery requires many elements and activities. Key among them are the presence of collective vision, effective planning, empowerment, cooperation and resourcefulness.

Collective vision. The disaster response period is often typified by clarity and unity of vision. Response organizations, volunteer organizations and the public at large all know that they must respond to the threat (or consequence) of the disaster. There is also general agreement about the priority of response activities: preservation of life, property and the environment. There is also a willingness to resort to extra–measures in order to meet the needs of the response effort.

The clarity and unity of vision often wears off as the response effort continues so that by the recovery stage, many issues become contentious. A significant reason for this lack of unified vision is the complete change of environment. No longer is everyone threatened by or exposed to a clear and present danger. Every individual and organization must now act to fulfil unique recovery needs. These needs may even be in conflict with the needs of others within the community.

There is a need, therefore, to recreate that unified vision, that overriding singular purpose that would galvanize the community action through the long period of recovery. That effort must be achieved if the community is to reach its objectives. Failure to create a 'vision' or purpose could result in the inability to raise needed funds, to complete needed development or to establish a sense of growth and harmony within the community.

One way to achieve this 'vision' is to develop a community forum which would decide how the community should proceed on significant matters. This forum should have a say regarding the major issues of the reconstruction process. These could include the following:

1. The relocation of affected businesses and residential sub–divisions.
2. The reconstruction/restoration of community facilities and historical landmarks.
3. The future 'look' of the municipality.

Effective planning. The recovery phase, like its predecessor the response phase, is dependent upon effective planning for its success. There are many similarities between the two planning processes. They both require the involvement of many organizations representing various jurisdictions, clarity of purpose, commitment to the task, extensive resources and cooperation.

Having stated the above, it is important to note that recovery planning is perhaps a more difficult task than the more traditional process of emergency planning. Planning for recovery must consider a longer period of time which often lacks a clear road map or a definite finish. Moreover, the process often involves a more diverse group of organizations and individuals in a more active 'political' arena.

Empowerment. The whole essence of 'recovery' is the (re)empowerment of individuals and organizations so that they can carry on with their normal routines. To that end, it is critical that the process of empowerment is started at the earliest possible time. In other words, the recovery process should not impede the willingness, commitment, capability and involvement of individuals (and organizations) in their own recovery.

Moreover, because the demands of communal recovery are so enormous, the more that can be done at the individual, family and organizational levels the less the burden is on communal organizations and resources. The more that can be done through volunteerism and the private sector the better. However, as noted earlier, the process must be guided by community–wide considerations. These considerations must not result in major delays of individual initiatives such as reopening business enterprises, reconstruction, resettlement and so on.

This criteria also demands that the survivors of disaster be seen for what they truly are: courageous, determined to rebuild their lives and in need of broad guidance and some support. As noted in Chapter 1, these are not helpless 'victims' who fall apart at the first sign of a crisis. They should be given the tools necessary for their own recovery efforts.

Cooperation. Successful efforts during both the response and the recovery phase are dependent upon cooperation of participating organizations. Because of the nature of the recovery phase, the element of cooperation is significant, but is more elusive than during the response phase. Gone is the clear mandate and obvious need to act quickly in unison.

Complete cooperation by all relevant organizations may not be achieved, but it is a goal worth striving for. It requires a clear notion of what 'the community' seeks to achieve and how that goal may be reached. One golden rule should prevail throughout the recovery process. That rule is "no one owns the process of recovery" and sticking by it will reduce turf war and discord.

Resourcefulness. The New Webster Dictionary defines 'resourcefulness' as the capability of using resources. The term is used here in a much broader sense. It is used to also mean the capability to secure these resources which one can then employ for a purpose.

The recovery process is exceptionally demanding on resources. It is likely to be more costly than the response effort. Affected communities will need, therefore, to secure additional resources in the form of grants, specialized equipment and services as well as other labour. The key here is creativity and ingenuity.

A community must seek and pursue all possible sources of funding (e.g., disaster relief or assistance programs). For example, each province and territory has at its disposal a process to allocate funds to disaster relief. These programs are not guaranteed and are not meant to be a substitute for insurance. These programs acknowledge that some disasters result in undue hardship on communities, organizations and individuals. They provide, therefore, financial assistance that will allow speedier and more effective recovery.

Municipal officials who are responsible for the emergency preparedness of their municipality should become familiar with these programs. They should establish contact with the appropriate provincial/territorial agency as part of the emergency planning process. Moreover, they should also be prepared to initiate their requests for assistance as soon as possible.

Regardless, all relevant avenues must be explored for the possibility of employing them to raise funds (or in–kind support) for the recovery effort. Wherever possible, organizations which can provide assistance should be alerted to the likely need for their support as soon as possible, even during the early response phase. This approach will greatly speed the process and will reduce the waiting period before support is received and action taken.

SUMMARY

The disaster response phase is not the end of the disaster period. It is followed by a crucial phase called the recovery phase. It is divided into two parts: short–term and long–term recovery. They are both important because they help solidify the activities undertaken during the response phase.

In fact, the recovery phase is often lengthier, costlier, less clear and contains greater contradictions than the response phase. It lacks the natural focus, commitment and cooperation which typify the response phase. And yet, without successful completion of this phase a community runs the risk of not having the disaster fully behind it.

The recovery process is intended to help the community and its affected members to return to a pattern of normal life. This does not mean life as it was before the disaster. That is a near impossibility. However, on the positive side, the disaster presents an opportunity to make life better, to learn from the event and grow from it. Failure to do so often leads to repeated crises with escalating consequences.

Picture 12.1

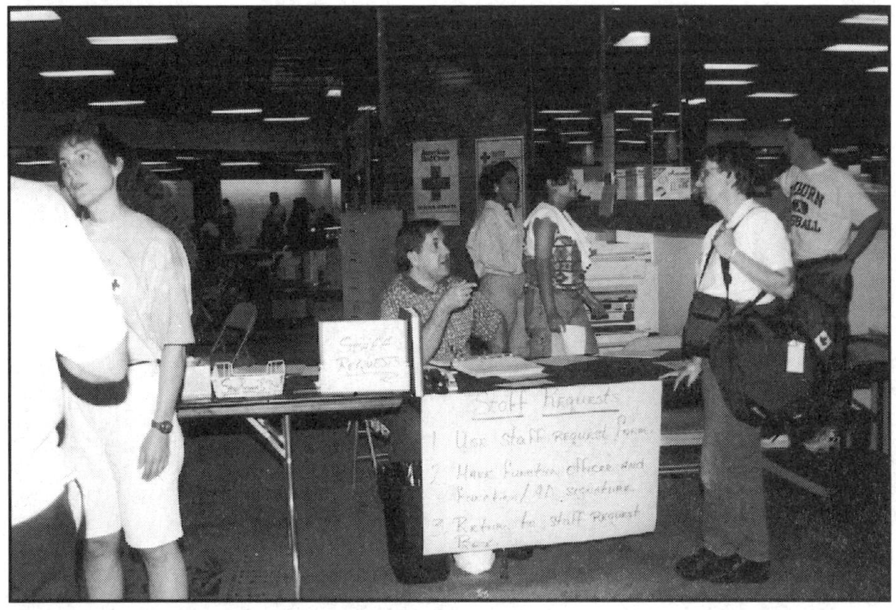

A reception centre in operations.
(Photo Courtesy of Terry Chicoine, Canadian Red Cross Society, Western Division.)

Picture 12.1

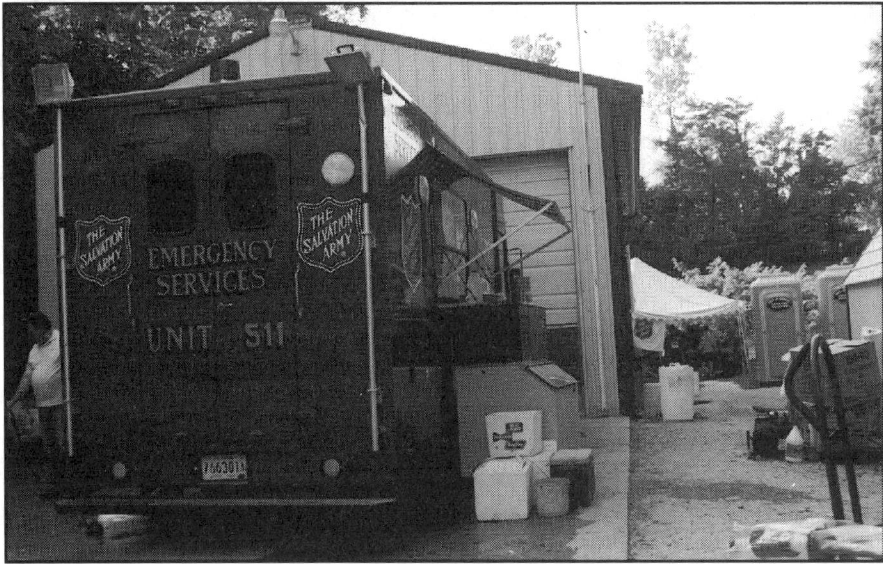

A reception centre in operations.
(Photo Courtesy of Terry Chicoine, Canadian Red Cross Society, Western Division.)

The Lessons For Canadian Fire Officers

By: Ron Kuban, Ph. D.
President, Turning Point Consulting Corp.

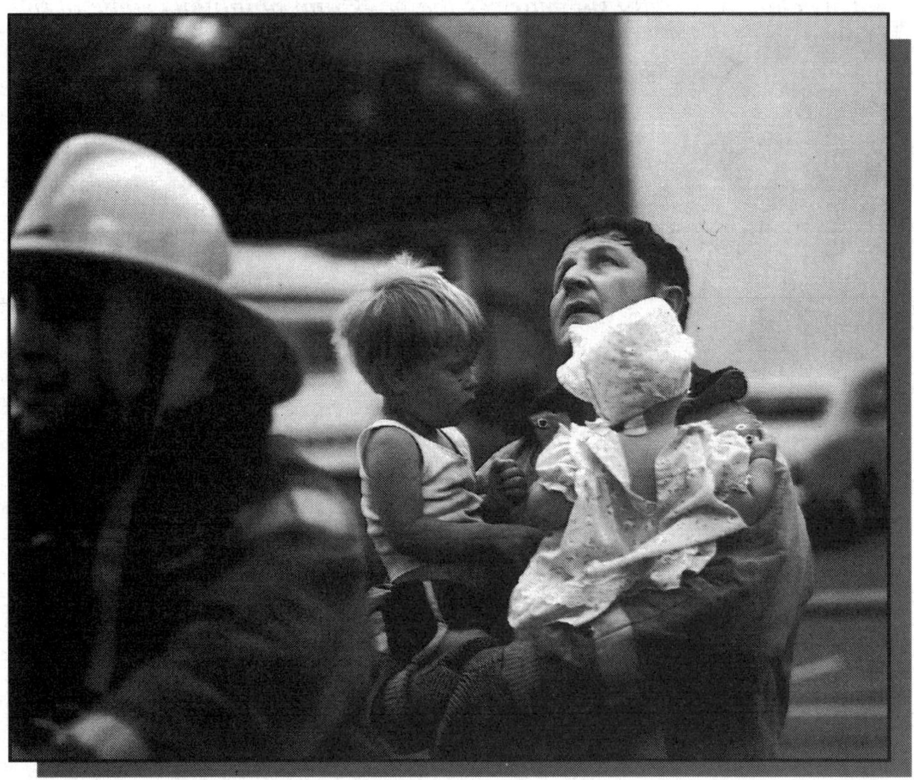

Photo Courtesy Gerry Emas, Edmonton Emergency Response Department.

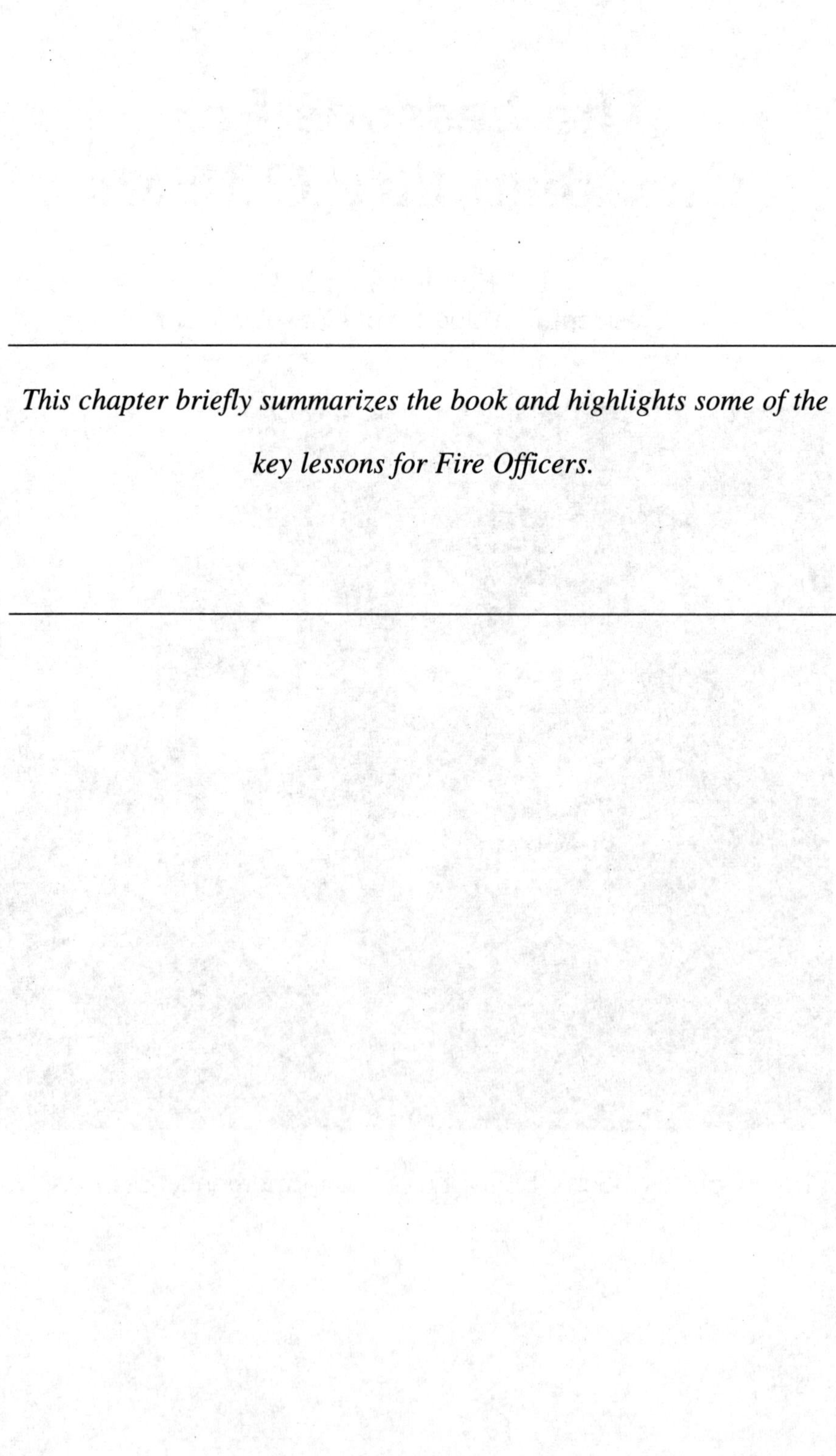

This chapter briefly summarizes the book and highlights some of the key lessons for Fire Officers.

This book was developed so that you would have a 'guide' relating to all the major facets of emergency management—planning (or preparedness), response and recovery. It was not intended to cover the 'technical' aspects of the various activities involved in emergency management. In other words, this book was designed to go beyond the expertise of fire fighting and Fire Command, to discuss disasters from the larger perspective of the 'community.'

This chapter is written to achieve two distinct goals. One, is to briefly summarize the content of the previous twelve chapters; the other is to highlight key lessons for Fire Officers.

A BRIEF SUMMARY

Disasters and crises are abnormal and unique events which occur with some degree of surprise to demand unusual, extensive and taxing response effort. The same might also be said of 'emergencies.' These events include a wide range of situations ranging from purely natural events (e.g., earthquake and tornadoes) to human acts of malice (e.g., riots and terrorism), with much in between.

Regardless of their nature, and the agent which instigates them, these events create an exceptionally stressful situation for both individuals and organizations. This stress, coupled with the hazards inherent to the situation and the damage caused by it, often affects all who experience the disaster.

Saying that disasters and crises affect individuals and organizations is an obvious understatement. What is less obvious are the various ways through which that affect is materialized. Both individuals and organizations will be affected in ways that will make routine life with its day–to–day functions difficult if not impossible. And, the truth of the matter is that disaster responders and their organizations are not immune to these effects.

Because of their nature, disasters and crises must be managed well and quickly. The luxury of time, which may exist in day–to–day operations is decidedly missing during crisis periods and the consequence of error or inaction is often severe. Consequently, if one is to respond effectively and manage these crises well, one must be ... prepared!

Any discussion relating to crises and disasters must put things in the context of 'emergency management.' This is an umbrella structure which includes four stages: Mitigation, preparedness (or planning), response and recovery. Fire Officers are likely to be involved, or have an input, in all four phases, but especially the last three.

It is important to note here that the whole process of emergency management must be rooted in law. This need is made particularly obvious during crisis situations which often demand extraordinary measures for response. Chapter 2 addressed this matter. Its intent was to emphasize the different aspects of the law (at federal, provincial and municipal levels) which assist (and hinder) Fire Officers to perform their emergency duties.

This chapter is important from a number of perspectives, least of which is the creation of barrack–room lawyers. Fire Officers need to know that they are supported by a wide range of statutes and case–law in the performance of their emergency duties. These duties do contain an inherent element of legal liability. However, that liability is not there to hinder action but to guide it.

The Chapter, and its related Appendix, presented a framework of the law as it relates to emergency preparedness. The topic area was covered in depth. However, you are strongly encouraged to seek legal advice, as appropriate.

Legal matters aside, effective disaster response requires effective emergency planning. This is the focus of Part two of this book. A number of things become readily apparent. First among them is the fact that crises often demand resources beyond the capability of any one individual, organization or community. There is a need, therefore, to involve a wide variety of organizations, each with its own special capabilities, resources and jurisdiction in the planning process.

The process of emergency planning (see Chapter 3) contains many facets which often culminate in the creation of an Emergency Plan. Emergency Plans are a valuable tool for effective response. However, the PROCESS of emergency planning is even more important. That is because people learn more by being part of the 'process' and working things out, than simply receiving a completed plan and being told to put it into action.

The planning process has three key by–products. One is the establishment of trust between individuals and organizations. This trust is exceptionally necessary for effective coordinated operations. A second by–product is the knowledge which everyone gains about each other's capabilities and limitations. This help create a more real and meaningful knowledge base regarding who can truly do what for whom. The third by–product is the Plan itself.

Emergency Plans are useful because they document all that has been agreed–to regarding roles and responsibilities, resource allocations, mutual aid agreements and so on. They are also a useful tool to identify the resources available to the community. And there are many of them, even in isolated and small communities. Chapter 5 identifies the range of possibilities. The secret is to be creative and inviting so that others in the community could feel welcome as members of the response network.

Many Fire Departments are currently responsible, to one degree or another, for the response to Dangerous Goods incidents. One of the resources which might be of interest to these departments is the Dangerous Goods Response Team (DGRT) which is discussed in Chapter 6. As noted, this resource need not be an integral part of the local Fire Department but should be available. It may be secured through Mutual Aid agreements, through industry or from private suppliers.

The planning process also includes the conduct of exercises to verify that the Plan is viable under disaster–like conditions. Disaster or emergency exercises are not intended to test individuals. They are designed to test key portions of the Plan to ensure that what should happen, could and would happen when needed.

Emergency exercises can be stressful for those who design, conduct and participate in them. However, they are invaluable and can significantly reduce stress during 'the real thing.' The reason is that people have had a chance to see the Plan unfold. They know its mechanics, what works and what does not (which, one hopes, was corrected). Additionally, these exercises present an ideal opportunity for both team and trust building.

Despite the best of plans, disasters do happen, often at the worst possible time and with catastrophic results. The fundamental purpose of emergency planning is to prepare for action. And so, disaster response must often be rapid, comprehensive and effective. Therefore, it needs to be coordinated and systematic. Hence, the various Fire Command Systems (see Chapter 8).

Fire Command systems have been applied effectively by the Fire Services and a select few other agencies. These systems, however, fail to address the complete needs of the community and its diverse response network. Enter the Emergency Site Management (ESM) system.

The ESM system is designed to complement the various Fire Command systems. Fire Officers at the Site are encouraged to operate using the Fire Command system desired by their department. This works well when most of the responders are Fire Services members and the problem at hand is primarily fire related. Anything else, which involves many other jurisdictions, should involve the Emergency Site Management system.

It seems that the ESM system is more adaptable for Canadian municipal needs. It focuses on coordination versus command and control. It facilitates the involvement of other response agencies and acknowledges the critical role which is played by the municipal Emergency Operations Centre.

Emergency response highlights many concerns. One of the more immediate ones, at personal level, is the health issue of responders at the Site. These responders are at risk. That is part of their job. However, it need not be made more risky by careless or thoughtless actions. Therefore, continued care should be taken by Fire Officers to ensure that they, their own staff and the staff of other response agencies are cognizant of the risks involved and the actions which may be necessary to prevent injury or exposure.

The other concerns are perhaps more subtle. They relate to being an isolated or small community. While neither factor may be remedied directly, their impact on emergency preparedness and response can clearly be overcome. Chapter 11 identifies both the challenges and the remedies. One must truly be open minded and creative in this enterprise, but isolation and size need not be a fatal flaw in the community's preparedness for disaster.

The last stage of emergency management is the recovery phase. It contains both short–term and long–term activities. Both sets of activities are critical for the return of individuals, organizations and the community as a whole, to their 'normal' pattern of life. Anything short of that goal will only prolong the pain and minimize the capability of individuals and their organizations to prepare for the next crisis or disaster.

The short–term recovery effort will likely begin while the response effort is still fully underway. It will be followed by the long–term recovery effort which will likely continue long after the response effort is completed. The long–term recovery process of some communities has been measured in decades!

LESSONS LEARNED

1. **Disaster response is a community affair.** Crises and disasters are events of such magnitude that no single individual or organization can effectively respond to them. That is not to belittle the capability of any response organization. On the contrary, it is to highlight the tremendous effort which is needed to effectively manage and overcome the disaster's outcomes. This effort goes beyond the use of one skill, one profession or one set of available resources. This begs, therefore, the use of 'collective action' during the response period.

Many response organizations embrace the notion of 'collective action.' Some of them, however, limit their partnerships to a select group of other response organizations. These typically include other Fire Departments (through mutual aid) as well as the local Police, Emergency Medical Services, hospital(s), Social Services, Public Works and Utilities.

The list of response partners must be more extensive than those mentioned in the previous paragraph. Fire Departments can not be all things to all people especially during crises and disasters. Therefore, Fire Service organizations should seek out organizations with disaster–related skills, resources and experience to complement the capabilities of the Fire Services.

These 'partners' could include non–government organizations, members of industry, select businesses, various government departments or agencies and many more.

2. **Risk is an inherent reality of the Fire Department's job.** That risk goes beyond the physical threat to the life and health of Fire Department personnel. It also includes

the risk of legal liability particularly in disaster situations which are abnormal, significantly complex and for which there are no set rules or specific response procedures.

While legal liability is a concern it need not cripple action. The advice of legal experts should be sought and considered. However, that advice should be balanced by the recognition that the Fire Services operations are often carried out in a high–risk environment. Stated differently, Fire Departments should balance the legal advice they receive with doing the necessary thing.

3. **When in doubt, prepare, prepare, PREPARE!** Effective disaster response is not accidental, haphazard or performed by the seat of one's pants. It is based on effective planning (which does not mean just having a plan).

Preparation should be conducted at three levels; at individual, fire team and community levels. Preparation at each of these levels should be connected into the others to form a web of response capabilities. Call it the disaster–response Internet and imagine it surviving despite being damaged or overwhelmed by disaster.

4. **Disasters are not normal events!** Much research and the accounts of experienced practitioners emphasizes the fact that disasters are not normal events. They represent a quantum leap of complexity, stress and repercussions even for practiced responders who deal with 'incidents' and 'emergencies' on a frequent basis. Consequently, the preparation for and the management of these events must take into consideration their uniquely complex nature.

Disasters and crises can not be managed as if they were day–to– day incidents requiring day–to–day practices. They need an extra set of skills, specialized resources and ... attitude. That 'attitude' begins with a recognition that the Fire Services are a key (perhaps a lead) agency within the community's response system. It is not, however, the only one. There are many other agencies with much needed skills and resources and they too have 'jurisdiction' within the response effort and the disaster site.

Another issue of 'attitude' relates to the two categories of 'victim' and 'rescuer.' As noted in Chapter 1, these two terms should best be replaced with the terms 'survivor' and 'responder.'

5. **The field is evolving rapidly and constantly.** Emergency management, as a field of study and practice, is evolving rapidly and constantly. Terminology, equipment, application practices, partnerships and related knowledge are rapidly outpacing traditional views and practices. To put it bluntly, the Fire Services are no longer seen as the only rescue/response organization in their community.

While true, that view is not necessarily unhealthy. It frees Fire Departments from the burden of being sole–provider and provides them an opportunity to define their niche within the response spectrum. It signals an opportunity for revisiting roles and partnerships. It also emphasizes the need to keep on top of their field to stay current.

6. **Empowerment and partnerships are the way of the future.** As has been noted extensively above, disasters and crises often overwhelm those organizations which are impacted by them. It makes sense, therefore, that members of the public are educated and encouraged to undertake disaster preparedness (and response) at the individual, family and organizational levels.

This will achieve two objectives. One, they will hopefully realize the importance of this activity. Two, an increase in their preparedness level will have a corresponding decrease in the demand on response agencies which will then be better able to concentrate on their primary disaster response functions.

Similarly, partnerships among the various community disaster response agencies can provide a safety net. The 'Emergency Response Internet' can then survive despite the incapacity of any of its member organizations.

7. **The positioning of the Fire Services.** The roles of the Fire Services can not remain static and must evolve with the field of emergency management. Failure to adapt could result in the Fire Services loosing their current primary (perhaps lead) role in this field of practice.

The difficulty is that the Fire Services are faced with a dichotomy. On the one hand they should seek a continued leadership role in the emergency management efforts of their community. That may require them to assume new and additional roles. But on the other hand they must maintain agency integration and focus of operations. In other words, the choice seems to be between broad diversification and resisting the temptation to become all things to all people. The challenge is to reach a meaningful and workable balance between the two extremes.

The Fire Services should also be prepared, when required, to assume a 'lead agency' role in their community's emergency management process. To do so effectively they also need to develop terminology and organizational systems that will facilitate the involvement of other response agencies as 'partners' in the process of emergency management. This system can not be the traditional 'command and control' system of the Fire Services.

CONCLUSION

The response to crises and disasters can not be left to chance. It must be well planned, coordinated and supplied with needed resources. Fire Departments have a critical and perhaps a leading role to play in the preparedness of their community for disasters. However, that role needs to be reviewed and defined within the changing bounds of the evolving emergency management profession.

This book was developed to highlight the challenges and identify ways to deal with them. We hope that we have met your needs. Our collective challenge now is to continue practicing, researching and writing the functions of emergency management. There is much to do and much to learn so that the knowledge base continues to grow.

May you have no reason to practice your emergency response skills. But if you do, may all your crises be manageable!

Appendix A

List Of Abbreviations And Terms

Disaster response often involves responders from different organizations. Some of them, perhaps most, may not be familiar with the abbreviations commonly used by the Fire Services. It is recommended, therefore, that abbreviations only be used when speaker and listener(s) alike understand their meaning. When in doubt, clarify their meaning to your listener.

ALS – Advance Life Support
BLEVE – Boiling Liquid Expanding Vapour Explosion
BCP – Business Continuity Planning
BLS – Basic Life Support
BRP – Business Recovery (or Resumption) Planning
CANUTEC – Canadian Transport Emergency Centre
CAPC – Civil Aviation Planning Committee
CASARA – Civil Air Search and Rescue Association
CCAS – Canadian Civil Alert System
CCPA – Canadian Chemical Producers' Association
CEM – Comprehensive Emergency Management
CISD – Critical Incident Stress Debriefing
CMRAS – Civil Marine Rescue Auxiliary Services
CPX – Command Post Exercise
DFAA – Disaster Financial Assistance Arrangements (usually between the federal and provincial governments)
DG – Dangerous Goods
DDS – Director of Disaster Services (typically at municipal level)
DO – Duty Officer
EBS – Emergency Broadcast System
EENET – Emergency Education Network (in the USA)
EFS – Emergency Feeding Services
EHS – Emergency Health Services
EMS – Emergency Medical Services
EMT – Emergency Medical Technician
EMO – Emergency Measures Organization (typically at provincial/territorial level)
EOC – Emergency Operations Centre
EOC–CG – Emergency Operations Centre (Control Group)
EPC – Emergency Preparedness Canada
EPIO – Emergency Public Information Officer
ERP – Emergency Response Plan
ERT – Emergency Response Team
ESM – Emergency Site Manager (also called Site Manager)
ESM (System) – The Emergency Site Management system
ESS – Emergency Social Services
FEMA – Federal Emergency Measures Agency
GEOC – Government Emergency Operations Centre
Haz. Mat. – Hazardous Materials (also called Dangerous Goods)

HF – High Frequency
ICDO – International Civil Defence Organization
ICS – Incident Command System
IRT – Industrial Response Team
JEPP – Joint Emergency Preparedness Program
LF – Low Frequency
LO – Liaison Officer
MA – Mutual Aid
MCI – Multiple Casualty Incident
MF – Medium Frequency
MFU – Mobile Feeding Unit
MIACC – Major Industrial Accident Council of Canada
NGO – Non–government Organization
OPREP – Operational Report
PMIR – Public and Media Inquiry Room
PSA – Public Service Announcement
PTSD – Post Traumatic Stress Disorder
PWC – Provincial Warning Centre
R&I – Registration and Inquiry
RC – Reception Centre
RCC – Rescue Coordination Centre
REET – Regional Environmental Emergency Team
SAR – Search And Rescue
SITREP – Situation Report
SHF – Super High Frequency
SOP – Standard Operating Procedure
TDG – Transportation of Dangerous Goods (often used in conjunction with related Acts and Regulations)
TEAP – Transportation Emergency Assistance Team
UCS – Unified Command System
UHF – Ultra High Frequency
VHF – Very High Frequency

Definition of Key Terms

BLEVE. Stands for Boiling Liquid Expanding Vapour Explosion. This occurs when a vessel containing a liquid under pressure is heated causing the liquid inside to boil. The resulting expansion inside the tank causes the tank to rupture explosively.

Business Continuity Planning. The process which ensure the availability of critical resources so that the business could continue its operation(s) despite major disruptions or crises.

Crisis. An abnormal and unique event which occurs with some degree of surprise to demand unusual, extensive and demanding response effort.

Disaster. (See Crisis)

Emergency. A situation out of the norm which demands a comprehensive response effort by a significant segment of an organization.
Emergency Management. The process which effectively manages all functions of mitigation, preparedness, response and recovery as they relate to crises and disasters.

Emergency Exercise. A simulated response effort by an organization to test the effectiveness of its emergency procedures and plans.

Emergency Manager. Any person or persons with formal (i.e., designated) or informal (i.e., assumed) responsibilities for emergency event mitigation. Depending on the event, this could range from First Responders (i.e., Police, Fire, or EMS personnel) to Chief Officers, City Managers or elected representatives.

Emergency Operations Centre. A location, often within a facility, which serves as the primary headquarters of an organization for its effort to manage the response to a specific event (i.e., disaster, crisis).

Emergency Planning. This process includes any activity that individuals and organizations undertake, prior to a disaster, to enhance their ability to effective response to that disaster. (This term is occasionally used interchangeably with 'emergency preparedness'.)

Emergency Preparedness. This process ensures that required resources are available, when needed, to effectively respond to disasters. The process includes a range of activities from the identification of needed resources to their acquisition and pre–positioning. (The term is occasionally used interchangeably with 'emergency planning'.)

Emergency Director. The person with the primary role of ensuring that emergency exercises unfold as they should.

Event. A situation, either episodic or chronic, which demands a specific response. It is typically handled by Standard Operating Procedures (SOPs) and may also be called an incident or an occurrence.

Hazard. The Webster dictionary defines hazard as a "fortuitous event; chance; danger; peril; risk."

Incident. See 'event.'

Incident Command. A system of scene management that applies basic management techniques to the emergency scene. The focus is on safety and systematic handling of the incident.

Mitigation. The Webster dictionary defines the verb mitigate as meaning "to alleviate or render less painful, rigorous, intense, or severe." Mitigation is a phase of emergency management. Its aim is to minimize the probability of an event and to reduce its negative impact.

Mutual Aid Agreement. Is a formal agreement between two or more entities (i.e., municipalities, Corporations) to be available to assist each other with specific resources and in specific circumstance(s).

Planning. The Webster Dictionary defines planning as "to arrange the parts of; or to have in mind." Planning links knowledge to action.

Risk. It is the combined effect of the probability that a particular event will take place and the consequence of that event.

APPENDIX B

EMERGENCY PREPAREDNESS AND THE LAW

APPENDIX B.1

EXAMPLE FIRE AND EMERGENCY SERVICES BY-LAW

MUNICIPALITY OF ________

BY-LAW NO. ________

A BY-LAW OF THE MUNICIPALITY OF _____, A MUNICIPAL CORPORATION IN THE PROVINCE OF _____, FOR THE ESTABLISHMENT AND OPERATION OF FIRE PROTECTION AND EMERGENCY SERVICES

WHEREAS by virtue of the power conferred upon it by the _______ Act (R.S. 19 , c. __ as amended or repealed and replaced from time to time); the ______ Act (R.S. 19 , c. __ as amended or repealed and replaced from time to time; the ______ Act (R.S. _ 1985, c. __ as amended or repealed and replaced from time to time); and the _____ Act (R.S. _ 19 , c. __ as amended or repealed and replaced from time to time), the Council of the Municipality of _____, duly assembled, enacts as follows:

SECTION 1

SHORT TITLE

1.1 This By-law shall be known and may be cited as the "Fire Protection and Emergency Services By-law" of the Municipality of

---

SECTION 2

INTERPRETATION

2.1 In this By-law the following terms shall have the following meanings:

2.1.1 "Adult" shall mean any person between the ages of _____ and _____ years, inclusive.

2.1.2 "Application Fee" shall mean a fee payable to the Fire Department as set out in Schedule "C", herein, which must accompany each Fire Permit Application.

2.1.3 "Contained Fire" shall mean a Fire which is totally confined within a non-combustible structure or container and which is ventilated in such a manner as to preclude the escape of combustible materials including ash.

2.1.4 "Council" shall mean the elected municipal council of the Municipality.

2.1.5 "Emergency Equipment" shall mean any vehicle, machine, device, apparatus, contrivance, tool or material designed or used for the purpose of alleviating or eliminating any Emergency Situation, which, without limiting the generality of the foregoing shall include the extinguishing of fires and the rescue of persons and property.

2.1.6 "Emergency Services" shall mean services provided by the Fire Department for the purpose of alleviating or eliminating any Emergency Situation, which, without limiting the generality of the foregoing shall include the extinguishing of fires and the protection of persons and property.

2.1.7 "Emergency Services Charge" shall mean any or all costs incurred by the Fire Department in providing Emergency Services.

2.1.8 "Emergency Situation" shall mean any condition, circumstance or event wherein there exists an imminent serious danger to persons or property.

2.1.9 "False Alarm" shall mean any notification to the Fire Department or any Member of the Fire Department of an Emergency Situation in circumstances where an Emergency Situation does not exist.

2.1.10 "Fire" shall mean any combustible material in a state of combustion.

2.1.11 "Fire Department" shall mean the Municipality of ________ Fire Department as established pursuant to this By-law, which, without limiting the generality of the foregoing shall include all Personnel of the Fire Department.

2.1.12 "Fire Hazard" shall mean any condition, circumstance or event wherein the possibility of fire is increased.

2.1.13 "Fire Investigation Services" shall mean services provided by the Fire Department for the purpose of investigating the cause, origin and circumstances of fires and explosions.

2.1.14 "Fire Permit" shall mean a document in the form set out in Schedule "B", herein, as endorsed by the Fire Department.

2.1.15 "Fire Permit Application" shall mean an application in writing in the form set out in Schedule "A", herein, and such other information as may be required by the Fire Department.

2.1.16 "Fire Prevention Services" shall mean services provided by the Fire Department for the purpose of preventing fires.

2.1.17 "Municipal Manager" shall mean the senior administrative officer of the Municipality.

2.1.18 "Municipality and "Municipal" shall mean the Municipality of ______ .

2.1.19 "Open Fire" shall mean any Fire which is not a Contained Fire, which, without limiting the generality of the foregoing shall include grass fires, pit fires, forest and brush fires, structure and building fires and chattel fires.

2.1.20 "Outstanding Accounts" shall mean Emergency Services Charges unpaid more than sixty (60) days after they have been levied.

2.1.21 "Personnel" shall mean any person employed by the Municipal Fire Department to provide fire protection services.

2.1.22 "Property" shall mean any real or personal property, which, without limiting the generality of the foregoing shall include land, buildings, structures, fixtures and chattels.

2.2 The provisions of this By-law, including the duties, responsibilities, powers and authority granted herein shall be subject to the operation of all validly enacted Federal or Provincial legislation.

SECTION 3

ESTABLISHMENT OF FIRE DEPARTMENT

3.1 The Municipality hereby authorizes the establishment of a Fire Department to provide the following services to the Municipality:

3.1.1 Emergency Services;

3.1.2 Fire Prevention Services;

3.1.3 Fire Investigation Services;

3.1.4 Emergency Rescue Services;

3.1.5 Emergency Medical Services.

SECTION 4

FIRE CHIEF

4.1 The Municipality shall appoint a Fire Chief (hereinafter referred to as the "Fire Chief"), who shall be an employee of the Municipality and shall report directly to the Municipal Manager.

4.2 The Fire Chief shall have the responsibility and the powers and authority necessary for the organization, administration and operation of the Fire Department, which, without limiting the generality of the foregoing shall include:

4.2.1 Make recommendations to the Municipal Manager with respect to the employment, promotion, discipline and dismissal of Fire Department Personnel.

4.2.2 Training of Fire Department Personnel.

4.2.3 Keeping detailed and accurate records of all matters relating to the organization, administration and operation of the Fire Department.

4.2.4 Establish committees to assist in the organization, administration and operation of the Fire Department.

4.2.5 Establish policies, rules, regulations, duties and responsibilities applicable to Fire Department Personnel for the organization, administration and operation of the Fire Department.

4.2.6 Fiscal management of the Fire Department, which, without limiting the generality of the foregoing shall include:

4.2.6.1 Allocation of financial resources provided to the Fire Department by the Municipality or by any other source;

4.2.6.2 Apply approved accounting procedures in the fiscal organization, administration and operation of the Fire Department;

4.2.6.3 Prepare fiscal budgets for the organization, administration and operation of the Fire Department;

4.2.6.4 Maintaining an accurate account of all Permit Fees and Fire Service Charges levied and received.

4.2.7 Assuming such other responsibilities as Council may direct or Provincial or Federal legislation may require, which, without limiting the generality of the foregoing shall include assumption of the position of ________ pursuant to the provisions of the ________ Act.

4.2.8 Provide information and make recommendations to the Municipality with respect to the organization, administration and operation of the Fire Department, which, without limiting the generality of the foregoing may include:

4.2.8.1 Acquisition, use and disposal of Emergency Equipment;

4.2.8.2 Establishment, organization, administration and operation of fire stations;

4.2.8.3 Establishment, organization, administration and operation of training facilities;

4.2.8.4 Establishment, organization, administration and operation of fire prevention programs and procedures.

4.2.8.5 Establishment, organization, administration and operation of systems for communication with respect to Emergency Situations, which, without limiting the generality of the foregoing may include fire alarms, telephone and radio communication;

4.2.8.6 Regulating the storage or transportation of explosives or other highly inflammable or dangerous materials;

4.2.8.7 Establishment of emergency plans and programs.

SECTION 5

DEPUTY FIRE CHIEF

5.1 The Fire Chief shall appoint a member of the Fire Department Personnel as Deputy Fire Chief.

5.2 The Deputy Fire Chief shall have the responsibilities, powers and authority of the Fire Chief in the absence of the Fire Chief or in the event that the Fire Chief is unable to perform his duties.

SECTION 6

GENERAL POWERS

6.1 Fire Department Personnel shall have the authority to enter any building, structure or place in which Fire Service Personnel have reason to believe an Emergency Situation exists for the purpose of alleviating or eliminating the Emergency Situation, which, without limiting the generality of the foregoing shall include the authority to enter any Property which is on fire to attempt to extinguish the fire or to prevent the spread thereof.

6.2 Fire Department Personnel shall have the authority to prevent interference with the efforts of persons engaged in alleviating or eliminating Emergency Situations by regulating the conduct of the public at or in the vicinity of any Emergency Situation.

6.3 Any person who interferes with the efforts of persons engaged in alleviating or eliminating Emergency Situations, which, without limiting the generality of the foregoing shall include interference with the efforts of persons engaged in the extinguishing of fires or prevention of the spread of fire shall be guilty of an offence.

6.4 Fire Department Personnel shall have the authority to compel any Adult person in the Municipality to assist in the extinguishing of fires and to assist in the prevention or spread thereof.

6.5 Any Adult person who refuses the direction of Fire Department Personnel to assist in the extinguishing of fires or to assist in the prevention or spread thereof in accordance with section 6.4, herein, is guilty of an offence.

SECTION 7

EMERGENCY SERVICES CHARGE

7.1 Upon providing Emergency Services on Property within or outside the municipal boundaries of the Municipality the Fire Department may in its sole and absolute discretion charge the owner or occupant of the Property an Emergency Services Charge.

7.2 An Emergency Services Charge shall be paid within sixty (60) days of the Emergency Service Charge being levied.

7.3 Collection of payment on Outstanding Accounts may be undertaken by civil action in a court of competent jurisdiction.

7.4 Any attempt to collect an Emergency Services Charge in accordance with section 7.3, herein, with respect to Emergency Services performed with respect to Property located within the municipal boundaries of the Municipality does not in any way invalidate any lien which the Municipality is entitled to on the Property in respect of which the indebtedness is incurred.

7.5 Emergency Services Charges imposed pursuant to this By-law with respect to Emergency Services performed with respect to Property located within the municipal boundaries of the Municipality shall constitute a preferential lien and charge on the Property and on the personal property of the debtor and may be levied and collected as municipal taxes due and owing in respect of that Property.

SECTION 8

FIRE PERMITS

8.1 Any person who ignites, fuels, supervises or otherwise maintains an Open Fire within the municipal boundaries of the Municipality must have a valid Fire Permit.

8.2 Any person who ignites, fuels, supervises or otherwise maintains an Open Fire within the municipal boundaries of the City without a valid Fire Permit is guilty of an offence.

8.3 Any person wishing to obtain a Fire Permit must:

8.3.1 Enter into a Fire Permit Application Agreement with the Municipality through the Fire Department as set out in Schedule "A", herein;

8.3.2 Complete a Fire Permit Application as set out in Schedule "B" herein;

8.3.3 Pay to the Municipality through the Fire Department the Application Fee as prescribed in Schedule "C" herein.

8.4 Any person who provides false, incomplete or misleading information to the Municipality or to the Fire Department on or with respect to a Fire Permit Application is guilty of an offence.

8.5 Upon receipt of a properly executed Fire Permit Application Agreement the Fire Department shall consider the Fire Permit Application, and may, in its sole and absolute discretion:

8.5.1 Refuse to grant a Fire Permit;

8.5.2 Grant a Fire Permit as set out in Schedule "E" herein, without terms and conditions;

8.5.3 Grant a Fire Permit as set out in Schedule "E" herein, upon such terms and conditions as the Fire Department deems appropriate.

8.6 In the event that the Fire Department elects to grant a Fire Permit either with or without conditions the person wishing to obtain the Fire Permit must:

8.6.1 Enter into a Fire Permit Agreement with the Municipality through the Fire Department as set out in Schedule "D", herein;

8.6.2 Pay to the Municipality through the Fire Department the Permit Fee as prescribed in Schedule "F", herein.

8.7 A Fire Permit shall not be transferrable.

8.8 A Fire Permit shall be valid for such period of time as determined by the Fire Department in its sole and absolute discretion, and which period of time shall be endorsed by the Fire Department on the Fire Permit.

SECTION 9

OFFENCES

9.1 Any person who contravenes any provision of this By-law is guilty of an offence and is liable to penalty as set out in Schedule "E", herein.

9.2 Under no circumstances shall any person contravening any provision of this By-law be subject to the penalty of imprisonment.

SECTION 10

REPEAL

10.1 Municipality of ____________ By-law No.______ and amendments made thereto shall be repealed upon this By-law coming into force in accordance with section 11.1, herein.

SECTION 11

EFFECTIVE DATE

11.1 This By-law shall come into force upon third and final reading.

Read for a first time this ____ day of __________, 199__.

Read for a second time this ____ day of __________, 199__ .

Read for a third time and passed this ____ day of __________, 199__.

____
(Signing Officer)

____
(Signing Officer)

SCHEDULE "A"

FIRE PERMIT APPLICATION AGREEMENT

BETWEEN:

Municipality of _________
a municipal corporation in the
Province of ______
(hereinafter referred to as the
"Municipality")

OF THE FIRST PART

-and-

a person residing in ______
in the Province of
____
(hereinafter referred to as the
"Applicant")

OF THE SECOND PART

SECTION 1

INTERPRETATION

1.1 In this Agreement the following terms shall have the following meanings:

1.1.1 "Agreement" shall mean this agreement.

1.1.2 "Application" shall mean the Fire Permit Application as set out in the By-law.

1.1.3 "Application Fee" shall mean a fee payable by the Applicant to the Municipality as prescribed in the By-law for the submission to the Municipality of a Fire Permit Application.

1.1.4 "By-law" shall mean Municipality of ________________ By-law No. ___________ as amended or repealed and replaced from time to time.

1.1.5 "Fire Department" shall mean the Municipality of Fire Department.

1.1.6 "Fire Permit" shall mean a Fire Permit as contemplated in the By-law..

1.1.7 "Property shall mean any land, building, structure, fixture or chattel.

SECTION 2

OBLIGATIONS AND DUTIES OF FIRE DEPARTMENT

2.1 The Municipality agrees to consider the Applicant's Application which, without limiting the generality of the foregoing shall include the performance of any inspections or investigations which the Fire Department in its sole and absolute discretion requires to be undertaken.

SECTION 3

OBLIGATIONS AND DUTIES OF THE APPLICANT

3.1 The Applicant warrants that he/she is the owner or occupant of, or has obtained the written permission of the owner or occupier of the Property described in the Application to carry out those purposes and acts for which a Fire Permit is being sought.

3.2 The Applicant agrees to allow the Fire Department to enter upon the Property for the purpose of carrying out the provisions of the By-law and this Agreement, which, without limiting the generality of the foregoing shall include the inspection of the Property.

3.3 The Applicant agrees to comply with all Federal, Provincial/Territorial and Municipal legislation, regulation and other requirements, and to observe all recognized safety standards and practices.

SECTION 4

LIABILITY WAIVER AND INDEMNITY

4.1 The Applicant Agrees:

4.1.1 not to make or bring any claim, action, suit, proceeding or demand against the Municipality, its elected officials, officers, employees, servants, agents and contractors with respect to any occurrence, incident, accident or happening relating in any manner whatsoever to this Agreement and the rights and obligations arising therefrom, which, without limiting the generality of the foregoing shall include any claim, action, suit, proceeding or demand arising in tort or contract;

4.1.2 to indemnify and save harmless the Municipality, its elected officials, officers, employees, servants, agents and contractors with respect to any claim, action, suit, proceeding or demand made or brought against the Municipality, its elected officials, officers, employees, servants, agents and contractors by any third party with respect to any occurrence, incident, accident or happening relating in any manner whatsoever to this Agreement and the rights and obligations arising therefrom, and which indemnity shall, without limiting the generality of the foregoing include all legal costs incurred by the Municipality in defending such a claim, action, suit, proceeding or demand.

ARTICLE 5

GENERAL MATTERS

5.1 If any term, covenant or condition of this Agreement or the application thereof to any party or circumstance shall be invalid or unenforceable to any extent, the remainder of this Agreement or application of such term, covenant or condition to a party or circumstance other than those to which it is held invalid or unenforceable shall not be affected thereby and each remaining term, covenant or condition of this Agreement shall be valid and shall be enforceable to the fullest extent permitted by law.

5.2 This Agreement constitutes the entire agreement between the Parties hereto relating to the subject matter hereof, and supersedes all prior and contemporaneous agreements, understandings, negotiations and discussions, whether oral or written, of the parties and there are no general or specific warranties, representations or other agreements by or among the Parties in connection with the entering into of this Agreement or the subject matter hereof except as specifically set forth herein.

5.3 The Applicant hereby covenants and agrees to do such things, obtain such approvals, permits and licenses and execute such further documents, agreements and assurances as may be necessary or advisable from time to time in order to carry out the terms and conditions of this Agreement in accordance with their true intent.

5.4 This Agreement may be altered or amended in any of its provisions when any such changes are reduced to writing and assigned by the Parties hereto but not otherwise.

5.5 No remedy herein conferred upon either Party is intended to be exclusive of any other remedy available to that party but each remedy shall be cumulative and shall be in addition to every other remedy given hereunder or now or hereafter existing by law or in equity or by statute.

5.6 No consent or waiver, express or implied, by either Party to or of any breach or default by the other party in the performance by the other party of its obligations hereunder shall be deemed or construed to be a consent or waiver to or of any other breach or default in the performance of obligations hereunder by such Party hereunder. Failure on the part of either Party to complain of any act or failure to act of the other party or to declare the other Party in default, irrespective of how long such failure continues, shall not constitute a waiver by such party of its rights hereunder.

5.7 Any notice required to be give hereunder by any Party shall be in writing and shall be deemed to have been well and sufficiently given if:

5.7.1 personally delivered to the Party to whom it is intended or if such party is a corporation to an officer of that corporation; or

5.7.2 if mailed by prepared registered mail, to the address of the Party to whom it is intended hereinafter set forth or to such other address as a Party may from time to time direct in writing as follows:

5.7.2.1 In case of notice to the Applicant,
to:

5.7.2.2 In case of notice to the Municipality,
to:

Any notice delivered as aforesaid shall be deemed to have been received on the date of delivery and any notice mailed shall be deemed to have been received seventy-two (72) hours after the date it is postmarked. If normal mail service is interrupted by strike, slow-down, force majeure or other cause after the notice has been sent the notice will not be deemed to be received until actually received. In the event normal mail service is impaired at the time of sending the notice, then personal delivery only shall be effective.

5.8 Time shall be of the essence of this Agreement and of every party hereof.

5.9 This Agreement may not be assigned in whole or in part by the Applicant without the express written permission of the Municipality.

5.10 This Agreement may not be assigned in whole or in part by the County without the express written permission of the City.

5.11 This Agreement shall enure to the benefit of and be binding upon the Parties hereto, their respective successors and permitted assigns.

____
(Applicant)

MUNICIPALITY OF

____

PER:__________________________

PER:__________________________

SCHEDULE "B"

FIRE PERMIT APPLICATION

1. NAME OF APPLICANT________________________________

2. ADDRESS________________________________

3. TEL. BUS.________________ TEL. RES.________________

4. REASON PERMIT REQUIRED________________________________

   ____

5. LEGAL DESCRIPTION OF PROPERTY
   FOR WHICH PERMIT IS REQUIRED________________________________

   ____

6. LOCATION OF FIRE________________________________

7. DESCRIPTION OF MATERIAL TO BE BURNED________________

   ____

8. PERIOD OF TIME FOR WHICH PERMIT IS REQUESTED _____ TO ________

9. PLANS/SPECIFICATIONS ATTACHED: YES________ NO________

10. WRITTEN PERMISSION OF OWNER/OCCUPIER
    OF PROPERTY ATTACHED YES________ NO________

________________________ ________________________
DATE SIGNATURE OF APPLICANT

SCHEDULE "C"

FIRE PERMIT APPLICATION FEES

Service Required	Rate	Fee
1. Site Inspection		
1.1 Inspection Time	$______	$______
1.2 Transportation	$______	$______
1.3 Administration/Clerical	$______	$______
1.4 Materials	$______	$______
1.5 Technical Assistance	$______	$______
Sub-Total	$______	
G.S.T. (7%)	$______	
Total	$______	

SCHEDULE "D"

FIRE PERMIT AGREEMENT

BETWEEN:

Municipality of ___________
a municipal corporation in the
Province of ________
(hereinafter referred to as the
"Permittee")

OF THE FIRST PART

-and-

a person residing in ________
in the Province of
___________ (hereinafter
referred to as the "Permittee")

OF THE SECOND PART

SECTION 1

INTERPRETATION

1.1 In this Agreement, the following terms shall have the following meanings:

1.1.1 "Agreement" shall mean this agreement.

1.1.2 "By-law" shall mean Municipality of __________ By-law No. ____ as amended or repealed and replaced from time to time.

1.1.3 "Fire Permit shall mean a Fire Permit as contemplated in the By-law.

1.1.4 "Permit Fee" shall mean a fee payable by the Permittee to the Municipality as prescribed in the By-law for the issuance of a Fire Permit to the Permittee by the Municipality.

SECTION 2

OBLIGATIONS AND DUTIES OF FIRE DEPARTMENT

2.1 The Municipality agrees to issue to the Permittee the Fire Permit set out in Section 5 herein.

SECTION 3

OBLIGATIONS AND DUTIES OF THE PERMITTEE

3.1 The Permittee warrants that he/she is the owner or occupier of, or has obtained the written permission of the owner or occupier of the property described in the Fire Permit to carry out those purposes and acts for which a Fire Permit is being sought.

3.2 The Permittee agrees to allow the Fire Department to enter upon the property for the purpose of carrying out the provisions of the By-law and this Agreement, which without limiting the generality of the foregoing shall include Fire Prevention, protection and investigation services.

3.3 The Permittee agrees to comply with all Federal, Provincial/Territorial and Municipal legislation, regulation and other requirements, and to observe all recognized safety standards and practices.

SECTION 4

LIABILITY WAIVER AND INDEMNITY

4.1 The Permittee agrees:

4.1.1 not to make or bring any claim, action, suit, proceeding or demand against the Municipality, its elected officials, officers, employees, servants, agents and contractors with respect to any occurrence, incident, accident or happening relating in any manner whatsoever to this Agreement and the rights and obligations arising therefrom, which, without limiting the generality of the foregoing shall include any claim, action, suit, proceeding or demand arising in tort or contract;

4.1.2 to indemnify and save harmless the Municipality, its elected officials, officers, employees, servants, agents and contractors with respect to any claim, action, suit, proceeding or demand made or brought against the Municipality, its elected officials, officers, employees, servants, agents and contractors by any third party with respect to any occurrence, incident, accident or happening relating in any manner whatsoever to this Agreement and the rights and obligations arising therefrom, and which indemnity shall, without limiting the generality of the foregoing include all legal costs incurred by the Municipality in defending such a claim, action, suit, proceeding or demand.

ARTICLE 5

GENERAL MATTERS

5.1 If any term, covenant or condition of this Agreement or the application thereof to any party or circumstance shall be invalid or unenforceable to any extent, the remainder of this Agreement or application of such term, covenant or condition to a party or circumstance other than those to which it is held invalid or unenforceable shall not be affected thereby and each remaining term, covenant or condition of this Agreement shall be valid and shall be enforceable to the fullest extent permitted by law.

5.2 This Agreement constitutes the entire agreement between the Parties hereto relating to the subject matter hereof, and supersedes all prior and contemporaneous agreements, understandings, negotiations and discussions, whether oral or written, of the parties and there are no general or specific warranties, representations or other agreements by or among the Parties in connection with the entering into of this Agreement or the subject matter hereof except as specifically set forth herein.

5.3 The Applicant hereby covenants and agrees to do such things, obtain such approvals, permits and licenses and execute such further documents, agreements and assurances as may be necessary or advisable from time to time in order to carry out the terms and conditions of this Agreement in accordance with their true intent.

5.4 This Agreement may be altered or amended in any of its provisions when any such changes are reduced to writing and assigned by the Parties hereto but not otherwise.

5.5 No remedy herein conferred upon either Party is intended to be exclusive of any other remedy available to that party but each remedy shall be cumulative and shall be in addition to every other remedy given hereunder or now or hereafter existing by law or in equity or by statute.

5.6 No consent or waiver, express or implied, by either Party to or of any breach or default by the other party in the performance by the other party of its obligations hereunder shall be deemed or construed to be a consent or waiver to or of any other breach or default in the performance of obligations hereunder by such Party hereunder. Failure on the part of either Party to complain of any act or failure to act of the other party or to declare the other Party in default, irrespective of how long such failure continues, shall not constitute a waiver by such party of its rights hereunder.

5.7 Any notice required to be give hereunder by any Party shall be in writing and shall be deemed to have been well and sufficiently given if:

5.7.1 personally delivered to the Party to whom it is intended or if such party is a corporation to an officer of that corporation; or

5.7.2 if mailed by prepared registered mail, to the address of the Party to whom it is intended hereinafter set forth or to such other address as a Party may from time to time direct in writing as follows:

5.7.2.1 In case of notice to the Applicant,
to:

5.7.2.2 In case of notice to the Municipality,
to:

Any notice delivered as aforesaid shall be deemed to have been received on the date of delivery and any notice mailed shall be deemed to have been received seventy-two (72) hours after the date it is postmarked. If normal mail service is interrupted by strike, slow-down, force majeure or other cause after the notice has been sent the notice will not be deemed to be received until actually received. In the event normal mail service is impaired at the time of sending the notice, then personal delivery only shall be effective.

5.8 Time shall be of the essence of this Agreement and of every party hereof.

5.9 This Agreement may not be assigned in whole or in part by the Applicant without the express written permission of the Municipality.

5.10 This Agreement shall enure to the benefit of and be binding upon the Parties hereto, their respective successors and permitted assigns.

____
(Applicant)

MUNICIPALITY OF

____

Per: ____________________________

Per: ____________________________

SCHEDULE "E"

FIRE PERMIT

PERMIT NUMBER ________________

EFFECTIVE DATE ________________

EXPIRY DATE ________________

APPLICANT: NAME ____

ADDRESS ____

BUSINESS NAME ____________________________________

LEGAL DESCRIPTION OF PROPERTY
FOR WHICH PERMIT IS REQUIRED ____________________________

LOCATION OF FIRE ____

DESCRIPTION OF MATERIAL
WHICH MAY BE BURNED ____________________________________

____

____

CONDITIONS ____

____

____

ADDITIONAL CONDITIONS ATTACHED YES ____ NO ____

MUNICIPALITY OF __________ FIRE DEPARTMENT ______________

SCHEDULE "F"

FIRE PERMIT FEES

Permit Duration		Fee
1.	1 Day	$_______
2.	3 Days	$_______
3.	7 Days	$_______
4.	14 Days	$_______
5.	30 Days	$_______

SCHEDULE "G"

PENALTIES

Offence	Section	Penalty
1. Interference with the efforts of persons engaged in alleviating or eliminating Emergency Situations.	6.3	$
2. Refusing to assist in the extinguishing of fires or to assist in the prevention or spread thereof.	6.5	$
3. Igniting, fuelling or maintaining an Outdoor Fire, Incinerator Fire or Structure Fire without a valid Fire Permit.	8.2	$
4. Providing false, incomplete or misleading information with respect to a Fire Permit.	8.4	$

APPENDIX B.2

EXAMPLE FIRE AND EMERGENCY SERVICES AGREEMENT

This Agreement made the _____ day of ______, 199__.

BETWEEN:

CITY OF ___________
a municipal corporation under
the laws of the Province of _______
(hereinafter referred to as the "City")

- and -

VILLAGE OF _________
a municipal corporation under
the laws of the Province of ________
(hereinafter referred to as the "Village")

FIRE AND EMERGENCY SERVICES AGREEMENT

WHEREAS:

A. The Village is desirous of obtaining from the City and the City is desirous of providing to the Village, fire and emergency services; and

B. The ____________ Act (R.S.__ 19__, c.__ (as amended or repealed and replaced from time to time) authorizes the City to establish and operate fire and emergency services; and

C. The ____________ Act (R.S._) 19_, c.___, (as amended or repealed and replaced from time to time) authorizes the City and the Village to enter into agreements with other persons or governments for the provision of fire and emergency services.

NOW THEREFORE THIS AGREEMENT WITNESSETH that, in consideration of these premises and of the terms, conditions and agreements herein contained, the Parties do hereby agree as follows:

ARTICLE 1

INTERPRETATION

1.1 In this Agreement unless there is something in the subject matter or context inconsistent therewith:

1.1.1 "Agreement" means this Agreement as the same may be amended from time to time in accordance with the terms hereof and the expressions "herein", "hereof", "hereto", "above", "below" and similar expressions used in any paragraph, subparagraph, section or article of this Agreement refer and relate to the whole of this Agreement and not to that paragraph, subparagraph, section or article only, unless otherwise expressly provided;

1.2 Unless otherwise defined, each capitalized word or phrase herein shall have the meaning ascribed to it in this Article.

1.3 The Parties hereby confirm and ratify the matters contained and referred to in the Preamble and the Schedules to this Agreement, and agree that same were expressly incorporated into and form part of this Agreement.

1.4 Wherever the singular, plural, masculine, feminine or neuter is used throughout this Agreement the same shall be construed as meaning the singular, plural, masculine, feminine, neuter, body politic or body corporate where the fact or context so requires, and the provisions hereof and all covenants herein shall be construed to be joint and several when applicable to more than one party.

1.5 The headings in this Agreement have been inserted for reference and as a matter of convenience only, and in no way define, limit or enlarge the scope or meaning of this Agreement or any provision hereof.

1.6 This Agreement shall be governed by and construed in accordance with the laws of the Province of _______ and the Parties hereby submit to the jurisdiction of the Courts in the Province of ________. The Parties agree that any litigation between the Parties which arises pursuant to or in connection with this Agreement, or any of its provisions, shall be referred to the courts in the Province of _________, and shall not be referred to the courts in any other jurisdiction.

ARTICLE 2

PROVISION OF FIRE AND EMERGENCY SERVICES

2.1 The City shall provide to the Village fire and emergency services as described in Schedule "A", herein.

2.2 The Village shall pay to the City the following charges for the provision of fire and emergency services pursuant to subsection 2.1 herein:

2.2.1 An annual payment in the amount of ________ ($______), which sum shall be due and payable on December 31 of each year during the term of this Agreement; and

2.2.2 Charges for the performance of fire and emergency services as calculated pursuant to Schedule "A" herein, which charges shall be due and payable within thirty (30) days of being invoiced by the County.

ARTICLE 3

INSURANCE

3.1 The City agrees to obtain and maintain during the term of this Agreement public liability and property damage insurance of such type and amount as is satisfactory to the Village in its sole and absolute discretion. Evidence of this insurance shall be given by the City to the Village upon request from time to time by the Village.

ARTICLE 4

PERFORMANCE FAILURE

4.1 If the Village shall fail to perform any of the obligations or agreements of the Village under or in respect of this Agreement the City may, from time to time, in its sole discretion, and without prejudice to its rights at law and in equity, perform or cause to be performed any such obligations or agreements, or any part thereof, and for such purpose may do such things as may be required. All costs and expenses incurred and expenditures made by or on behalf of the City under this section shall be paid by the Village within _____ (__) days of receiving notice thereof.

4.2 If the City shall fail to perform any of the obligations or agreements of the City under or in respect of this Agreement the Village may, from time to time, in its sole discretion, and without prejudice to its rights at law and in equity, perform or cause to be performed any such obligations or agreements, or any part thereof, and for such purpose may do such things as may be required. All costs and expenses incurred and expenditures made by or on behalf of the Village under this section shall be paid by the City within _____ (__) days of receiving notice thereof.

ARTICLE 5

TERM OF AGREEMENT

5.1 The term of this Agreement shall be _____ (__) years commencing from the date of this Agreement, unless terminated earlier pursuant to the terms of subsection 5.2 herein.

5.2 Either Party may at any time terminate this Agreement upon providing to the either Party ____________________ (____) months written notice of intention to terminate.

ARTICLE 6

GENERAL MATTERS

6.1 If any term, covenant or condition of this Agreement or the application thereof to any party or circumstance shall be invalid or unenforceable to any extent, the remainder of this Agreement or application of such term, covenant or condition to a party or circumstance other than those to which it is held invalid or unenforceable shall not be affected thereby and each remaining term, covenant or condition of this Agreement shall be valid and shall be enforceable to the fullest extent permitted by law.

6.2 This Agreement constitutes the entire agreement between the Parties hereto relating to the subject matter hereof, and supersedes all prior and contemporaneous agreements, understandings, negotiations and discussions, whether oral or written, of the Parties and there are no general or specific warranties, representations or other agreements by or among the Parties in connection with the entering into of this Agreement or the subject matter hereof except as specifically set forth herein

6.3 The Parties hereto and each of them do hereby covenant and agree to do such things, obtain such approvals, permits and licenses and execute such further documents, agreements and assurances as may be necessary or advisable from time to time in order to carry out the terms and conditions of this Agreement in accordance with their true intent.

6.4 This Agreement may be altered or amended in any of its provisions when any such changes are reduced to writing and assigned by the Parties hereto but not otherwise.

6.5 No remedy herein conferred upon either Party is intended to be exclusive of any other remedy available to that Party but each remedy shall be cumulative and shall be in addition to every other remedy given hereunder or now or hereafter existing by law or in equity or by statute.

6.6 No consent or waiver, express or implied, by either Party to or of any breach or default by the other Party in the performance by the other Party of its obligations hereunder shall be deemed or construed to be a consent or waiver to or of any other breach or default in the performance of obligations hereunder by such Party hereunder. Failure on the part of either party to complain of any act or failure to act of the other party or to declare the other Party in default, irrespective of how long such failure continues, shall not constitute a waiver by such party of its rights hereunder.

6.7 Any notice required to be give hereunder by either Party shall be in writing and shall be deemed to have been well and sufficiently given if:

6.7.1 personally delivered to the Party to whom it is intended or if such Party is a corporation to an officer of that corporation; or

6.7.2 if mailed by prepared registered mail, to the address of the Party to whom it is intended hereinafter set forth or to such other address as a Party may from time to time direct in writing as follows:

6.7.2.1 In case of notice to the City,
to:

6.7.2.2 In case of notice to the Village,
to:

Any notice delivered as aforesaid shall be deemed to have been received on the date of delivery and any notice mailed shall be deemed to have been received seventy-two (72) hours after the date it is postmarked. If normal mail service is interrupted by strike, slow-down, force majeure or other cause after the notice has been sent the notice will not be deemed to be received until actually received. In the event normal mail service is impaired at the time of sending the notice, then personal delivery only shall be effective.

6.8 Time shall be of the essence of this Agreement and of every party hereof.

6.9 This Agreement may not be assigned in whole or in part by the Village without the express written permission of the City.

6.10 This Agreement may not be assigned in whole or in part by the City without the express written permission of the Village.

6.11 This Agreement shall enure to the benefit of and be binding upon the parties hereto, their respective successors and permitted assigns.

CITY OF ________

PER: _____________

PER: _____________

VILLAGE OF ________

PER: _____________

PER: _____________

SCHEDULE "A"

FIRE AND EMERGENCY SERVICES/CHARGES

		Service	Charge
1.	Inspections		
	1.1	Inspection time	$______
	1.2	Transportation	$______
	1.3	Administration/Clerical	$______
	1.4	Materials	$______
	1.5	Outside Technical Assistance	$______
2.	Fire Suppression Apparatus		
	2.1	Pumper Truck	$______
	2.2	Ladder Truck	$______
	2.3	Command Vehicle	$______
	2.4	Water Truck	$______
3.	Fire Suppression Personnel		
	3.1	Command Personnel	$______
	3.2	Senior Field Personnel	$______
	3.3	Junior Field Personnel	$______
	3.4	Support Personnel	$______
	3.5	Outside Technical Assistance	$______
4.	Dangerous Goods Apparatus		
	4.1	Dangerous Goods Response Unit	$______
	4.2	Dangerous Goods Removal Unit	$______
	4.3	Dangerous Goods Disposal Site	$______
	4.4	Outside Technical Apparatus	$______
5.	Dangerous Goods Personnel		
	5.1	Command Personnel	$______
	5.2	Senior Field Personnel	$______
	5.3	Junior Field Personnel	$______
	5.4	Support Personnel	$______
	5.5	Outside Technical Personnel	$______

APPENDIX B.3

EXAMPLE JOINT FIRE AND EMERGENCY SERVICES AGREEMENT

This Agreement made the _____ day of ______, 199__.

BETWEEN:

COUNTY OF ___________
a municipal corporation under
the laws of the Province of _______
(hereinafter referred to as the "County")

- and -

TOWN OF __________
a municipal corporation under
the laws of the Province of _______
(hereinafter referred to as the "Town")

JOINT FIRE AND EMERGENCY SERVICES AGREEMENT

WHEREAS:

A. The County and the Town are desirous of providing fire and emergency services to residents located within their respective municipal boundaries; and

B. The _____________ Act (R.S._) 19_, c.__ (as amended or repealed and replaced from time to time) authorizes the County to establish and operate fire and emergency services; and

C. The County and the Town are desirous of jointly establishing and operating a fire and emergency service;

D. The ____________ Act (R.S._) 19_, c.___, (as amended or repealed and replaced from time to time) authorize the County and the Town to enter into agreements with other persons or governments for the provision of fire and emergency services.

NOW THEREFORE THIS AGREEMENT WITNESSETH that, in consideration of these premises and of the terms, conditions and agreements herein contained, the Parties do hereby agree as follows:

ARTICLE 1

INTERPRETATION

1.1 In this Agreement unless there is something in the subject matter or context inconsistent therewith:

1.1.1 "Agreement" means this Agreement as the same may be amended from time to time in accordance with the terms hereof and the expressions "herein", "hereof", "hereto", "above", "below" and similar expressions used in any paragraph, subparagraph, section or article of this Agreement refer and relate to the whole of this Agreement and not to that paragraph, subparagraph, section or article only, unless otherwise expressly provided;

1.2 Unless otherwise defined, each capitalized word or phrase herein shall have the meaning ascribed to it in this Article.

1.3 The Parties hereby confirm and ratify the matters contained and referred to in the Preamble and the Schedules to this Agreement, and agree that same are expressly incorporated into and form part of this Agreement.

1.4 Wherever the singular, plural, masculine, feminine or neuter is used throughout this Agreement the same shall be construed as meaning the singular, plural, masculine, feminine, neuter, body politic or body corporate where the fact or context so requires, and the provisions hereof and all covenants herein shall be construed to be joint and several when applicable to more than one party.

1.5 The headings in this Agreement have been inserted for reference and as a matter of convenience only, and in no way define, limit or enlarge the scope or meaning of this Agreement or any provision hereof.

1.6 This Agreement shall be governed by and construed in accordance with the laws of the Province of _______ and the Parties hereby submit to the jurisdiction of the Courts in the Province of ________. The Parties agree that any litigation between the Parties which arises pursuant to or in connection with this Agreement, or any of its provisions, shall be referred to the courts in the Province of _________, and shall not be referred to the courts in any other jurisdiction.

ARTICLE 2

FIRE AND EMERGENCY SERVICES AUTHORITY

2.1 The County and the Town agree to establish an authority which shall be known as the "_________" Fire and Emergency Services Authority" (hereinafter referred to as the "Authority").

2.2 The County and the Town agree that the Authority shall have the following powers:

ARTICLE 3

JOINT ASSUMPTION OF LIABILITY

3.1 The County agrees to jointly and severally assume responsibility with respect to any claim, action, suit, proceeding or demand against the Town, its elected officials, officers, employees, servants, agents and contractor by any third party with respect to any occurrence, incident, accident or happening, relating in any manner whatsoever to this Agreement and the rights and obligations arising therefrom, and which responsibility shall, without restricting the generality of the foregoing, include all legal costs incurred by the Town in defending such a claim, suit, proceeding or demand.

3.2 The Town agrees to jointly and severally assume responsibility with respect to any claim, action, suit, proceeding or demand against the County, its elected officials, officers, employees, servants, agents and contractor by any third party with respect to any occurrence, incident, accident or happening, relating in any manner whatsoever to this Agreement and the rights and obligations arising therefrom, and which responsibility shall, without restricting the generality of the foregoing, include all legal costs incurred by the County in defending such a claim, suit, proceeding or demand.

ARTICLE 4

INSURANCE

4.1 The Parties each agree to obtain and maintain during the term of this Agreement public liability and property damage insurance in the amount of ___________ DOLLARS ($________). Evidence of this insurance shall be given by each party to the other party upon request from time to time by the other party.

ARTICLE 5

PERFORMANCE FAILURE

5.1 If the Town shall fail to perform any of the obligations or agreements of the Town under or in respect of this Agreement the County may, from time to time, in its sole discretion, and without prejudice to its rights at law and in equity, perform or cause to be performed any such obligations or agreements, or any part thereof, and for such purpose may do such things as may be required. All costs and expenses incurred and expenditures made by or on behalf of the County under this section shall be paid by the Town within _______ (__) days of receiving notice thereof.

5.2 If the County shall fail to perform any of the obligations or agreements of the County under or in respect of this Agreement the Town may, from time to time, in its sole discretion, and without prejudice to its rights at law and in equity, perform or cause to be performed any such obligations or agreements, or any part thereof, and for such purpose may do such things as may be required. All costs and expenses incurred and expenditures made by or on behalf of the Town under this section shall be paid by the County within ________ (__) days of receiving notice thereof.

ARTICLE 6

TERM OF AGREEMENT

6.1 The term of this Agreement shall be _____ (__) years commencing from the date of this Agreement, unless terminated earlier pursuant to the terms of subsection 6.2 herein.

6.2 Either Party may at any time terminate this Agreement upon providing to the other. Party _____________ (____) months within written notice of intention to terminate.

ARTICLE 7

GENERAL MATTERS

7.1 If any term, covenant or condition of this Agreement or the application thereof to any party or circumstance shall be invalid or unenforceable to any extent, the remainder of this Agreement or application of such term, covenant or condition to a party or circumstance other than those to which it is held invalid or unenforceable shall not be affected thereby and each remaining term, covenant or condition of this Agreement shall be valid and shall be enforceable to the fullest extent permitted by law.

7.2 This Agreement constitutes the entire agreement between the parties hereto relating to the subject matter hereof, and supersedes all prior and contemporaneous agreements, understandings, negotiations and discussions, whether oral or written, of the parties and there are no general or specific warranties, representations or other agreements by or among the parties in connection with the entering into of this Agreement or the subject matter hereof except as specifically set forth herein.

7.3 The Parties hereto and each of them do hereby covenant and agree to do such things, obtain such approvals, permits and licenses and execute such further documents, agreements and assurances as may be necessary or advisable from time to time in order to carry out the terms and conditions of this Agreement in accordance with their true intent.

7.4 This Agreement may be altered or amended in any of its provisions when any such changes are reduced to writing and assigned by the Parties hereto but not otherwise.

7.5 No remedy herein conferred upon either Party is intended to be exclusive of any other remedy available to that party but each remedy shall be cumulative and shall be in addition to every other remedy given hereunder or now or hereafter existing by law or in equity or by statute.

7.6 No consent or waiver, express or implied, by either Party to or of any breach or default by the other party in the performance by the other Party of its obligations hereunder shall be deemed or construed to be a consent or waiver to or of any other breach or default in the performance of obligations hereunder by such Party hereunder. Failure on the part of either Party to complain of any act or failure to act of the other Party or to declare the other Party in default, irrespective of how long such failure continues, shall not constitute a waiver by such Party of its rights hereunder.

7.7 Any notice required to be give hereunder by either Party shall be in writing and shall be deemed to have been well and sufficiently given if:

7.7.1 personally delivered to the Party to whom it is intended or if such party is a corporation to an officer of that corporation; or

7.7.2 if mailed by prepared registered mail, to the address of the Party to whom it is intended hereinafter set forth or to such other address as a party may from time to time direct in writing as follows:

7.7.2.1 In case of notice to the County,
to:

7.7.2.2 In case of notice to the Town,
to:

Any notice delivered as aforesaid shall be deemed to have been received on the date of delivery and any notice mailed shall be deemed to have been received seventy-two (72) hours after the date it is postmarked. If normal mail service is interrupted by strike, slow-down, force majeure or other cause after the notice has been sent the notice will not be deemed to be received until actually received. In the event normal mail service is impaired at the time of sending the notice, then personal delivery only shall be effective.

7.8 Time shall be of the essence of this Agreement and of every party hereof.

7.9 This Agreement may not be assigned in whole or in part by the Town without the express written permission of the County.

7.10 This Agreement may not be assigned in whole or in part by the County without the express written permission of the Town.

7.11 This Agreement shall enure to the benefit of and be binding upon the parties hereto, their respective successors and permitted assigns.

COUNTY OF ________

PER: ______________

PER: ______________

TOWN OF ________

PER: ______________

PER: ______________

APPENDIX B.4

EXAMPLE FIRE AND EMERGENCY SERVICES MUTUAL ASSISTANCE AGREEMENT

This Agreement made the _____ day of _____, 199__.

BETWEEN:

COUNTY OF ___________
a municipal corporation under
the laws of the Province of _______
(hereinafter referred to as the "County")

- and -

CITY OF _________
a municipal corporation under
the laws of the Province of ______
(hereinafter referred to as the "City")

FIRE AND EMERGENCY SERVICES MUTUAL ASSISTANCE AGREEMENT

WHEREAS:

A. The County and the City have each established and operated their own fire and emergency services pursuant to the provisions of the _______ Act (R.S._) 19_, c.___ (as amended or repealed and replaced from time to time); and

B. The County and the City are desirous of providing to and receiving from each other fire and emergency services from time to time when the need arises; and

C. The ___________ Act (R.S._) 19_, c.___, (as amended or repealed and replaced from time to time) authorizes the County and the City to enter into agreements with other persons or governments for the joint provision of fire and emergency services.

NOW THEREFORE THIS AGREEMENT WITNESSETH that, in consideration of these premises and of the terms, conditions and agreements herein contained, the Parties do hereby agree as follows:

ARTICLE 1

INTERPRETATION

1.1 In this Agreement unless there is something in the subject matter or context inconsistent therewith:

1.1.1 "Agreement" means this Agreement as the same may be amended from time to time in accordance with the terms hereof and the expressions "herein", "hereof", "hereto", "above", "below" and similar expressions used in any paragraph, subparagraph, section or article of this Agreement refer and relate to the whole of this Agreement and not to that paragraph, subparagraph, section or article only, unless otherwise expressly provided;

1.1.2 "City Fire and Emergency Services" means the fire and emergency services established and operated by the City.

1.1.3 "City Chief Fire and Emergency Services Officer" means the City ___.

1.1.4 "County Fire and Emergency Services" means the fire and emergency services established and operated by the County.

1.1.5 "County Chief Fire and Emergency Services Officer" means the County ________.

1.2 Unless otherwise defined, each capitalized word or phrase herein shall have the meaning ascribed to it in this Article.

1.3 The Parties hereby confirm and ratify the matters contained and referred to in the Preamble and the Schedules to this Agreement, and agree that same are expressly incorporated into and form part of this Agreement.

1.4 Wherever the singular, plural, masculine, feminine or neuter is used throughout this Agreement the same shall be construed as meaning the singular, plural, masculine, feminine, neuter, body politic or body corporate where the fact or context so requires, and the provisions hereof and all covenants herein shall be construed to be joint and several when applicable to more than one party.

1.5 The headings in this Agreement have been inserted for reference and as a matter of convenience only, and in no way define, limit or enlarge the scope or meaning of this Agreement or any provision hereof.

1.6 This Agreement shall be governed by and construed in accordance with the laws of the Province of _______ and the Parties hereby submit to the jurisdiction of the Courts in the Province of _______. The Parties agree that any litigation between the Parties which arises pursuant to or in connection with this Agreement, or any of its provisions, shall be referred to the courts in the Province of _________, and shall not be referred to the courts in any other jurisdiction.

ARTICLE 2

MUTUAL ASSISTANCE

2.1 Subject to subsection 2.4 herein, the County shall make available to the City those fire and emergency services described in Schedule "A" herein, upon receiving a request from the City in accordance with subsection 2.2 herein.

2.2 If in the opinion of the City Chief Fire and Emergency Services Officer or his designate, the City Fire and Emergency Services is unable to adequately respond to an incident or occurrence within its municipal boundaries requiring fire and emergency services, the City Chief Fire and Emergency Services Officer, or his designate may contact by whatever means are expedient the County Chief Fire and Emergency Services Officer or his designate and request that the County provide any or all of its Fire and Emergency Services described in Schedule "A" herein.

2.3 Fire and emergency services provided to the County by the County pursuant to subsection 2.1 herein, are subject to those charges described in Schedule "A" herein, and which charges shall be paid to the County by the City within thirty (30) days of being invoiced by the County.

2.4 Upon receiving a request from the City in accordance with subsection 2.2 herein, the County shall not be obligated to make available to the City the County's Fire and Emergency Services requested if such services are already engaged in the provision of fire and emergency services or if, in the opinion of the County Chief Fire and Emergency Services Official, or his designate, making such services available to the City would result in the County Fire and Emergency Service being unable to adequately respond to an incident or occurrence requiring fire and emergency service within the municipal boundaries of the County.

2.5 Subject to subsection 2.8 herein, the City shall make available to the County those fire and emergency services described in Schedule "B" herein, upon receiving a request from the County in accordance with subsection 2.2 herein.

2.6 If in the opinion of the County Chief Fire and Emergency Services Officer or his designate, the County Fire and Emergency Services is unable to adequately respond to an incident or occurrence within its municipal boundaries requiring fire and emergency services, the County Chief Fire and Emergency Services Officer, or his designate may contact by whatever means are expedient the City Chief Fire and Emergency Services Officer or his designate and request that the City provide any or all of its Fire and Emergency Services described in Schedule "A" herein.

2.7 Fire and emergency services provided to the City by the City pursuant to subsection 2.1 herein, are subject to those charges described in Schedule "A" herein, and which charges shall be paid to the City by the County within thirty (30) days of being invoiced by the City.

2.8 Upon receiving a request from the County in accordance with subsection 2.2 herein, the City shall not be obligated to make available to the County the City's Fire and Emergency Services requested if such services are already engaged in the provision of fire and emergency services or if, in the opinion of the City Chief Fire and Emergency Services Official, or his designate, making such services available to the County would result in the City Fire and Emergency Service being unable to adequately respond to an incident or occurrence requiring fire and emergency service within the municipal boundaries of the City.

ARTICLE 3

INSURANCE

3.1 The Parties each agree to obtain and maintain during the term of this Agreement public liability and property damage insurance in the amount of __________ DOLLARS ($_______). Evidence of this insurance shall be given by each party to the other party upon request from time to time by the other party.

ARTICLE 4

PERFORMANCE FAILURE

4.1 If the County shall fail to perform any of the obligations or agreements of the County under or in respect of this Agreement the City may, from time to time, in its sole discretion, and without prejudice to its rights at law and in equity, perform or cause to be performed any such obligations or agreements, or any part thereof, and for such purpose may do such things as may be required. All costs and expenses incurred and expenditures made by or on behalf of the City under this section shall be paid by the

County within ________ (__) days of receiving notice thereof.

4.2 If the City shall fail to perform any of the obligations or agreements of the City under or in respect of this Agreement the County may, from time to time, in its sole discretion, and without prejudice to its rights at law and in equity, perform or cause to be performed any such obligations or agreements, or any part thereof, and for such purpose may do such things as may be required. All costs and expenses incurred and expenditures made by or on behalf of the County under this section shall be paid by the City within ________ (__) days of receiving notice thereof.

ARTICLE 5

TERM OF AGREEMENT

5.1 The terms of this Agreement shall be _____ (__) years commencing from the date of this Agreement, unless terminated earlier pursuant to the terms of subsection 5.2 herein.

5.2 The Parties may at any time terminate this Agreement upon providing to the other party _______________________ (___) months written notice of intention to terminate.

ARTICLE 6

GENERAL MATTERS

6.1 If any term, covenant or condition of this Agreement or the application thereof to any party or circumstance shall be invalid or unenforceable to any extent, the remainder of this Agreement or application of such term, covenant or condition to a party or circumstance other than those to which it is held invalid or unenforceable shall not be affected thereby and each remaining term, covenant or condition of this Agreement shall be valid and shall be enforceable to the fullest extent permitted by law.

6.2 This Agreement constitutes the entire agreement between the Parties hereto relating to the subject matter hereof, and supersedes all prior and contemporaneous agreements, understandings, negotiations and discussions, whether oral or written, of the parties and there are no general or specific warranties, representations or other agreements by or among the Parties in connection with the entering into of this Agreement or the subject matter hereof except as specifically set forth herein.

6.3 The Parties hereto and each of them do hereby covenant and agree to do such things, obtain such approvals, permits and licenses and execute such further documents, agreements and assurances as may be necessary or advisable from time to time in order to carry out the terms and conditions of this Agreement in accordance with their true intent.

6.4 This Agreement may be altered or amended in any of its provisions when any such changes are reduced to writing and assigned by the Parties hereto but not otherwise.

6.5 No remedy herein conferred upon either Party is intended to be exclusive of any other remedy available to that party but each remedy shall be cumulative and shall be in addition to every other remedy given hereunder or now or hereafter existing by law or in equity or by statute.

6.6 No consent or waiver, express or implied, by either Party to or of any breach or default by the other party in the performance by the other party of its obligations hereunder shall be deemed or construed to be a consent or waiver to or of any other breach or default in the performance of obligations hereunder by such Party hereunder. Failure on the part of either Party to complain of any act or failure to act of the other party or to declare the other Party in default, irrespective of how long such failure continues, shall not constitute a waiver by such party of its rights hereunder.

6.7 Any notice required to be give hereunder by any Party shall be in writing and shall be deemed to have been well and sufficiently given if:

6.7.1 personally delivered to the Party to whom it is intended or if such party is a corporation to an officer of that corporation; or

6.7.2 if mailed by prepared registered mail, to the address of the Party to whom it is intended hereinafter set forth or to such other address as a Party may from time to time direct in writing as follows:

6.7.2.1 In case of notice to the County,
to:

6.7.2.2 In case of notice to the City,
to:

Any notice delivered as aforesaid shall be deemed to have been received on the date of delivery and any notice mailed shall be deemed to have been received seventy-two (72) hours after the date it is postmarked. If normal mail service is interrupted by strike, slow-down, force majeure or other cause after the notice has been sent the notice will not be deemed to be received until actually received. In the event normal mail service is impaired at the time of sending the notice, then personal delivery only shall be effective.

6.8 Time shall be of the essence of this Agreement and of every party hereof.

6.9 This Agreement may not be assigned in whole or in part by the City without the express written permission of the County.

6.10 This Agreement may not be assigned in whole or in part by the County without the express written permission of the City.

6.11 This Agreement shall enure to the benefit of and be binding upon the Parties hereto, their respective successors and permitted assigns.

COUNTY OF ________

PER: ______________

PER: ______________

CITY OF __________

PER: ______________

PER: ______________

SCHEDULE "A"

COUNTY FIRE AND EMERGENCY SERVICES AVAILABLE FOR MUTUAL ASSISTANCE TO THE CITY

	Services Available	Charge
1.	Fire Suppression Apparatus	
	1.1	$_______
	1.2	$_______
	1.3	$_______
2.	Fire Suppression Personnel	
	1.1	$_______
	1.2	$_______
	1.3	$_______

SCHEDULE "B"

CITY FIRE AND EMERGENCY SERVICES AVAILABLE FOR MUTUAL ASSISTANCE TO THE COUNTY

	Services Available	Charge
1.	Fire Suppression Apparatus	
	1.1	$_______
	1.2	$_______
	1.3	$_______
2.	Fire Suppression Personnel	
	1.1	$_______
	1.2	$_______
	1.3	$_______

APPENDIX C

CHECKLIST OF HAZARDS

Checklist of Hazards

The following is a partial list of the type of hazards which may be encountered at community level. These hazards are listed in alphabetical order because separating them into categories may only be misleading. Disasters and emergencies do not come in neat little packages which scream out their names to be recognized. Rather, each disaster often contains a number factors and disaster agents.

- Air crashes
- Assaults
- Avalanches
- Blackouts/Brownouts
- Bomb threats
- Building and structure collapses
- Chemical spills
- Civil disturbances
- Dam and Levee failures
- Dangerous Goods occurrences
- Droughts
- Earthquakes
- Epidemics
- Explosions
- Extreme heat/cold
- Fires (i.e., structural)
- Flash floods
- Floods
- Forest fires
- Frost situations
- Fuel shortages
- Hostage incidents
- Hurricanes
- Kidnapping
- Land–shifts
- Marine accidents
- Mine collapse
- Missing persons
- Multi–casualty incidents
- Nuclear accidents
- Pipeline ruptures
- Plagues
- Pollution
- Product tampering
- Riots
- Sink holes
- Slides (Snow, mud, rock)
- Storms (Snow, wind, dust, lightening, hail, ice)
- Strikes
- Terrorism
- Tidal waves
- Tornadoes
- Train derailments
- Tsunamis
- Volcanic eruptions

APPENDIX D
DGRT SOPs AND PROCEDURES

EMERGENCY RESPONSE DEPARTMENT
STANDARD OPERATING PROCEDURES
FIRE/RESCUE BRANCH
DANGEROUS GOODS

PAGE: 1 of 3

PROCEDURE: FS NOV 01 94 906

SUPERSEDES: FS MAY 17 94 906

AFFECTS: FC/FS/FA

TITLE: RESPONSE TO LEVEL I AND LEVEL II DANGEROUS GOODS INCIDENTS

PURPOSE:

1. To establish immediate control, define roles, and provide a standard system to be utilized for the purpose of managing personnel and resources at the scene of a Dangerous Goods Incident.
2. To ensure that all Department and other safety considerations and standards are maintained during the process.

PROCEDURE: 1. LEVEL I RESPONSE

The minimum response to a Dangerous Goods Incident shall consist of one Pumper. The initial response shall operate utilizing the following considerations:

a) Single unit response may be utilized for minor spills involving automotive fluids such as gasoline, diesel fuel, antifreeze, motor oil, transmission fluid, and hydraulic fluid. The total volume of all fluids should not exceed 25 litres. These spills may be contained and absorbed using the spill kits which are carried on all pumpers.

b) Minor spills may be cleaned up by responding personnel. Upon completion of the cleanup process, the Incident Commander shall ensure the product is packaged and labelled, and will attempt to leave the product in the care of a responsible person at the scene. If no such person is available, the Incident Commander shall contact the on-duty Dangerous Goods Captain, via Fire Central, and shall arrange to have a disposal contractor dispatched to the scene.

c) In cases where the Incident Commander determines that a contactor is required for both cleanup and disposal, the Incident Commander shall contact the on-duty Dangerous Goods Captain, via Fire Central, and shall arrange to have a cleanup/disposal contractor dispatched to the scene.

EMERGENCY RESPONSE DEPARTMENT
STANDARD OPERATING PROCEDURES
FIRE/RESCUE BRANCH
DANGEROUS GOODS

PAGE: 2 of 3

PROCEDURE: FS NOV 01 94 906

d) When a routine Level I response becomes identified as beyond the capabilities of a single pumper, the Incident Commander shall notify Fire Central immediately, relaying as much information as possible regarding the scene and materials involved, and shall request the Dangerous Goods Response Team. The Incident Commander shall remove all personnel and equipment to a safe distance from the scene. When an incident is suspected, or known to be a Level II or III dangerous goods incident, Fire Central will automatically dispatch D.G. units at the same time as the station response.

e) Upon arrival on the scene of a Level I Dangerous Goods incident, the Incident Commander will immediately designate a safe perimeter, and mark it using yellow BANNER GUARD.

f) The Incident Commander will retain complete control of the incident until such time as the incident is concluded, or command is transferred to another officer.

g) Evacuation may be initiated by the Incident Commander as the situation dictates.

h) No life-saving rescue, fire suppression, or control operation will be initiated until the product or material has been identified.

2. LEVEL II RESPONSE

The minimum response to a Level II Dangerous Goods Incident shall consist of one Pumper with support provided by the D.G. Team. The initial response shall operate utilizing the following considerations:

a) Units responding to a known Level II D.G. Incident will locate no closer than 100 metres from the point of the incident if nothing is visible. If the product is unknown, then the initial responding units will stage at a greater dis tance until more information can be obtained.

b) Units will approach incident from upwind and uphill if at all possible. Vapour clouds and potential liquid run-off are important considerations. Monitor readings will be taken as soon as possible.

EMERGENCY RESPONSE DEPARTMENT
STANDARD OPERATING PROCEDURES
FIRE/RESCUE BRANCH
DANGEROUS GOODS

PAGE: 3 of 3

PROCEDURE: FS NOV 01 94 906

c) When a routine response is identified as a D.G. Incident, the Incident Commander will notify Fire Central immediately, relaying as much information as possible regarding the scene and materials involved, and will request the Dangerous Goods Response Team. The Incident Commander will remove personnel and equipment to a safe distance from the scene.

   When an incident is suspected, or known to be a Level II dangerous goods incident, Fire Central will automatically dispatch D.G. units at the same time as the station response.

d) Upon arrival at a Level II Dangerous Goods incident, the Incident Commander will immediately designate a safe perimeter and mark it, using yellow BANNER GUARD. This will define the "Warm Zone." On arrival of the Dangerous Goods Team, the D.G. Officer will consult with the Incident Commander and designate the "Hot Zone" using red BANNER GUARD. The D.G. officer will also establish a Staging Area at which incoming personnel and equipment will assemble.

e) The Incident Commander will retain complete control of the incident, working in cooperation with the Dangerous Goods Officer until such time as the incident is concluded, or command is transferred to another officer, other than a D.G. officer.

f) Evacuation may be initiated by the Incident Commander as the situation dictates.

g) No life-saving rescue, fire suppression, or control operation will be initiated until the product or material has been identified.

BRANCH MANAGER DEPUTY CHIEF

EMERGENCY RESPONSE DEPARTMENT
STANDARD OPERATING PROCEDURES
FIRE/RESCUE BRANCH
DANGEROUS GOODS

PAGE: 1 of 2

PROCEDURE: FS NOV 01 94 907

SUPERSEDES: FS MAY 17 94 907

AFFECTS: FS/ / /

TITLE: DANGEROUS GOODS RESPONSE TEAM RESPONSE (LEVEL III)

PURPOSE: To identify minimum response procedures to be initiated by the Dangerous Goods Response Team at Level III Dangerous Goods incidents.

PROCEDURE:

The Dangerous Goods Response Team will utilize the Incident Command System for the systematic management of a Dangerous Goods Incident.

a) All Dangerous Goods Incidents will be initially treated as a "Worst Case" potential scenario.

b) Immediately upon arrival, the Dangerous Goods Officer will report to the Incident Commander to be briefed on status and particulars of the incident. The Dangerous Goods officer will not be required to assume the position of Incident Commander during the entire incident operation.

c) The accurate identification of the involved product(s) or material(s) is a Top Priority in the effective handling of a dangerous goods incident. Three separate sources of reference should be used in the product identification process, including but not limited to CAMEO, CCINFO and EMERGENCY ACTION GUIDE, etc.

d) As soon as possible, the D.G. Officer will establish restricted entry zones. Red BANNER GUARD will designate the "Hot Zone", and yellow BANNER GUARD will designate the "Warm Zone." If the incident condition dictates, a Safety Monitor will be appointed. The Safety Monitor will be responsible for recording the names and time of all personnel entering and exiting the "warm" and "hot" zones.

e) **ONLY PERSONNEL APPROPRIATELY PROTECTED ARE PERMITTED INTO THE "WARM" OR "HOT" ZONES AT ANY TIME !**

EMERGENCY RESPONSE DEPARTMENT
STANDARD OPERATING PROCEDURES
FIRE/RESCUE BRANCH
DANGEROUS GOODS

PAGE: 2 of 2

PROCEDURE: FS NOV 01 94 907

f) A dry chemical extinguisher and a charged protective hoseline staffed by a minimum of two fire fighters will be stationed in the WARM ZONE at the point of entry to the HOT ZONE whenever entry or approach is made into the hot zone.

g) Personnel exiting the HOT ZONE must pass through controlled access points, and must undergo proper decontamination and medical evaluation.

h) All entries into the HOT ZONE will be done in pairs of properly clad workers, with an additional pair of properly equipped personnel in a state of readiness as a backup.

i) A Dangerous Goods EMERGENCY Incident shall be deemed to be concluded at a point when:

1. the commodities have been neutralized, or restored to a controlled state.
2. a state of "no risk" exists.
3. a licensed and qualified hazardous waste cleanup/disposal firm accepts custody and responsibility for "clean-up".

The Incident Commander, upon determining that the initial emergency has been resolved, may turn over responsibility for clean-up:

a. To the custody of the City of Edmonton (the department having jurisdiction) if ownership of the property involved or affected is that of the City of Edmonton (e.g. Transportation, Drainage, Parks & Recreation, etc.).

b. A certified and licensed hazardous waste cleanup and/or disposal agency, where private property is involved. Police will act on advisement from the Incident Commander in regards to closing or opening of roads.

BRANCH MANAGER DEPUTY CHIEF

Appendix E

References

References

American Academy of Orthopaedic Surgeons (1995). Emergency care and transportation of the sick and injured, Sixth Edition. New York, NY: Author.

Anderson, M. B., & Woodrow, P. J. (1989). Rising from the ashes: Development strategies in time of disaster. Boulder, CO: Westview–Press.

Auf der Heide, E. (1989). Disaster response: Principles of preparation and coordination. St. Louis, MO: C. V. Mosby.

Bahme, C. W., & Kramer, W. M. (1992). Fire officer's guide to disaster control (2nd ed.). Saddle Brook, NJ: Penwall.

Barton, L., Crisis in organizations: Managing and communicating in the heat of chaos (1993). Cincinnati, OH: South–Western

Beare, H. (1980). Cyclone Tracy and the Darwin educators: A study in crisis management. In R. H. Farquhar & I. E. Housego (Eds.), Canadian and comparative educational administration (pp. 76–87). Vancouver, BC: Education–Extension.

Bowen, J. E. (1995). Emergency management of hazardous materials incidents. Quincy, MA: National Fire Protection Association (NFPA).

Burton, C. R. (1990). Civilians to the rescue. Fire Engineering, 143 (4), pp. 55–57.

Brunacini, A. V. (1985). Fire Command. College Park, MA: YOS Productions.

Bryn, K. (1974). Disaster brings out the best in people. Emergency Planning Digest, 1 (2), pp. 9–11.

Brigham, J. C. (1991). Social psychology (2nd ed.). New York, NY: Harper Collins.

Canada. Emergency Preparedness Canada (EPC). (1990). Guidelines for national emergency arrangements. Ottawa, ON: Author.

Canada. Emergency Preparedness Canada (EPC). (1992). Federal crisis management procedures – Alberta. Edmonton, AB: Author.

Canada. Environment Canada. (1991). Crisis management planning manual. Ottawa, ON: Author.

Canada. Health and Welfare. (1990). Personal services: Psycho–logical planning for disasters. Ottawa, ON: Author.

Canada. Privy Council Office (PCO). (n.d.). Crisis management. Ottawa, ON: Queen's Printers.

Carlson, G. P. (Ed.), Incident command system, Fire Protection Publications, Oklahoma State University, OK, 1983.

Charles, M. T., & Kim, J. C. K. (Eds.). (1988). Crisis management: A case book. Springfield, IL: Charles C. Thomas.

Charles, M. T. (1989). The last flight of space shuttle Challenger. In Rosenthal, U., Charles, M. T., & Hart, P. 't (Eds.), Coping with crises: The management of disasters, riots, and terrorism (pp. 141–168). Springfield, IL: Charles C. Thomas.

Clarke, J. N., Gerber, L. M., & Macionis, J. J. (1994). Sociology: Canadian edition. Scarborough, ON: Prentice Hall.

Cohen, R. E., & Ahearn, F. L. (1980). Handbook for mental health care of disaster victims. Baltimore: John Hopkins University.

Cohen, E. (1989). Disaster planning trends 1989. Emergency: Journal of Emergency Services, 21 (2), pp. 38–44.

Coleman, R. J., & Granito, J. A. (Eds).. (1988). Managing fire services (2nd ed.). Washington, DC: International City Management Association.

Comfort, L. K. (1988). Managing disasters: Strategies and policy perspectives. Durham, SC: Duke University.

Crocker, W. P., & Alp, E. (1993). Risk assessment: Preventing major industrial accidents. Engineering Dimensions, 5, pp. 37–40.

Daines, G. E. (1991). Planning, training and exercising. In Drabek, T. E., & Hoetmer, G. J. (Eds.), Emergency management: Principles and practices for local government (pp. 161–193). Washington, DC: International City Management Association.

Dernocoeur–Boyd, K., & Mackie–Wells, J. J. (1980). Disaster equipment: A weak link in the rescue chain. Emergency: Journal of Emergency Services, 12 (12), pp. 56–60.

Drabek, T. E. (1986). Human system response to disaster: An inventory of sociological findings. New York, NY: Springer– Verlag.

Drabek, T. E. (1991). The evolution of emergency management. In Drabek, T. E., & Hoetmer, G. J. (Eds.), Emergency management: Principles and practices for local government (pp. 3–26). Washington, DC: International City Management Association.

Drabek, T. E., & Hoetmer, G. J. (Eds.). (1991). Emergency management: Principles and practices for local government. Washington, DC: International City Management Association.

Dynes, R. R. (1967). Societal and community problems in disaster. EMO National Digest, 7 (5), pp. 16–18.

Dynes, R. R. (1970). Organized behaviour in disaster. New York, NY: Heath.

Duguay, J. (1994). Looking ahead: Emergency preparedness training for Canada in the nineties and beyond. Emergency Preparedness Digest, 21 (1), pp. 16–21.

ECRU. Emergency Communication Research Unit (1985). The 1978 San Diego air crash: Emergency response to an urban disaster (Research Rep.). Ottawa, ON: Scanlon, J., & Pawzick, A.

ECRU. Emergency Communication Research Unit (1987). The Gander air crash, December 1985 (Research Rep. 87–01–01). Ottawa, ON: Scanlon, J., & Pawzick, A.

EPC. Emergency Preparedness Canada. (1995). Did you know that...? Emergency Preparedness Digest, 22 (1), p. 11.

Erikson, K. (1991). A new species of trouble. In Couch, S. R., & Kroll–Smith, S. (Eds.), Communities at risk: Collective responses to technological hazards. New York, NY: Peter Lang.

FEMA. Federal Emergency Management Agency. (1981). Disaster planning guidelines for fire chiefs. Washington, DC: International Associations of Fire Chiefs and FEMA.

Fink, S. (1986). Crisis management: Planning for the inevitable. New York, NY: American Management Association.

Flynn, M. E. (1995a). Stormy weather: Is Canada's weather system up to the challenge? Emergency Preparedness Digest, 22 (1), pp. 4–8.

Flynn, M. E. (1995b). Newfoundland: Where volunteers make the difference. Emergency Preparedness Digest, 22 (1), pp. 9– 10.

Fowlkes, M. R., & Miller, P. Y. (1988). Unnatural disaster at love canal. In Charles, M. T., & Kim, J. C. K. (Eds.), Crisis management: A case book (pp. 23–41). Springfield, IL: Charles C. Thomas.

Fritz, C. E. (1961). Disaster. In R. K. Merton & R. A. Nisbet (Eds.), Contemporary social problems. New York, NY: Harcourt, Brace & World.

Fritz, C. E., & Mathewson, J. H. (1957). Convergence behavior in disasters: A problem in social control. Washington, DC: National Academy of Sciences / National Research Council.

Gillespie, D. F. (1991). Coordinating community resources. In Drabek, T. E., & Hoetmer, G. J. (Eds.), Emergency management: Principles and practices for local government (pp. 55–77). Washington, DC: International City Management Association.

Gargan, J. B. (1991). DPW: A valuable resource. Fire Engineering, 144 (10), pp. 49–51.

Godschalk, D. R. (1991). Disaster mitigation and hazard management. In Drabek, T. E., & Hoetmer, G. J. (Eds.), Emergency management: Principles and practices for local government (pp. 131–157). Washington, DC: International City Management Association.

Granito, J. A. (1995). Planning for disaster: Emergency management today. NFPA Journal, 89 (4), pp. 44–53.

Hamblin, R. L. (1958). Leadership and crises. Sociometry, 21, pp. 322–335.

Hart, P. 't., & Pijnenburg, B. (1989). The Heizel stadium tragedy. In Rosenthal, U., Charles, M. T., & Hart, P. 't (Eds.), Coping with crises: The management of disasters, riots, and terrorism (pp. 197–224). Springfield, IL: Charles C. Thomas.

Hawkins, T. M., & McClees, H. (1988). Emergency management. In Coleman, R. J., & Granito, J. A. (Eds), Managing fire services (2nd ed.) (pp. 319–345). Washington, DC: International City Management Association.

Hoetmer, G. J. (1991). Introduction. In Drabek, T. E., & Hoetmer, G. J. (Eds.), Emergency management: Principles and practices for local government (pp. xvii–xxxiii). Washington, DC: International City Management Association.

Hoffman, J. M. (1988). Regional perspectives on coordination in emergency preparedness and response. Edmonton, AB: Emergency Preparedness Canada (EPC).

IFSTA. International Fire Services Training Association. (1983). Incident Command System. Stillwater, OK: Fire Protection Publication, Oklahoma State University.

IFSTA. International Fire Services Training Association. (1984). Chief Officer. Stillwater, OK: Fire Protection Publication, Oklahoma State University.

Janis, I. L. (1982). Group think: Psychological studies of policy decisions and fiascoes (2nd ed.). Boston, MA: Houghton Mifflin.

Jasanoff, S. (1988). The Bhopal disaster and the right to know. Social Science Medical Review, 27 (10), pp. 1113–1123.

Jenaway, W. J. (1992). Pre–emergency planning (2nd ed.). Ashland, MA: International Society of Fire Service Instructors.

Kartez, J. D., & Lindell, M. K. (1987). Planning for uncertainty: The case for local disaster planning. APA Journal, Fall issue.

Kasperson, R. E., & Pijawka, D. K. (1985). Societal response to hazards and major hazard events: Comparing natural and technological hazards. Public Administration Review, 45 (1), pp. 7-18.

Kelly, R. B. (1989). Industrial emergency preparedness. New York, NY: Van Nostrand Reinhold.

Kepner, C. H., & Tregoe, B. B. (1981). The new rational manager. Princeton, NJ: Princeton Research.

Kramer, W. M. (1990). Introduction to disaster and fire defence planning. In National Fire Academy, Disaster and fire defence planning. Emmitsburg, MA: Open Learning Fire Service Program, National Fire Academy.

Kreps, G. A. (1991). Organizing for emergency management. In Drabek, T. E., & Hoetmer, G. J. (Eds.), Emergency management: Principles and practices for local government (pp. 30–52). Washington, DC: International City Management Association.

Kuban, R. (1993). Management of community–wide crises. Canadian Emergency News, 16 (4), pp. 6–10.

Kuban, R. (1994). Dialogue on Crisis: Attitude, the basis of effective crisis management. Canadian Emergency News, 17 (5), pp. 16–17.

Kuban, R. (1995a). Crisis management in Canada: A study of its practice. Calgary, AB: Pendragon.

Kuban, R. (1995b). Dialogue on Crisis: The role of fire departments in emergency preparedness. Canadian Emergency News, 18 (3), pp. 28–29.

La Plante, J. M., & Kroll–Smith, J. S. (1989). Coordinated emergency management: The challenge of the chronic technological disaster. International Journal of Mass Emergencies and Disasters, 7(2), pp. 134–150.

Mann, B. W. (1994). The crucial role of radio amateurs in emergency response. Emergency Preparedness Digest, 21 (1), pp. 6–9.

Mazur, A. (1987). Does public perception of risk explain the social response to potential hazard? Quarterly Journal of Ideology. 2, pp. 41-45.

Mileti, D. S., Drabek, T. E., & Haas, J. E. (1975). Human systems in extreme environments: A sociological perspective. Boulder, CO: Institute of Behavioral Sciences, University of Colorado.

Mintzberg, H. (1973). The nature of managerial work. New York, NY: Harper & Row.

Myers, K. N. (1993). Total contingency planning for disasters. New York, NY: John Wiley & Sons.

Mushkatel, A. H., & Perry, R. W. (1984). Disaster management: Warning, response and community relocation. Wesport, CT: Quorom Books.

NRC. National Research Council of Canada. (1995). Total cost of fire: An initial estimate. Ottawa, ON: Author.

Palmer, C. J. (1993). Taking command of disaster. Emergency: Journal of Emergency Services, 25 (4), pp. 37–40.

Perrow, C. (1984). Normal accidents: Living with high risk technology. New York, NY: Basic.

Petak, W. J. (1985). Emergency management: A challenge for public administration. Public Administration Review, 45 (1), pp. 3–7.

Plunkett, L. C., & Hale, G. A. (1982). The proactive manager: The complete book of problem solving and decision making. New York, NY: John Wiley & Sons.

Quarantelli, E. L. (1978). Disasters: Theory and research. Beverly Hills, CA: SAGE.

Quarantelli, E. L. (1982). Social and organizational problems in a major community emergency. Emergency Planning Digest, 9(1), pp. 7–10,21.

Quarantelli, E. L. (1985). Organizational behaviour in disasters and implications for disaster planning (Report Series 18). Newark, DE : University of Delaware, The Disaster Research Center.

Raphael, B. (1986). When disaster strikes: How individuals and communities cope with catastrophe. New York, NY: Basic Books.

Ritti, R. R., & Funhouser, G. R. (1977). The ropes to skip and the ropes to know: Studies in organizational behavior. Columbus, OH: Grid.

Rosenthal, U., Charles, M. T., Hart, P. 't, Kouzmin, A., & Jarman, A. (1989). From case studies to theory and recommendations: A concluding analysis. In Rosenthal, U., Charles, M. T., & Hart, P. 't (Eds.), Coping with crises: The management of disasters, riots, and terrorism (pp. 436– 472). Springfield, IL: Charles C. Thomas.

Rosenthal, U., Hart, P. 't, & Charles, M. T. (1989). The world of crises and crisis management. In Rosenthal, U., Charles, M. T., & Hart, P. 't (Eds.), Coping with crises: The management of disasters, riots, and terrorism (pp. 3– 33). Springfield, IL: Charles C. Thomas.

Routley, G. J. (1991). Fire department operations. In Cote, P. E., & Linville, J. L. (Eds.), Fire Protection Handbook (17th ed.), (pp. 9–55 to 9–67). Quincy, MA: National Fire Protection Association.

Rubin, C. B. (1991). Recovery from disaster. In Drabek, T. E., & Hoetmer, G. J. (Eds.), Emergency management: Principles and practices for local government (pp. 224–258). Washington, DC: International City Management Association.

Saint–Pierre, P. (1992). Evacuation planning. Emergency Preparedness Digest, 19 (3), pp. 18–19.

Scanlon, J. (1990). Political leadership and Canadian emergency planning: The role of the mayor. In Sylves, R. T., & Waugh, W. L. (Eds.), Cities and disaster: North American studies in emergency management (pp. 165–181). Springfield, IL: Charles C. Thomas.

Scanlon, J., & Sylves, R. T. (1990). Conflict and coordination in responding to aviation disaster: The San Diego and Gander experiences compared. In Sylves, R. T., & Waugh, W. L. (Eds.), Cities and disaster: North American studies in emergency management (pp. 109–129). Springfield, IL: Charles C. Thomas.

Scanlon, J. T. (1991). Reaching out: Getting the community involved in preparedness. In Drabek, T. E., & Hoetmer, G. J. (Eds.), Emergency management: Principles and practices for local government (pp. 79–99). Washington, DC: International City Management Association.

Shrivastava, P. (1989). Managing the crisis at Bhopal. In Rosenthal, U., Charles, M. T., & Hart, P. 't (Eds.), Coping with crises: The management of disasters, riots, and terrorism (pp. 92–116). Springfield, IL: Charles C. Thomas.

Synder, J. (1993). Saskatchewan: Blessed with the volunteer spirit. Emergency Preparedness Digest, 20 (2), pp. 2–3.

Sylves, R. T., & Waugh, W. L. (Eds.). (1990). Cities and disaster: North American studies in emergency management. Springfield, IL: Charles C. Thomas.

Turner, B. A., & Toft, B. (1989). Fire at Summerland leisure centre. In Rosenthal, U., Charles, M. T., & Hart, P. 't (Eds.), Coping with crises: The management of disasters, riots, and terrorism (pp. 169–196). Springfield, IL: Charles C. Thomas.

Warheit, G., & Dynes, R. R. (1969). Organizations in disasters. EMO National Digest, 9(2), pp. 12–13,19.

Withers, R. (1988). Communicator/decision–maker: A dual role for the successful senior government manager. Emergency Preparedness Digest, 15(1), pp. 18–22.

AUTHORS' BIOGRAPHIES

The following, in alphabetic order are the biographies of each of the writers involved in this book.

Chief, Laird Burton

Chief Laird Burton has had over 26 years of Fire and Emergency Service Experience. He has been a Fire Fighter, Course Development Officer and Supervisor (i.e., Director) of the Alberta Fire Training School (AFTS). In 1994, Laird left his post with AFTS for his current role as Manager, Emergency Services and Fire Chief of Strathcona County.

Laird has had extensive experience teaching and writing about Fire related issues. He was the co–author of material for IFSTA, and produced numerous course materials for AFTS. He has also written international professional qualification materials for the National Professional Qualification Board and for the International Fire Services Accreditation Congress.

Chief Burton continues his education through formal studies and field application of management theories. He is currently working on a Bachelor of Science degree through the University of Cincinnati.

Ron Kuban, Ph.D.

Ron has served for over 23 years in the Department of National Defence, the federal government and the Alberta government. During much of this period he taught management and interpersonal skills, organizational behaviour and emergency preparedness at all levels.

Ron graduated with a B.A. from the Royal Military College of Kingston, an M.Ed. (Adult and Higher Education) and a Ph.D.
(Educational Administration) from the University of Alberta. His doctoral research into the management of community–wide crises in Canada has been published under the title *Crisis Management in Canada: A study of its practice.*

Ron has had numerous crises and disaster related experiences. His latest involved a month in China as a delegate of the International Federation of Red Cross and Red Crescent Societies following the 1995 floods. Ron is the President of **Turning Point Consulting Corp.** specializing in emergency preparedness, the management of crises and business recovery.

Deputy Chief Mike Lowing

Mike Lowing is the Deputy Fire Chief of the City of Yellowknife, NWT. He began his career in the fire service in 1984 when he joined the Yellowknife Fire Department as a volunteer fire fighter.
Mike moved to the hamlet of Tuktoyaktuk, NWT, in 1967 and has since travelled

extensively throughout Canada's North. He also resided in the Towns of Inuvik (1969) and Iqaluit (1972). In 1974 Mike moved to City of Yellowknife in 1974 where he has lived ever since.

Mike has been active in all facets of emergency planning. He is currently actively involved in fire and pre–hospital care training in the Northwest Territories as well as critical incident stress management.

Deputy Chief Lowing is also the secretary/treasurer for the NWT Fire Chief's Association. He is an enthusiastic proponent of continued education for Fire Officers and is near completion of his degree from the University of Cincinnati.

Jack V. McAllister

Born and lived in Collingwood Ontario where his father was the Fire Chief for 37 years. Jack served for 32 years with the Barrie Fire Department in the following positions:

Fire Fighter	1963 – 1968
Fire Prevention Officer	1968 – 1974
Deputy Fire Chief	1974 – 1976
Fire Chief	1976 – 1995

Chief McAllister is a graduate of the Ontario Fire College and various other courses and institutions. He has held various posts including:

* President of the Canadian Division International Association of Fire Chiefs, the Ontario Association of Fire Chiefs, and Fire Prevention Canada
* Member, Board of Directors of the Canadian Association of Fire Chiefs
* Member of Various Committees including I.A.F.C., C.A.F.C., O.A.F.C., F.P.C., Underwriters Laboratories of Canada and
  Simcoe County Fire Coordinator.

John Oakley

John Oakley has been actively involved in Public Safety at municipal, provincial, national and international levels since 1974. He completed his Emergency Paramedic diploma in 1983 from the Northern Alberta Institute of Technology (NAIT). John served with Edmonton's Ambulance Authority as Paramedic and as Supervisor, Training Division. In 1988, he moved to Vancouver, British Columbia to work as a contract program developer with the Professional Health Programs of the Emergency Health Services Academy at the Justice Institute of British Columbia. In 1990 he was appointed Vancouver Zone Manager, Provincial Emergency Program.

In 1991 John assumed the position of Director, Office of Emergency Management for the City of Vancouver. In May, 1996, he returned to the Justice Institute of British

Columbia, as an Emergency Management Instructor with the Provincial Emergency Program Academy.

John currently holds membership with the following associations:

- The Earthquake Engineering Research Institute
- National Coordinating Council on Emergency Management
- Emergency Planners and Managers Association of British Columbia (Vice Chair)
- Regional Emergency Planning Committee (Past Chair)
- National Association of EMS Physicians (associate member)
- World Association for Emergency and Disaster Medicine

Larry Reynolds

Larry A. Reynolds B.A., B.Ed., LL.B., LL.M. is a practising lawyer in Alberta and the Northwest Territories, and is currently a fellow with the University of Alberta Eco-Research Chair in Environmental Risk Management and with the Social Sciences and Humanities Research Council of Canada (SSHRC). In addition to being the author of numerous publications in the areas of fire and emergency services law, municipal law, public authority liability law and environmental law, Larry Reynolds is also a sessional instructor with the Alberta Fire Training School, Vermilion, Alberta. Currently, Larry Reynolds is working in cooperation with the the Alberta Fire Training School and the Alberta Fire Commissioner in the development of *Fire, Emergency and Safety Services Law in Alberta*, a series of guide books and courses designed to assist fire and emergency services personnel from across Canada in addressing a wide variety of legal and regulatory issues including civil and regulatory liability, administrative law, contracts and agreements, environmental law and judicial process and court procedure.

Chief Gary Richardson

Chief Richardson joined the Winnipeg Fire Department in 1973. Over the following 16 years he was assigned to a wide variety of apparatus and Fire Stations. In 1980 he became a first responder and added medical response to his standard duties. In 1984 he became first responder instructor/examiner. Gary then spent 11 years working with volunteer fire fighters and ambulance attendants from across Manitoba.

In 1991 Gary was promoted to Fire Prevention Officer and in 1994 became Captain in the Training Division. In late 1994 he was again promoted to Assistant Deputy Chief and held the position for a short period until promoted to Deputy Chief. In September 1995, Gary assumed his current role of Fire Chief for the City of Ottawa.

Chief Richardson completed his B.A. (Administrative Studies) in 1990 at the University of Winnipeg. He was immediately accepted into its Masters of Public Administration program. His thesis deals with Fire Ambulance integration. Gary is due to complete his Masters degree by mid 1996.

Doug G. Skelding

Born and educated in Windsor, Ontario. He was employed by Bell Canada for many years and retire, in 1985, in Barrie, Ontario.

Doug became involved with emergency services in 1979 and organized a civilian response team. For many years, and in conjunction with the local Fire Department, he supervised activities related to both major and minor disasters. The association with the Barrie Fire Department was natural given the earlier involvement of both his father and uncle in that Department.

In 1994 the Barrie Fire Department celebrated its 150th anniversary. To commemorate this occasion, beginning in 1991, we researched the history of the Department from it's beginning in 1844. This culminated in a book titled "FORGED IN THE FLAMES".

Doug is the unofficial historian for the Barrie Fire Department and has restored two antique fire trucks and a number of pieces of antique memorabilia for display. He still operates, on volunteer basis, a canteen service for fire fighters during extended emergencies.

Battalion Chief Glenn Spratt

Battalion Chief Spratt is with the City of Edmonton's Emergency Response Department. He joined the Department in 1970, promoted to Training Officer in 1988 and to Lieutenant in 1990. From 1993 to 1996, when he was promoted to his current position, he held the position of Chief of Dangerous Goods. Glenn is currently enrolled in and near completion of the Bachelor of Fire Science Technology Program at the University of Cincinnati.

Glenn has been trained as a Dangerous Goods Second Responder and has served as an instructor on a number of Dangerous Goods training courses, exercises and drills. He is a strong proponent of the need for municipal emergency response teams to work closely with industry. He has established many joint exercises, demonstrations and information sharing sessions with various industrial groups and organizations. Glenn was instrumental in developing many of the policies and procedures currently in place for Edmonton's Dangerous Goods Response Team.

Training Officer Gordon Sweetnam

Training Officer Gordon Sweetnam has had over 20 years experience with the Calgary Fire Department, with the last 10 years in the role of Training Officer. Gordon is a keen educator and extensively active in training development, training delivery, public speaking and volunteer work.

He is certified to teach many programs from Incident Command, to Officer Development, First Response and the NFPA Fire Officer courses. He has delivered many of these courses both at the community and national level.

Gordon continues to enjoy taking courses and has completed a number of fire and management–related programs through Western Oregon State College, Mount Royal College (Calgary, Alberta), the University of Calgary, the Alberta fire Training School (Vermilion, Alberta) and various other institutions.

Training Officer Sweetnam has been actively involved as a volunteer in a wide variety of organizations and associations. These include the Canadian Automotive Rescue Society (Director), the Accident Review Board and the Transportation Emergency Rescue Committee.

Deputy Chief Bernie Williams, Ph.D.

Deputy Chief Williams has been employed with the City of Edmonton's Emergency Response Department since 1980. He earned his Bachelor's and Master's degrees at the University of Alberta and his Doctoral degree from the University of Toronto. He is currently enrolled in the Executive Fire Officer Program at the U.S. National Fire Academy. He is also an adjunct instructor at that Academy.

Bernie presently works primarily in the administrative area of the Emergency Response Department and responds to major emergencies on a call–out basis. He previously served as Deputy Chief in the Operations Bureau for two years. During that time period he was involved in the planning, administration and training of Fire/Rescue Branch, including the Dangerous Goods Response Team.

Bernie chairs the Emergency Response Department's Regional Initiative Committee. It is designed to facilitate the sharing of Departmental expertise and resources with customers and clients outside the City of Edmonton.

Dave Worman

Mr. Worman is the Protective Services Director of the City of Fort Saskatchewan (pop. 12,000), located 25 kilometres East of Edmonton. Dave is responsible for Emergency Medical Services, R.C.M. Police contract services, the City's Fire Department and Emergency Preparedness, as well as Bylaw Services, Environmental Standards and Employee Health and Safety programs. He is also the City's Director of Disaster Services.

Dave has been exceptionally active in his community's emergency preparedness programs. He is one of five Canadians to receive (in 1989) the Corpus Occupational Health and Safety Certificate of Merit in recognition of significant contribution to Occupational Health and Safety.

He is a member of the Canadian Society of Safety Engineers, the Alberta Safety Council and the Alberta Branch of the Major Industrial Accident Council of Canada (MIACC). He is also the Chairman of the Planning and Administration Group of the Northern Region Community Awareness Emergency Response (NR CAER) organization. It is a mutual aid organization consisting of ten municipalities and 40 industrial members.

Mr. Worman has been the President of the Alberta Cities Safety Association. He has been the Chairman of a number of organizations including: the Board of Directors of the Alberta Municipal Health and Safety Association, the National Working Group of MIACC (to develop emergency planning standards for municipalities).

Dave is a graduate of the University of Alberta's Safety Certificate Program and Public Administration Certificate Program.